LYLE PRICE GUIDE
FURNITURE

While every care has been taken in compiling the information contained in this volume, the publishers cannot accept any liability for loss, financial or otherwise, incurred by reliance placed on the information herein.

The publishers wish to express their sincere thanks to the following for their involvement and assistance in the production of this volume:

Editor	TONY CURTIS
Text By	EELIN McIVOR
Editorial	ANNETTE CURTIS
	DONNA RUTHERFORD
	CLAIRE COSSAR
Art Production	CATRIONA DAY
	DONNA CRUICKSHANK
	NICKY FAIRBURN
Graphics	JAMES BROWN
	MALCOLM GLASS
	DOROTHY GLASS

British Library Cataloguing-in-Publication Data.
A catalogue record for this book is available from the British Library.
ISBN 86248-150-3

I.S.B.N. 86248 - 150 - 3

Copyright © Lyle Publications   MCMXCIV
Glenmayne, Galashiels, Scotland

Typeset by Word Power, Berwickshire
Printed and bound in Great Britain by
Butler & Tanner Ltd, Frome and London

LYLE PRICE GUIDE
FURNITURE

TONY CURTIS

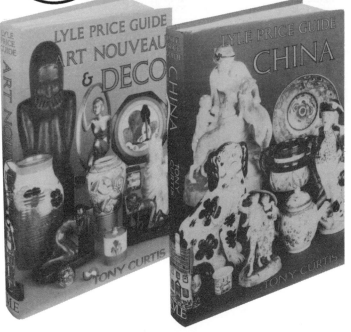

JUST £14.95

With comprehensive illustrations, descriptions and up-to-date prices for over 3,000 items, these Lyle Price Guides provide a unique and indispensable work of reference for the dealer and collector alike. Every item is given its current market value! Prices actually paid, based on accurate sales records - and with sources quoted.

CONTENTS

ACKNOWLEDGEMENTS

AB Stockholms Auktionsverk, Box 16256, 103 25 Stockholm, Sweden

Abbotts Auction Rooms, The Auction Rooms, Campsea Ash, Woodbridge, Suffolk

Allen & Harris, St Johns Place, Whiteladies Road, Clifton, Bristol BS8 2ST

Anderson & Garland, Marlborough House, Marlborough Crescent, Newcastle upon Tyne NE1 4EE

Auktionshaus Arnold, Bleichstr. 42, 6000 Frankfurt a/M, Germany

Bearnes, Rainbow, Avenue Road, Torquay TQ2 5TG

Bigwood, The Old School, Tiddington, Stratford upon Avon

Bonhams, Montpelier Street, Knightsbridge, London SW7 1HH

Bonhams Chelsea, 65–69 Lots Road, London SW10 0RN

Bonhams West Country, Dowell Street, Honiton, Devon

British Antique Exporters, School Close, Queen Elizabeth Avenue, Burgess Hill, Sussex

Butterfield & Butterfield, 220 San Bruno Avenue, San Francisco CA 94103, USA

Butterfield & Butterfield, 7601 Sunset Boulevard, Los Angeles CA 90046, USA

Christie's (International) SA, 8 place de la Taconnerie, 1204 Genève, Switzerland

Christie's Monaco, S.A.M, Park Palace 98000 Monte Carlo, Monaco

Christie's Scotland, 164–166 Bath Street, Glasgow G2 4TG

Christie's South Kensington Ltd., 85 Old Brompton Road, London SW7 3LD

Christie's, 8 King Street,London SW1Y 6QT

Christie's East, 219 East 67th Street, New York, NY 10021, USA

Christie's, 502 Park Avenue, New York, NY 10022, USA

Christie's, Cornelis Schuytstraat 57, 1071 JG Amsterdam, Netherlands

Christie's SA Roma, 114 Piazza Navona, 00186 Rome, Italy

Christie's Swire, 2804–6 Alexandra House, 16–20 Chater Road, Hong Kong

Christie's Australia Pty Ltd., 1 Darling Street, South Yarra, Victoria 3141, Australia

Dreweatt Neate, Donnington Priory, Donnington, Newbury, Berkshire RG13 2JE

Hy. Duke & Son, 40 South Street, Dorchester, Dorset

Sala de Artes y Subastas Durán, Serrano 12, 28001 Madrid, Spain

Eldred's, Box 796, E. Dennis, MA 02641, USA

Ewbanks, Burnt Common Auction Rooms, London Road, Sand, Woking, Surrey, GU23 7LN

Finarte, 20121 Milano, Piazzetta Bossi 4, Italy

Galerie Moderne, 3 rue du Parnasse, 1040 Bruxelles, Belgium

Geering & Colyer (Black Horse Agencies), Highgate, Hawkhurst, Kent

Graves Son & Pilcher, 71 Church Road, Hove, East Sussex, BN3 2GL

Greenslade Hunt, Magdalene House, Church Square, Taunton, Somerset, TA1 1SB

FURNITURE

Andrew Hartley Fine Arts, Victoria Hall, Little Lane, Ilkely

Giles Haywood, The Auction House, St John's Road, Stourbridge, West Midlands, DY8 1EW

P Herholdt Jensens Auktioner, Rundforbivej 188, 2850 Nerum, Denmark

Hobbs & Chambers, 'At the Sign of the Bell', Market Place, Cirencester, Glos

Jacobs & Hunt, Lavant Street, Petersfield, Hants, GU33 3EF

G A Key, Aylsham Saleroom, 8 Market Place, Aylsham, Norfolk, NR11 6EH

Kunsthaus am Museum, Drususgasse 1–5, 5000 Köln 1, Germany

Lawrence Butler Fine Art Salerooms, Marine Walk, Hythe, Kent, CT21 5AJ

Lawrence Fine Art, South Street, Crewkerne, Somerset TA18 8AB

Lawrence's Fine Art Auctioneers, Norfolk House, 80 High Street, Bletchingley, Surrey

David Lay, The Penzance Auction House, Alverton, Penzance, Cornwall TA18 4KE

Lots Road Chelsea Auction Galleries, 71 Lots Road, Chelsea, London SW10 0RN

John Nicholson, 1 Crossways Court, Fernhurst, Haslemere, Surrey GU27 3EP

Onslow's, Metrostrore, Townmead Road, London SW6 2RZ

Phillips Manchester, Trinity House, 114 Northenden Road, Sale, Manchester M33 3HD

Phillips Son & Neale SA, 10 rue des Chaudronniers, 1204 Genève, Switzerland

Phillips West Two, 10 Salem Road, London W2 4BL

Phillips, 11 Bayle Parade, Folkestone, Kent CT20 1SQ

Phillips, 49 London Road, Sevenoaks, Kent TN13 1UU

Phillips, 65 George Street, Edinburgh EH2 2 JL

Phillips, Blenstock House, 7 Blenheim Street, New Bond Street, London W1Y 0AS

Phillips Marylebone, Hayes Place, Lisson Grove, London NW1 6UA

Phillips, New House, 150 Christleton Road, Chester CH3 5TD

Pinney's, 5627 Ferrier, Montreal, Quebec, Canada H4P 2M4

Russell, Baldwin & Bright, The Fine Art Saleroom, Ryelands Road, Leominster HR6 8JG

Schrager Auction Galleries, 2915 North Sherman Boulevard, Milwaukee, WI 53210, USA

Selkirk's, 4166 Olive Street, St Louis, Missouri 63108, USA

Skinner Inc., Bolton Gallery, Route 117, Bolton MA, USA

Sotheby's, 34–35 New Bond Street, London W1A 2AA

Sotheby's, 1334 York Avenue, New York NY 10021

Sotheby's, 112 George Street, Edinburgh EH2 2LH

Sotheby's, Summers Place, Billingshurst, West Sussex RH14 9AD

Sotheby's Monaco, BP 45, 98001 Monte Carlo

Henry Spencer, 20 The Square, Retford, Notts. DN22 6BX

G E Sworder & Son, Northgate End Salerooms, 15 Northgate End, Bishop Stortford, Herts

Tennants, Harmby Road, Leyburn, Yorkshire

Woolley & Wallis, The Castle Auction Mart, Salisbury, Wilts SP1 3SU

FURNITURE

When one speaks of 'antiques' perhaps the first image that flits across the mind is that of a piece of furniture, be it Auntie Mabel's treacly Victorian sideboard or an elegant 18th century satinwood and ormolu commode. For furniture may be said to form the basis of the antiques trade, whether it be the £1.76 million paid for the Anglesey desk, or the £8.5 million for the Badminton cabinet, or just a few pounds for humbler 'brown' pieces at the bottom end of the scale. It is also the sector which seems to prove the most resilient to the wilder vicissitudes of the market.

*The Badminton cabinet made for the 3rd Duke of Beaufort, 152ins. high.
(Christie's)* £8,580,000

Furniture is, after all, something we all have, and it is one of the most basic of human requirements. Even the law testifies to this, in that, when the bailiffs finally catch up with you to relieve you of all your worldly possessions, they are nevertheless obliged to leave you with a chair, a table, and a bed. Nowadays more and more people not normally active in the collecting

field seem to be realising that buying furniture of a certain age for their homes is both cheaper and a much better potential investment than spending out on what can be very expensive modern or reproduction items.

True to form, the furniture market has, over the last year, been one of the first sectors to throw off the doldrums of recession, with both auctioneers and dealers reporting a buoyant upswing in the market. Top class pieces of good provenance have always been easy to shift, but more prosaic items too are also beginning regularly to outstrip their estimates. One such example was a pleasant but unexceptional Victorian mahogany extending dining table which sold at Phillips in Edinburgh recently for over £10,000 against a top estimate of half that. Interestingly, it was a private buyer who secured this particular item, and against others of his ilk, the trade having dropped out at around £5,000. It is perhaps the strength of the private sector at just about every level in this field which is instrumental in keeping it so buoyant.

Apart from pieces of a traditional nature, more modern items continue to attract avid followers. Charles Rennie Mackintosh has been a name to conjure with for a number of years now, and his popularity shows no signs of waning. 'Landmark' was the adjective used by Christie's to describe the sale, early in 1994, of a very special collection of his work owned by the leading Mackintosh scholar, Dr. Thomas Howarth. Furniture made up only a small proportion of the whole, but attracted the highest prices, with a superb writing cabinet fetching £793,500 and a single highbacked oak chair selling for £309,500. Remarkably, almost half the lots on offer were purchased by Japanese interests, and the writing cabinet was only purchased by the Fine Arts Society against very stiff Japanese competition. The chair did go to a Japanese, outbidding an equally determined American, and between them they took the price to over ten times the lower estimate.

Mackintosh items are highly characteristic and demand for them is very much a matter of fashion, (he was almost completely unrecognised until the 1970s) albeit, it seems, a very enduring one. More vulnerable, too, to the

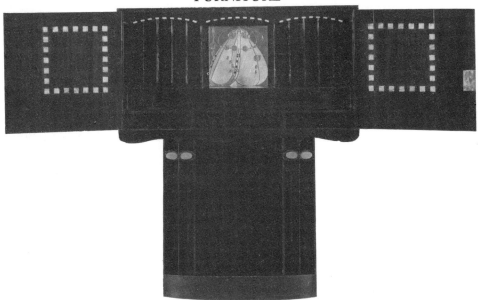

A highly important ebonised mahogany writing cabinet by CHARLES RENNIE MACKINTOSH, 1904. (Christie's) £793,500

A rare and important high back oak chair by CHARLES RENNIE MACKINTOSH, circa 1898-99. (Christie's) £309,500

swings of taste is the modern designer furniture which finds its way now into several specialist sales each year. Bonhams have established a regular niche early in the year for 20th century furniture and design, dominated largely by Scandinavian, Italian and American designers. In the past it had been the more 'traditional' items in this field which had proved easiest to sell, pieces, for example, by Marcel Breuer and Mies van der Rohe. In 1994, however, something of a sea change occurred. The rooms, always healthily full for the sale, were this time packed to overflowing, with a high proportion of the bidders being new young private buyers who seemed intent on snapping up the less expensive pieces rather than the higher-estimated design classics. A certain distance still seems to be necessary for these modern items to become 'desirable', but this had shunted forward from the 30s to the 50s, while items from the 70s and 80s were still altogether too familiar to attract much interest.

It seems that this is an area to watch, with a rich, hitherto uptapped seam of new buyers.

Furniture then does have its speculative areas. However, mainstream items at all levels still represent excellent investment potential, as anyone who has made even modestly sensible purchases over the last twenty years has reason to know.

This large cupboard, which consists basically of one or two long doors with one or more drawers in the interior or under, originated in 16th century France. *Armoire* is simply the French word for a cupboard or wardrobe. The armoire was treated monumentally by Boulle and his studio, and as a piece of furniture it is generally characterised by the solidity and massiveness of its appearance. It survived into the early Regency period, but all but disappeared thereafter as rooms became smaller.

A 17th century Flemish rosewood and ebony armoire with massive bun feet, 91in. wide. £3,250

A French Provincial fruitwood armoire on squat cabriole legs, 61in. wide. £2,200

A French mahogany collapsible armoire of Empire style with moulded rectangular cornice above a pair of doors with two geometrically-glazed panels, on bracket feet, 54¹/₂in. wide. (Christie's) £1,210

A German armoire, in pine and other softwoods, with a projecting cornice, a frieze inlaid with geometric panels and above two doors decorated in Renaissance style, 18th/19th century, 74in. wide. (Lawrence Fine Art) £1,760

Louis XV Transitional pickled oak armoire, the cavetto cornice over triple panel sides and a pair of wire mesh double panel doors well carved with plumes, 4ft. 10in. wide. (Butterfield & Butterfield) £5,781

An antique French Louis XV cherrywood bonnetière with two inset shaped panels and an outset cornice on scroll feet, circa 1760, 44in. wide. (Selkirk's) £2,949

An 18th century Dutch mahogany and floral marquetry armoire, with moulded undulating pediment, on splayed claw and ball feet, 165cm. wide. (Finarte) £5,505

A French Provincial walnut and fruitwood armoire with a drawer below and waved apron on cabriole legs, late 18th/early 19th century, 65in. wide. (Christie's) £1,210

A Louis XVI amaranth, tulipwood and parquetry armoire, possibly Dutch, 41in. wide. £4,350

A classical mahogany armoire, attributed to Chas. H. Lannvier, circa 1800-15, 55in. wide. £17,500

A mid 18th century French Provincial cherrywood armoire with moulded cornice, 56in. wide. £2,150

A Flemish oak, walnut, ebony and ebonised armoire with fielded panelled frieze flanked and divided by volutes above a pair of small fielded panelled doors and a larger conforming pair of doors, late 17th century, 60¹/₂ in. wide. (Christie's) £4,950

A Franco-Flemish walnut armoire with moulded rectangular cornice above a panelled frieze carved with vases and foliage above three pairs of panelled doors, incorporating some earlier panels, 180in. wide. (Christie's) £7,150

Louis XV/XVI Provincial oak armoire, late 18th century, the pair of grilled doors centring a reserve carved with scrolling tendrils issuing foliage and flowerheads, 4ft. 9¹/₂ in. wide. (Butterfield & Butterfield) £1,734

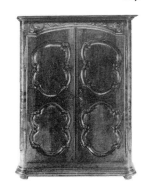

A French Provincial walnut and elm armoire, with a pair of triple shaded panel cupboard doors, on short cabriole legs, 52³/₄ in. wide, mid 18th century. (Bonhams) £1,500

An antique Italian rococo Venetian green painted wood armadio with silver-gilt highlights, 18th century, 7ft. 6in. wide. (Selkirk's) £4,237

A fine antique French Régence oak armoirette with a pair of doors, each with arched tops and two scroll-carved fielded panels, circa 1730, 4ft. 4in. wide. (Selkirk's) £2,966

A Dutch fruitwood armoire with a pair of shaped panelled doors, 76in. wide, 96in. high. £6,000

A Louis XV carved oak armoire with foliate vase and scroll motifs, 5ft.6in. wide, circa 1770. £2,000

An 18th century South German figured and burr walnut armoire, 74in. wide. £16,000

A French Provincial oak armoire with moulded rectangular cornice above two long panelled doors with waved mouldings and carved with flowerheads and baskets of flowers, second half 18th century, 66in. wide. (Christie's) £2,750

A late 18th century Wesphalian oak armoire with moulded rectangular cornice above two carved fielded doors and two drawers, monogrammed in pewter *ICF 1776*, 174cm. wide. (Kunsthaus am Museum) £1,953

A French Provincial oak armoire, the frieze carved with a basket of flowers above two doors with shaped fielded panels carved with flowers and foliage, 18th century, 62in. wide. (Christie's London) £3,520

A 17th century Flemish oak armoire, the projecting moulded cornice above a frieze carved with scrolling foliage, on massive bun feet, 79in. wide. (Bearne's) £2,300

A French Provincial oak armoire, the arched moulded cornice carved with a cabochon within scrolls and foliage, mid-18th century. (Christie's London) £1,540

An early 19th century German walnut armoire, the moulded cornice with a pair of shaped panel doors on block feet, 6ft. 3in. wide. (Phillips) £460

Fine Victorian mahogany and walnut armoire with two keys, 1865.   £700

A French gold and parcel gilt armoire squat cabriole feet.   £2,150

An 18th century German walnut veneered and marquetry armoire, 78in. wide.   £12,000

A Tyrolean painted and marbled armoire, the frieze dated 1810 above two panelled doors painted with roses, early 19th century, 61½in. wide. (Christie's London)   £6,050

A fine Dutch mahogany armoire, the pair of panelled cupboard doors applied with ribbon and tassel tied pendant husk swags and urns, 68in. wide, late 18th century.
(Bonhams)   **£3,600**

An Italian walnut armadio with two panelled doors carved with cabochons in guilloche borders framed by strapwork scrolls, foliage and masks. 59½in. wide. (Christie's London)   £11,000

A South African stinkwood armoire on claw and ball feet, with silver handles stamped IB, 64in. wide.   £2,300

A Dutch walnut floral marquetry armoire, the bombe base fitted with two short and two long drawers, 78in. wide. (Christie's)   £17,600

Mid 18th century Tyrolean cream and black-painted armoire on later bun feet, 55in. wide, 73½in. high. (Christie's)   £2,750

A Liberty & Co. inlaid mahogany armoire, England, circa 1905, 7ft. high.   £750

An 18th century French Provincial oak armoire, 6ft. 2in. wide.   £1,400

An 18th century Scandinavian walnut armoire, 57in. wide.   £5,000

A 19th century armoire with moulded arched cornice over two conforming arched doors painted with drapery and urns and inscribed *M A D 1813*, Scandinavian, 128cm. wide. (Auktionsverket)   £3,940

A Dutch burr walnut armoire banded in ash with arched moulded cornice above two arched panelled doors, on shaped bracket feet, mid-18th century, 65in. wide. (Christie's London)   £8,250

A Dutch mahogany armoire with two panelled doors carved with ribbon-tied paterae and baskets of flowers flanked by fluted column-angles, late 18th century, 105½in. high. (Christie's)   £8,800

Mid 18th century French Provincial oak armoire with moulded foliate cornice, 64in. wide, 88in. high.   £5,500

An 18th century Dutch burr walnut and feather banded armoire, the upper part of ogee arched form with moulded cornice, 1.75m. wide. (Phillips London)   £4,000

An 18th century French oak armoire with two doors each with three shaped fielded panels and on bun feet, 58in. wide. (Bearne's)   £840

A French Provincial walnut armoire with arched moulded cornice, panelled sides and scrolled feet, 61in. wide. (Christie's) £3,300

An 18th century Dutch walnut armoire, the bombe lower part fitted with three drawers, 1.83m. wide. £3,000

A Flemish oak armoire with a moulded cornice, fluted and flower head-carved frieze, 61in. wide, part late 17th century. (Bearne's) £1,850

A Louis XVI boulle cabinet en armoire, the upper part with convex frieze above two cupboard doors, inlaid with engraved pewter scrolling foliage, 42½in. wide. (Christie's London) £8,800

A Dutch mahogany and marquetry armoire with moulded dentil cornice above two fielded panelled doors, each inlaid with vases of flowers, birds and butterflies, 70in. wide. (Christie's) £7,150

A Polish polychrome pine armoire with a pair of cupboard doors painted with flowers, Saint Dorata and Saint Maria Boskowska, 18th century, 51in. wide. (Christie's London) £7,920

A Louis XV Provincial oak armoire with brass barrel hinges and escutcheon plates, 60in. wide. £1,200

A 17th century Dutch walnut and ebony armoire, 76in. wide. £1,750

A Louis XV cherrywood armoire with moulded chamfered cornice, 56in. wide. £5,500

BEDS

The earliest beds, of a form that would be recognised and accepted today, date from the 16th century – in Britain, anyway. Before that time the most important feature of the rich man's bed was the drapery, often of velvet or silk intricately embroidered with hunting or hawking scenes, which was suspended from the ceiling by means of rings.

This drapery would enclose a simply constructed oak framework of such crude design and make that it was rarely considered worth taking when the family moved house. The framework was usually made with holes drilled through ends and sides, a length of rope being threaded through the holes to form an open-mesh base on which would be supported a rush-work pallet and a couple of feather mattresses. Coverings would include sheets, often of silk, blankets and an embroidered bedspread probably trimmed with fur.

The poor man's bed was more often than not a heap of leaves or straw laid in a shallow box – and the most important feature as far as he was concerned was whether or not the leaves were dry.

Up and coming families, rich enough to afford large coffers, would sleep on these, the lids made more hospitable by means of straw palliasses.

Once the idea of beds caught on, however, the family bed soon became the most important item of furniture in the household. One of the best extant examples of this is the Great Bed of Ware, made in 1595, which was a massive ten feet eight inches wide.

A French Louis XV style walnut and carved bedstead, 48in. wide. (J. M. Welch & Son) £160

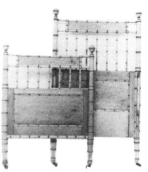

American Victorian maple and bird's-eye maple veneer bamboo crib, circa 1870, 53½in. long. £400

Important Moorish style gilt-metal-mounted, mother-of-pearl and ivory inlaid ebony bedstead and pair of matching nightstands, circa 1878. (Butterfield & Butterfield) £52,006

An American 'Aesthetic' Movement double bed, in the manner of the Herter Brothers, New York, circa 1880, the headboard with a carved pierced, gilt and ebonised cresting, 5ft. wide. (Sotheby's) £2,035

A Robert 'Mouseman' Thompson oak double bed, on casters, the panelled adze finished headboard carved with two rosettes and with three grotesque carved terminals, 152cm. wide. (Christie's) £1,100

A French mahogany, parquetry and giltmetal mounted bed of Louis XVI design, each end with a pierced laurel floral ribbon-tied cresting, 49in. wide. (Christie's S. Ken) £1,870

17

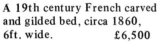

Gustav Stickley double bed, circa 1907, no.. 923, tapering vertical posts centring five wide slats, signed, 57½in. wide. (Skinner Inc.) £1,910

A 19th century French carved and gilded bed, circa 1860, 6ft. wide. £6,500

A Gustav Stickley oak bed, designed by Harvey Ellis, 59½in. wide. £17,500

Late 19th century American walnut bed of Eastlake influence, 58½in. wide. £800

A German figured walnut single bedstead on turned tapering legs and bun feet, 74in. long, 34in. wide. £750

Late Victorian brass and iron bedstead of parallel tubing, circa 1880, 3ft. wide. £225

One of a pair of Arts & Crafts inlaid beds, attributed to Herter Bros., circa 1870, oak burl and other veneers, 26½in. wide. £1,250

A rare George III oak bed-bureau, the front faced as a sloping fall above four long graduated drawers, with the folding bed enclosed at the back, 27½in. wide. (Bonhams) £1,300

An oak headboard with three gadrooned shallow arches filled with geometric inlay, above a gadrooned panel, mostly 17th century with later braces, 65½ x 62½in. (Christie's) £550

Mission oak double bed with exposed tenons, circa 1907, 58½in. wide. £1,400

Mid 19th century Louis XV style walnut bed with scrolled and moulded headboard, 5ft.6in. wide, made in France. £750

A classical mahogany sleigh bed, New York, 1820–1840, on rectangular moulded feet and casters, 60¾in. wide. (Christie's) £954

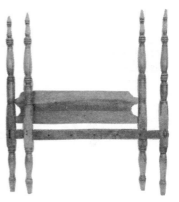

Pair of Gustav Stickley oak twin beds, 40in. wide. £2,500

Chinese opium bed, 19th century, open lattic work and carved canopy with gilded frieze, raised on a base fitted with drawers, 81in. wide. (Skinner Inc.) £1,250

Antique American Sheraton field bed in maple with pine headboard, turned posts, with canopy, 50in. wide. (Eldred's) £767

An oak bed, the footboard with two rectangular relief panels of lozenges flanked by carved caryatid panels, basically 17th century, 84in. long. (Christie's) £2,420

PEL chromed tubular steel B4 single bed with double-hoop bed head, 1930's, 90.5cm. wide. £600

"Tady" headboard, designed by Ferruccio Tritta, produced by Studio Nove, New York, offset geometric design marquetry of walnut and ebony, 63½in. wide. (Skinner Inc.) £675

An Italian parcel gilt, walnut and ebonised bed with distressed padded solid headboard, shaped foot rest and sides with turned finials, 70 x 85in.
(Christie's London) £3,520

Art Nouveau marquetry bed, France, early 20th century, headboard and footboard inlaid with floral designs and carved tendrils, 54in. wide.
(Skinner Inc.) £722

A Biedermeier bird's eye maple and ebony bed with conforming headboard and foot-board each with scrolled top, with boxspring and mattress, the seat-rail with replaced backboard, 86in. wide.
(Christie's) £2,420

An English Art Deco Egyptian style bed, the tall headboard with beaten copper panel of Egyptian style foliage, 108cm. wide. (Christie's) £550

A Chinese black lacquered marriage bedstead, the pierced profusely carved gilded frieze and serpentined apron flanking interior picture panels, 96½in. high. (Christie's S. Ken.) £2,640

One of a pair of mahogany Mission oak beds, possibly Roycroft, circa 1912, 42in. wide.
(Skinner Inc.) £400

Fine Aesthetic inlaid, gilt-incised and carved walnut and burled walnut three-piece bedroom suite by Herter Brothers, New York, circa 1880.
(Butterfield & Butterfield) £12,607

American maple faux bamboo bed, circa 1880, headboard, footboard, side rails, turned finials, incised details, 72½in. long. (Skinner Inc.) £451

A Leleu Art Deco three-piece bedroom suite, comprising: a grand lit with arched headboard and two bedside tables, with circular overhanging tops, 191cm. long measurement of bed.
(Christie's) £6,050

FOUR POSTER

A 17th century oak four-poster bed with panelled headboard, 64in. wide, 93in. high.　　£3,500

A mahogany four-post bed with waved shaped and moulded cornice, 94in. wide.　　£2,000

A 17th century oak four-poster bed, the tester with moulded cornice and carved frieze, 156cm. wide. £3,000

A mahogany four-post bed with pale green-painted arched canopy and two reeded baluster columns, part early 19th century, 58in. wide. (Christie's)　　£3,080

An oak four poster bed, the tester panels carved with lozenges, the frieze carved with lunettes and foliage, basically 17th century. (Christie's London)　　£6,050

A mahogany and cream-painted four-poster bed with cream floral chintz upholstery, the front-posts and headboard 18th century, 66in. wide. (Christie's)　　£3,300

A mahogany four-post bed with box spring and mattress covered in pale green repp, 18th century and later, 82½in. long.　　£8,500

A Federal birchwood and maple four-post bedstead, New England, circa 1810, on tapered feet, with tester. (Sotheby's)　　£3,783

A mahogany four-poster bed with moulded canopy and floral chintz hangings, George III and later, 60in. wide.　　£3,750

FOUR POSTER

A Federal maple highpost bedstead, New England, 1800-20, 54in. wide. £3,750

A rare red-painted cherrywood and pine, child's bedstead, American, first half 19th century, has full set of cotton crocheted hangings, width 36in. (Sotheby's) £1,967

A Federal carved maple high-post bedstead, Mass., 1790-1810, 57in. wide. £6,500

A mahogany and parcel gilt four poster bed, the arched canopy with foliate moulded cornice hung with ribbon tied tasselled drapery swags, 18th century and later, 87in. long. (Christie's London) £6,050

An oak four poster bed of panelled construction, the headboard with arched architectural panel inlaid with birds and flowers, the footboard carved with lozenges, 76in. long. (Christie's London) £3,300

A black and gilt-japanned four poster bed decorated overall with chinoiserie scenes, the rectangular canopy pierced with open-fretwork centred by pagodas and hung with black and gilt chinoiserie-pattern silk, 86in. long. (Christie's) £3,080

A Federal carved mahogany four-post bedstead, American, probably Salem, Massachusetts, 19th century, the feet with foliate caps, 80in. long. (Sotheby's) £1,654

A Federal turned curly maple four-post bedstead, American, circa 1815, having an arched tester, 6ft. 7in. long. (Sotheby's) £2,812

A parcel gilt and cream-painted four-post bed, with padded headboard and yellow repp pleated hangings, box spring and mattress, 83.5in. wide. £1,400

FOUR POSTER

A mahogany four-poster bed
in the manner of Chippendale,
with moulded canopy, 62 x84in.
(Christie's)   £3,300

A late Federal carved mahogany bedstead, the footposts
on brass ball feet, 57in. wide.
                    £8,000

A mahogany four-post bed
with box-spring and mattress,
59in. wide.   £2,200

A George III mahogany four
post bedstead, the two foot
posts fluted and stop- fluted
above acanthus carved baluster and square bases, 224cm.
high. Lawrence Fine Arts)
                    £3,080

A carved mahogany four poster
bed, the tester supported by
floral-carved cluster column and
octagonal supports with
panelled square section legs,
55in. wide.
(Christie's)   £1,100

A George III green, buff, red
and blue painted four post bed,
the arched canopy decorated
with panels of flowers and
beading, extensively restored
and redecorated, 79in. wide.
(Christie's London)   £23,100

Fine 19th century mahogany
four poster bedstead, the foot
post carved with The Prince of
Wales Feathers and reeded, 6ft.
9in. wide.
(G.A. Key)   £1,900

Early 19th century Federal
painted walnut pencil-post
bedstead, North Carolina,
52½in. wide, overall.
                    £3,750

A Federal carved mahogany
four-post bedstead, Mass.,
circa 1820, 76in. long, 47¼in.
wide.   £5,750

FOUR POSTER

A Victorian papier-mâché bed by H. Schmurmoff & Co., Birmingham.
£6,000

A mahogany four-poster bed with box spring, 60in. wide.
£2,500

A George III mahogany four-post bedstead, 5ft.2in. wide, 6ft.9in. long, 7ft.6in. high.
£5,300

A mahogany four-post bed with blind-fret carved canopy, hung with aquamarine watered silk, 54½in. wide, 97in. high. (Christie's)   £3,520

A mahogany four-poster bedstead, labelled Heal & Son, Makers of Bedsteads and Bedding, London W, 74in. wide, 92in. high. (Christie's)   £3,520

A Georgian mahogany four-post bed, the canopy with breakfront cornice on reeded posts inlaid with satinwood panels, 72in. wide.
£5,500

19th century canopy bed, the upholstery with coloured bunches of flowers with braided edges.
(Finarte)   £4,007

A fine Federal carved mahogany bedstead, Philadelphia, circa 1800, having a shaped headboard, 7ft. long.
(Sotheby's)   £9,925

A four-poster bedstead decorated with leafage, six drawing curtains, 97in. high.
(Lawrence Fine Art)
£1,210

HALF TESTER

A Victorian Gothic style half tester bed, complete with original drapes, 4ft. 7ins. wide. £1,000

Late Victorian brass and iron half tester bedstead with ornamental head and foot rail, 7ft. 3ins. high. £500

An early Victorian oak half-tester bed with fluted pointed arched rear supports by a central panel and supporting a crenellated canopy, 90in. long. (Christie's) £990

'The Yatman', a half-tester bed, designed by William Burges, the walnut panelled footboard and framework surmounted by an elaborate and ebonised frieze and dentillated cornice, 157.5cm. wide. (Christie's) £28,600

A grey and blue-painted lit à la polonaise with domed hanging canopy with waved moulded rail, centred by flowerheads and foliage and hung with floral chintz, 61in. wide. (Christie's) £7,700

Fine American Renaissance figured maple and rosewood three-piece bedroom suite comprising a bedstead, nightstand, and dresser, by Herter Brothers, New York, circa 1872. (Butterfield & Butterfield) £7,211

A Victorian mahogany half tester double bed, the shaped footboard decorated with applied fielding and scallop motif, 4ft.6in. wide. £800

A Victorian walnut half-tester bed, with tasselled moulded canopy hung with printed cotton drapes, 67 x 68in. (Christie's) £935

Extremely fine Victorian figured walnut half tester bedstead, the foot of serpentine form with applied panelled designs. (G.A. Key) £3,000

25

HIGH POST

A Federal mahogany high-post bedstead, Mass., 1790-1810, with D-shaped head-board, 53½in. wide. £3,500

An Empire grain painted tall post bed, possibly Mahantango Valley, Penn., circa 1825, 51in. wide. (Skinner Inc.) £2,250

A Portuguese rosewood bed with pierced open headboard and with box spring, 18th century, 42in. wide. £2,750

A 19th century Italian blue-painted and parcel gilt four-post double bed-stead, 71in. wide, 103in. high. (Christie's) £1,750

A Federal maple and birch tall post tester bed, New England, circa 1820, 57in. wide, 80in. long. £3,250

A late Federal carved cherry-wood four-post bedstead, probably New York, circa 1825, 53¼in. wide. £5,320

Italian baroque style carved walnut posted bed, the massive cylindrical posts carved with three bands of vertical acanthus, 6ft. 9in. long.
(Butterfield & Butterfield)
£2,891

A mahogany four-poster bed with plain headboard and square pillars, 61in. wide, 84in. high. £2,500

An oak single bed, the panelled headboard carved with lozenges enclosing stylised flowerheads, partly 17th century, 42in. wide. (Christie's) £1,265

26

LIT EN BATEAU

A Charles X elmwood and
fruitwood inlaid lit en bateau,
the curved ends with scroll
terminals, 218cm. long.
(Finarte)   £3,444

A mahogany lit en bateau,
three-quarter size, circa 1830,
43½in. high.   £1,000

Empire mahogany and ormolu
lit en bateau decorated with
sirens, stars, arabesques and
mythological figures.
(Finarte)   £15,385

An Empire ormolu mounted
mahogany lit en bateau, each of
the panelled ends with a
rounded toprail and with box
spring and mattress. (Christie's
London)   £1,980

A walnut and parcel-gilt lit en
bateau with panelled ends
between column angles with
bands of foliage and gadrooned
ball feet, the shaped concave side
edged with ribbon-tied reeding
and scrolls carved with laurel
foliage, early 19th century,
probably German, 82in. long.
(Christie's)   £16,500

An Empire brass-inlaid
mahogany lit-en-bateau banded
overall with ebony, the scrolling
head and foot-board with
paterae, on ebonised lion's paw
feet, 103½in. wide.
(Christie's)   £5,500

An Empire mahogany lit en
bateau with box spring
mattress, 48in. wide, 86in.
long. (Christie's)   £5,000

An Empire gilt-bronze mounted
'lit en bateau', the swept ends and
front support applied with a
band of trailing poppies and
foliage, raised on scroll feet,
possibly Portuguese.
(Tennants)   £3,600

An Empire mahogany lit en
bateau with box spring, 54in.
wide, 73in. long.
(Christie's)   £5,000

A Charles I oak tester bedstead, circa 1640, 4ft.7½in.
wide.   £9,500

A North Country Charles
II oak tester bedstead,
circa 1670, 5ft.9in. wide,
7ft.7in. long.   £4,250

Charles I design carved
oak tester bed with foliate
carved cornice, 4ft. 3ins.
wide, circa 1640.   £2,500

Italian baroque carved giltwood
tester bed, composed of late 17th
century and later elements, the
spirally twisted endposts carved
in high relief with fruiting vines,
5ft. 9in. wide.
(Butterfield & Butterfield)
£1,518

An Elizabethan oak tester
bed with box-spring mat-
tress, 7ft. wide overall, circa
1580-1603.   £22,500

An Elizabethan oak, walnut
and painted tester bedstead,
the panelled canopy with
lunette and foliate moulded
cornice, late 16th century,
restorations, 66in. wide.
(Christie's)   £33,000

An oak tester bed, the canopy
with arcaded frieze, the panelled
backboard carved with foliage
and arcading above foliage-filled
lozenges, 17th century and later,
77½in. wide. (Christie's)
£2,970

An oak tester bedstead of
panelled construction carved
throughout with stylised
scrolls and foliage, the canopy
with a dentilled cornice, 62in.
wide. (Christie's)   £5,500

A mahogany tester bed, the
canopy with waved fringe and
padded backboard covered in
blue floral silk damask with two
George III turned stop-fluted
front posts, 82in. long.
(Christie's)   £1,540

28

Most early bookcases were designed by architects and made to fit a particular wall as the house was built. Fortunately for us, furniture designers such as Chippendale, Hepplewhite and the Adams, designed bookcases in sections in order that they might be moved into and out of houses.

Chippendale was among the first designers to build bookcases as separate units and it is clear that the architectural feeling of existing designs had some influence on the manner in which his were styled.

There were any number of open bookshelves designed at the end of the 18th century and such is their practicality that they have remained popular ever since.

The Georgian variety, elegantly tall and narrow with nicely graduated shelves, are made or mahogany, rosewood or satinwood, often japanned black or green and decorated with painted scenes or brass inlay. Some have cupboards or drawers in the base and they are supported on a variety of feet: bracket, scroll, claw, turned or with a shaped apron.

The revolving bookcase is the ideal piece of furniture for the idle bibliophile or for the family which lacks the wall space necessary for the more conventional methods of book display and storage.

Made in significant quantities between 1880 and 1920, many were given as free gifts by fast talking sales representatives, who offered them as inducements to potential purchasers of the innumerable home educator or encyclopaedia volumes in vogue at the time.

A French green painted pharmacy cupboard, with a pair of cupboard doors painted with book spines between fluted column pilasters, on bun feet, 19th century, 60in. wide. (Christie's S. Ken)   £1,320

An early Victorian mahogany breakfront bookcase with moulded bolection cornice and pediment above a frieze applied with the letters *XYZ*, 129in. wide. (Christie's)   £13,200

A Regency mahogany breakfront bookcase in six sections with moulded rectangular cornice, the angles with antifixes filled with paterae, above four glazed doors with arcaded glazing bars, 115in. wide. (Christie's)   £18,700

A George II mahogany breakfront bookcase, the broken architectural pediment above four rectilinear astragal glazed doors, the lower section with four panelled cupboard doors, 93in. wide. (Bonhams)   £6,000

An attractive mahogany serpentine front bookcase in the Georgian style, with fret carved broken swan neck pediment, 6ft. 11in. wide. (Spencer's)   £2,600

A very fine Federal inlaid mahogany breakfront bookcase, Salem, Massachusetts, circa 1800, in two parts, on tapering legs, 5ft. 7³/₄in. wide. (Sotheby's)   £76,090

An unusual mahogany centre bookcase, each side with two glazed doors, 21¼in. square. (Lawrence Fine Arts) £3,410

An early 19th century mahogany veneered open bookcase, the figured shaped and banded raised back with a central anthemion motif and fan corners, 6ft. 6in. wide. (Woolley & Wallis) £1,600

A second Empire walnut bookcase, the finialled serpentined cornice with cartouche and foliate cresting, 43½in. wide. (Christie's S. Ken) £660

A 19th century carved mahogany breakfront library bookcase in the Chippendale style, the stepped upper part with pierced lattice swan-neck pediment, 6ft. 5in. wide. (Phillips) £12,000

A Georgian mahogany open bookcase fitted with two graduated and adjustable shelves, containing two drawers below, on ring-turned tapering legs, 2ft. 8in. wide. (Phillips) £2,400

An early 19th century figured walnut and ebonised bookcase, the stepped moulded dentil carved cornice over frieze inlaid with heart motifs and husks, 4ft. 9in. wide. (Spencer's) £2,000

A George III mahogany bookcase with moulded dentilled gothic arcaded cornice above a pair of geometrically glazed cupboard doors, 65in. wide, 92in. high. (Christie's) £3,080

A giltmetal-mounted tortoiseshell and ebony boulle bibliothèque basse with breakfront rectangular top above a panelled door inlaid with foliate scrolls and mounted with a figure of Pomona flanked by musical trophies. (Christie's) £198,000

A late George III mahogany and satinwood banded bookcase, the lower section with rectangular top above two marquetry eared panelled doors with classical urns and swags, 44½in. wide. (Christie's) £2,750

An early 19th century pine open bookcase, with brass carrying handles, 18¹/₂in. wide.
(Dreweatt Neate) £520

A William IV breakfront bookcase, on a plinth base, 64in. wide.
(Dreweatt Neate) £780

A Chinese hualiwood bookcase, carved with lion scaped panels depicting figures, on block feet, 48in. wide. (Christie's S. Ken) £715

A mahogany breakfront bookcase in six sections with moulded cornice above four glazed doors enclosing shelves, each with arched glazing bars, 120in. wide.
(Christie's) £7,150

A Victorian mahogany bookcase, the moulded cornice above three pointed arch glazed sliding doors, on a plinth base, 79in. wide.
(Bonhams) £1,300

A late George III mahogany breakfront library bookcase with four astragal-glazed doors, four panelled doors applied with beading and on a plinth base, 105in. wide.
(Bearne's) £2,700

A Scottish oak bookcase, in two parts, rectangular overhung top above glazed folding cupboard doors, enclosing adjustable shelves, 128cm. wide.
(Christie's) £880

A mid-Victorian ormolu-mounted ebony, ebonised, brass and brown tortoiseshell bibliothèque basse inlaid à contre partie, decorated overall with birds and masks, 74in. wide.
(Christie's) £2,750

A Regency mahogany dwarf bookcase, the shaped back above open shelving with two panel doors below, 56¹/₂ x 48¹/₂in.
(Christie's S. Ken) £3,080

A French inspired walnut bookcase, upper section with three velvet-lined shelves, 49in. wide. (Locke & England) £2,700

A Regency rosewood and brass-inlaid breakfront dwarf bookcase with three-quarter pierced brass gallery above a frieze inlaid with foliate motifs, 96½in. wide. (Christie's S. Ken) £2,750

A late George III mahogany open bookcase on chest, the four graduated shelves above three long graduated drawers, 29in. wide. (Bonhams) £1,200

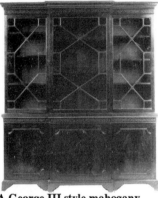

A George III style mahogany breakfront bookcase, the dentil moulded cornice with a blind fretwork frieze, above three astragal glazed doors, on bracket feet, 80in. wide, late 19th century. (Bonhams) £2,600

A Chippendale period carved mahogany secrétaire bookcase, the fall enclosing a fitted interior with tooled leather lined surface, chequer strung and tulipwood crossbanding and central cupboard, 3ft. 9in. wide. (Phillips) £5,500

A mahogany breakfront library bookcase fitment with a moulded cornice and enclosed by four glazed doors above four radial panelled doors, 92in. wide, late 18th century and later. (Christie's S. Ken) £5,280

A Regency mahogany breakfront secretaire library bookcase with a moulded cornice above pointed arched astragal glazed doors enclosing shelves, 103in. wide x 106in. high. (Christie's S. Ken) £8,800

A mahogany library breakfront bookcase carved with acanthus scrolls and foliate lunette borders, on cabriole legs with claw-and-ball feet, stamped *Gillows*, 91in. wide. (Christie's S. Ken) £4,620

A Victorian mahogany library bookcase with rounded rectangular and moulded cornice above three arched glazed panelled doors, on plinth base, 84in. high. (Christie's) £1,375

One of a pair of Regency mahogany bookcases each with moulded rectangular top and two glazed doors enclosing four shelves, 53in. wide.
(Christie's) (Two) £8,250

A Regency mahogany secretaire breakfront-bookcase, with moulded cornice above four glazed doors with arcaded glazing bars headed by acanthus, 113in. wide.
(Christie's) £20,900

An Irish William IV mahogany bookcase by Williams & Gibton, the bolection moulded inverted-breakfront cornice carved with Greek key, on plinth base, 62in. wide.
(Christie's) £9,350

A Federal mahogany bookcase, Philadelphia, 1790–1810, the two bookcase sections each with double cupboard doors glazed in a Gothic-arch pattern enclosing adjustable shelves, on a moulded base, 119in. wide.
(Christie's) £13,552

A Regency rosewood and simulated rosewood small bookcase with three-quarter brass scroll-galleried portor marble top, the frieze centred by anthemia and a patera above two open shelves and a door simulated as two shelves filled with books, 15in. wide.
(Christie's) £11,000

A George III mahogany breakfront bookcase, the moulded cornice above a pair of geometrically-glazed doors flanked by two doors enclosing shelves, 93¾in. wide.
(Christie's) £18,700

A George III mahogany breakfront library bookcase attributed to Thomas Chippendale, the centre with scrolled pediment outlined with ebony and with ebony dentils, 79in. wide.
(Christie's) £374,000

A mid-Georgian mahogany bookcase with moulded cornice above a pair of geometrically-glazed doors, on bracket feet, 63in. wide.
(Christie's) £23,100

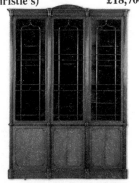

A Regency mahogany bookcase with moulded eared rectangular cornice with central arch above three long geometrically-glazed cupboard doors, each enclosing shelves, 75in. wide.
(Christie's) £6,600

A Regency mahogany break-front bookcase with raspberry moire silk lined interior, 108in. wide. £20,000

A George III mahogany standing bookcase, the apexed moulded cresting above graduating open rectangular shelves. (Christie's) £1,100

A George IV mahogany breakfront bookcase, in-laid with brass medallions, 8ft.4in. wide, circa 1825. £5,000

Empire style gilt-bronze-mounted mahogany bibliothèque, circa 1900, of slight breakfront outline, the shaped top above an elaborate gilt-bronze frieze, 6ft. 6in. wide. (Butterfield & Butterfield) £2,294

An impressive George IV-early Victorian mahogany breakfront library bookcase, the architectural cornice above four doors with gothic-arch astragals and four panelled doors, 145in. wide. (Bearne's) £8,300

A George III mahogany breakfront bookcase, the top with three sections, with moulded cornice above four geometrically-glazed doors enclosing shelves, on plinth base, 111in. wide. (Christie's) £6,050

A Georgian carved mahogany breakfront library bookcase with four glazed astragal doors, 2.50m. wide. (Phillips) £19,000

A Victorian oak breakfront library bookcase, the top section enclosed by four glazed panel doors, 88in. wide. £2,000

A George III mahogany break-front bookcase with moulded cornice above two pairs of gothic-glazed doors, on a plinth base, 100in. wide. (Christie's) £17,600

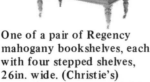

A late Victorian mahogany breakfront bookcase, the bookshelves enclosed by glazed tracery doors, 8ft. 2in. wide. £5,350

One of a pair of Regency mahogany bookshelves, each with four stepped shelves, 26in. wide. (Christie's) (Two) £6,050

A Regency mahogany breakfront bookcase in the manner of Gillows, with six glazed doors, 143½in. wide. £28,500

A William IV mahogany breakfront library bookcase, with four gothic arched glazed doors applied with honeysuckle and divided by reeded pilasters with acanthus capitals, 122in. wide.
(Christie's London) £35,200

A Victorian walnut and marquetry library bookcase with a cavetto cornice above inverted breakfront with four doors, each inlaid with sprays of flowers, 87in. wide.
(Lawrence Fine Art) £6,050

A George III carved mahogany and inlaid secrétaire library breakfront bookcase, the fall enclosing a fitted satinwood and decorated interior having cupboards below, on a plinth base, 8ft. 4in. wide.
(Phillips) £16,000

A Regency mahogany library bookcase, the top section with moulded cornice above four glazed doors. 95in. wide.
(Christie's) £7,150

A large Regency mahogany breakfront bookcase, the base with six panelled cupboard doors, 176in. wide. £5,500

George III mahogany breakfront bookcase having double-opening glazed doors, 7ft. wide.
(Giles Haywood) £3,800

A George III mahogany breakfront bookcase with moulded cornice above two pairs of rectangular-glazed doors enclosing shelves.
(Christie's) £6,050

An early Victorian rosewood dwarf bookcase with rectangular top and moulded cornice above two sets of two shelves, 72in. wide.
(Christie's) £4,620

A George III mahogany bookcase with moulded rectangular cornice above a band of entrelac and a pair of geometrically-glazed doors, 80in. wide.
(Christie's) £4,950

A George III mahogany bookcase in two sections, the moulded rectangular cornice carved with stiff leaves above a pair of chicken-wire-filled doors, and two George III mahogany and grained bookcases, en suite, 96¼in. high.
(Christie's) £7,700

Fine George III inlaid mahogany breakfront bookcase, circa 1790, the glazed doors with 'Gothik' mullions enclosing shelves, the lower section with four panelled cupboard doors, 8ft. 10in. wide.
(Butterfield & Butterfield) £18,911

One of a pair of Irish George III mahogany library bookcases, each with rectangular dentilled cornice above a pair of geometrically-glazed doors enclosing four shelves, 78¾in. wide.
(Christie's) £20,900

A mid-Georgian oak bookcase in two sections, with moulded rectangular cornice, on shaped bracket feet, 50½in. wide.
(Christie's) £3,300

A Regency mahogany breakfront bookcase, with stepped cornice above two pairs of horizontally-glazed doors each enclosing four shelves, on plinth base, the locks stamped *TURNERS*, 97¼in. wide.
(Christie's) £8,250

A George IV rosewood bookstand, the rectangular black leather-lined top with gadrooned edge above three shelves to front and back, 26in. wide.
(Christie's) £5,280

BUREAU BOOKCASES

The introduction, at the end of the 17th century, of higher ceilings encouraged the development of taller items of furniture and one of the most successful adaptations of existing designs to the new fashion was the bureau bookcase, which entailed quite simply the placing of a cabinet on top of the already popular sloping front bureau.

The earliest Queen Anne bureau cabinets had panelled doors to the upper section, often containing Vauxhall mirror glass, which enclosed a multitude of small drawers and pigeon holes.

Since bureau bookcase carcasses tend to be very similar, the pattern made by the glazing bars is a good aid to establishing the date of a piece. Unfortunately, however, it is not infallible, since many of the designs were used throughout the different periods.

Broadly, however, in the late 17th century, the glazing was of plain rectangles secured with putty behind substantial, half round mouldings. In the 1740's, the glass was mounted in a wavy frame and the establishment of mahogany soon after meant that, by the 1750's, the glazing bars could be finer and more decorative – usually forming 13 divisions or shaped in the fashion of Gothic church windows.

At the end of the 18th century, Hepplewhite introduced diamond glazing and also flowing curves and polygonal shapes, often enriched with foliate designs, in the glazing of his furniture. Sheraton too, used similar forms, often enhanced by their super-impositions on pleated silks.

An 18th century walnut and ebony banded bureau bookcase, the upper section having two arched mirrored doors, on scroll feet, Lombardy, 114cm. wide.
(Finarte) £44,393

A fine George I walnut and burr-walnut bureau cabinet, the upper part with a broken arched pedimented cornice centred with a giltwood figure of Atlas, on bracket feet, 3ft. 4in. wide.
(Phillips) £65,000

A mid-Georgian mahogany bureau, the broken pediment cornice with later turned vases above and a pair of mirror-glazed arched doors, on bracket feet, 38in. wide.
(Christie's) £3,475

An early 18th century burr walnut bureau bookcase of bombé outline, the upper part with broken arch pediment above two incised glass mirrors, Lombardy, 123cm. wide.
(Finarte) £41,322

A late 18th century Ligurian palisander veneer bureau bookcase, the lower section comprising two herringbone banded drawers, the upper section with two glazed doors, 126cm. wide.
(Finarte) £27,103

A fine 18th century Venetian walnut bureau cabinet, the base with a sloping flap, enclosing an interior of pigeonholes and two drawers around a cupboard, 3ft. 1in. wide.
(Phillips) £28,000

A German stained birch bureau cabinet, with hinged slope above a concave kneehole, on bracket feet, mid 18th century, 44in. wide. (Christie's) £8,800

A Chippendale mahogany blockfront secretary desk, circa 1780, 42in. wide. £38,000

A Chinese padoukwood bureau cabinet, the pair of doors each with a mirrored glass painting, circa 1780, 3ft.8in. wide. £35,000

A walnut bureau bookcase, the double dome upper section with a pair of astragal glazed doors, the fall front enclosing a stepped interior, on bracket feet, 39in. wide.
(Bonhams) £2,700

An early George III mahogany bureau cupboard in three sections, inlaid with stringing and above four long graduated drawers, 42in. wide. (Lawrence Fine Arts) £4,620

A Queen Anne walnut bureau bookcase, the fall front enclosing a stepped interior of drawers and pigeonholes around a cupboard door inlaid with a foliate oval, 41in. wide.
(Bonhams) £6,500

An 18th century Anglo-Dutch kingwood, burr yew-wood and amboyna oyster veneered bureau cabinet, 1.98m. high. £3,750

A Queen Anne brown and gold lacquer bureau cabinet, the mirror cupboard doors enclosing a fitted interior, 40½in. wide. £42,000

A walnut bureau bookcase, the arched top with two glazed doors above a feather banded slope, 36in. wide. (Christie's S. Ken) £2,090

BUREAU BOOKCASES

A walnut bureau bookcase with moulded cornice above a pair of glazed cupboard doors, 35¾in. wide. (Christie's) £8,250

A late 18th/early 19th century Dutch walnut and floral marquetry bureau cabinet in three parts, 1.39m. wide. (Phillips) £10,500

A George II oak bureau bookcase, the fall-front with concealed well, drawers, pigeon holes and central cupboard, 39in. wide. £1,950

A mid-18th century oak bureau cabinet with two fielded panelled doors enclosing shelves, sloping flap enclosing a cupboard, pigeon holes, drawers and a well, 40in. wide. (Bearne's) £1,250

An unusual Edwardian mahogany inlaid bureau bookcase, the breakfront cornice with chequer inlaid frieze, 126cm. wide. (Phillips) £1,700

German mid-18th century walnut and burr walnut tabernacle bureau cabinet, the door and drawers with secret locks, on bun feet, 116cm. wide. (Kunsthaus am Museum) £13,975

A George III mahogany bureau bookcase with astragal glazed doors, 124cm. wide, circa 1770. £1,430

Baroque walnut and kingwood inlaid bureau cabinet, with faceted mirror, 200cm. high, 120cm. wide. (Auktionshaus Arnold) £7,885

A George III oak bureau cabinet with cream painted paterae above two panelled doors, on bracket feet, 50in. wide. (Christie's London) £2,860

A George I black japanned and parcel gilt bureau cabinet, the fall front enclosing drawers and pigeonholes around a cupboard door, above a well, 28in. wide. (Bonhams) £7,000

A South German walnut and ebonised bureau-cabinet in three sections inlaid overall with geometrical stringing in stained wood, mid-18th century, 48in. wide. (Christie's) £3,960

A George III mahogany bureau bookcase, in four sections, the breakfront central section with arched cornice headed by an acanthus-scrolled cresting, probably North Country, 50¹/₂in. wide. (Christie's) £5,500

An Anglo-Dutch figured-walnut bureau-cabinet feather-banded and inlaid overall with bands and panels of seaweed marquetry, with later waved apron and shaped bracket feet, 18th century, the marquetry 19th century, 43¹/₄in. wide. (Christie's) £7,150

A George I walnut crossbanded and feather strung bureau cabinet, the upper part with an ogee moulded cornice and angular arched sides centred by a mirrored panel in the frieze, 3ft. 5in. wide. (Phillips) £28,000

An early Georgian burr walnut and walnut bureau-cabinet inlaid overall with featherbanding, the moulded rectangular cornice above two mirrored doors enclosing shelves, on bracket feet, 42³/₄in. wide. (Christie's) £8,800

William and Mary walnut veneered double-domed bureau cabinet, circa 1700, in three sections, the upper part enclosed by a pair of shaped arched mirrored doors, raised on bun feet, 40¹/₂in. wide. (Butterfield & Butterfield) £10,277

A South German walnut, fruitwood and marquetry bureau-cabinet in three sections, the hinged flap enclosing a fitted interior, the concave-fronted waved base with three long drawers, on bun feet, 47³/₄in. wide. (Christie's) £14,300

A Queen Anne walnut bureau cabinet, inlaid overall with feather-banding, the double dome cornice with vase-shaped finials, above two mirrored doors each with bevelled plate, on later bracket feet, 38in. wide. (Christie's) £15,400

A George III mahogany bureau bookcase with a pair of geometrically-glazed doors enclosing three shelves, on shaped bracket feet, 42in. wide. (Christie's)   £9,350

A black and gilt-japanned bureau cabinet decorated overall with chinoiserie scenes, with arched moulded cornice, 18th century, 40½in. wide. (Christie's)   £29,700

A George I walnut and parcel-gilt bureau-cabinet with a pair of later mirror-glazed doors enclosing two shelves, pigeon-holes and four drawers. (Christie's)   £35,200

A George I red and gilt-japanned bureau-cabinet decorated overall with chinoiserie figures in European poses hunting, riding and drinking tea, the upper section with broken arched cresting with cavetto cornice, 40¾in. wide. (Christie's)   £61,600

South German baroque inlaid walnut secretary bookcase, first quarter 18th century, in three parts, the centre section with a slant-lid centring a scene of hunters and a boar, raised on compressed-ball feet, 4ft. 1in. wide. (Butterfield & Butterfield)   £14,183

A George I brass-mounted figured and burr-walnut bureau-cabinet, the cavetto cornice above a pair of doors, the later mirror plates engraved with arches, on shaped bracket feet, 40in. wide. (Christie's)   £30,800

A walnut bureau bookcase, with two candle-slides, the lower section with fall-front enclosing a fitted interior above four graduated long drawers, on shaped bracket feet, basically early 18th century, 39in. wide. (Christie's)   £8,800

A George I figured walnut bureau-cabinet, with broken semi-circular pediment centred by a plinth above a pair of later mirror-glazed doors, 39½in. wide. (Christie's)   £31,900

A George III mahogany bureau-cabinet, the upper section with broken triangular pediment carved with foliage, egg-and-dart and dentilling, above a pair of glazed, shaped panelled doors, on ogee bracket feet. 45in. wide. (Christie's)   £8,250

A Dutch marquetry and mahogany bureau bookcase in three sections, circa 1760, 3ft.9in. wide. £11,000

A Victorian mahogany cylinder bureau bookcase, the ogee moulded cornice above a pair of arched glazed doors. (Bonhams) £1,800

A Chippendale block front desk and bookcase in two sections, Mass., 1760-80, 40½in. wide. £27,000

An 18th century Dutch walnut bombé miniature bureau cabinet, in two sections, crossbanded in oak, the arched moulded domed cornice with domed sides above a mirror panel door, 1ft. 5in. wide. (Phillips) £2,800

A good Gordon Russell English walnut yew and ebony bureau bookcase, the panelled doors inlaid with yew banding and ebony stringing and enclosing shelves, 1.90m. high. (Phillips) £5,520

A late 18th/early 19th century Dutch walnut bureau display cabinet of small size with canted sides, the upper part with floral carved platform cresting and fitted with carved laurel gilt serpentine shelves, 4ft. 11in. wide. (Phillips) £3,600

A Chippendale walnut desk and bookcase with four grad-uated long drawers, on ogee bracket feet, 85in. high. (Christie's) £3,072

A George III mahogany bureau bookcase with quarter veneered and inlaid fall front, fully fitted marquetry inlaid interior, 48in. wide. (Andrew Hartley) £3,000

A Chippendale style faded mahogany bureau bookcase on ogee bracket feet, 4ft. wide. £3,600

The writing desk was born in the monasteries of the Middle Ages, originally as a small, Gothic style oak box with a sloping lid hinged at the back like old fashioned school desk tops.

As time passed and men of letters increased their output, the writing box grew and was made a permanent fixture in the copying rooms of the monasteries, being built upon a stand, usually high enough to be used by a man standing or seated on a high stool.

Later, the hinges of the lid were moved from the back to the front, allowing the lid to fall forward on supports and form a writing platform in the open position. The practice on the Continent was the cover this area with a 'burel' or russet cloth, probably named from the Latin *burrus* (red), the colour of the dye used in its manufacture. It is doubtless from here that we gain the word bureau, though the connotations of the word have changed somewhat since it was first coined.

The bureau remained little more than a box on a stand until the close of the 17th century when it was married to a chest of drawers for obvious practical reasons. From that time onward, there have been few changes in the design beyond relatively small stylistic alterations which were reflections of the changing tastes of the fashionable rather than modifications dictated by practical usage.

Most reproductions of this period are of plain mahogany enhanced with a boxwood string inlay and a conch shell in the centre of the bureau flap.

A Dutch walnut and marquetry bureau inlaid throughout with medallions, baskets of flowers, foliage and swags, 38in. wide. (Bearne's)   £2,800

An oyster veneered walnut bureau, the sloping flap enclosing a fitted interior including a well above a pair of short and two graduated long drawers, on bun feet, 32in. wide. (Christie's London)
£3,850

A George I walnut veneered bureau outlined with feather stringing and crossbanding, on bracket feet, 34½in. wide. (Bearne's)   £1,700

An 18th century Italian walnut and bone inlaid bureau, the sloping flap enclosing a fitted interior, 50in. wide.   £6,500

A George II walnut bureau, the hinged flap enclosing a fitted interior with a door flanked by columns, pigeon holes and stepped drawers, on bracket feet, 36½in. wide. (Christie's London)   £1,650

A Chippendale mahogany slant lid serpentine desk, Mass., circa 1780, 41½in. wide. (Skinner Inc.)   £4,213

A Chippendale figured maple slant-front desk, Pennsylvania, 1770–1780, the rectangular top above a moulded slant-lid enclosing an elaborately fitted interior, on ogee bracket feet, 41in. wide.
(Christie's) £10,846

An oak bureau by Sidney Barnsley, sloping panelled flap enclosing a fitted interior, with frieze drawer and two panelled cupboard doors, 86.1cm. wide.
(Christie's) £2,420

A 19th century Dutch kingwood crossbanded and marquetry bureau, the top, sloping fall and front with all over panels of birds, flowers and foliage, 3ft. 4in. wide.
(Phillips) £6,500

A Queen Anne cherrywood desk-on-frame, probably New Hampshire, 1760–1780, the upper section with thumbmoulded slant-lid opening to a fitted interior with five valanced pigeonholes, on short cabriole legs, 41in. wide.
(Christie's) £4,620

A fine and rare pair of 18th century North Italian walnut and fruitwood bureaux, of small size and undulating outline, on moulded base and turned feet with casters, probably Venetian or Genoese, 2ft. 7in. wide.
(Phillips) £110,000

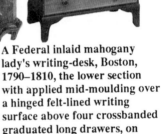

A Federal inlaid mahogany lady's writing-desk, Boston, 1790–1810, the lower section with applied mid-moulding over a hinged felt-lined writing surface above four crossbanded graduated long drawers, on bracket feet, 20in. wide.
(Christie's) £4,928

A late 18th century Continental fruitwood, marquetry and boxwood strung bureau à cylindre, the cylinder top with a harbour scene enclosing a fitted baize-lined interior, on cabriole legs, 3ft. 8in. wide.
(Phillips) £4,200

A Regency brass-inlaid rosewood cylinder bureau, the three-quarter galleried rectangular top above a solid roll-top inlaid with scrolls, 41½in. wide.
(Christie's) £5,500

A Chippendale cherrywood slant-front desk, Eastern Connecticut, 1760–1780, the slant lid enclosing an interior fitted with a shell-carved small drawer over two shaped small drawers flanked by fluted pilasters, 40¾in. wide.
(Christie's) £8,008

An early Georgian walnut bureau, the rectangular top and hinged flap enclosing two slides, drawers, pigeon-holes and secret drawers, on later shaped bracket feet, 37in. wide. (Christie's) £5,500

An 18th century South German walnut bureau, the serpentine flap enclosing a stepped interior of seven drawers about an open area, on cabriole legs with gilt bronze sabots, Dresden, 2ft. 6in. wide.(Phillips) £2,100

A late 18th century Continental kingwood and purplewood bureau of serpentine bombé shape, the top, front and sides veneered 'à quatre faces' within shaped reserves, 2ft. 10in. wide. (Phillips) £4,000

A Chinese export black and gilt lacquer bureau-on-stand decorated overall with foliage and chinoiserie landscapes, the rectangular top above a hinged slope enclosing an interior of drawers, pigeon-holes and a well, second half 18th century, 28½in. (Christie's) £2,420

A William and Mary stained burr-elm bureau banded overall in walnut, the rectangular top and hinged flap enclosing a fitted interior with walnut-lined drawers, on later bun feet, 42in. wide. (Christie's) £3,080

An early Georgian walnut and burr-walnut bureau inlaid overall with feather-banding, the hinged flap enclosing a fitted interior with slide, on later bracket feet, 29¾in. wide. (Christie's) £2,420

An Edwardian inlaid satinwood and crossbanded cylinder bureau, with a panelled shutter enclosing a fitted interior with leather-lined slide, on square tapering legs with brass castors, 41¾in. wide. (Christie's) £5,280

A diminutive Chippendale carved cherrywood slant-front desk, Woodbury, Connecticut, 1760–1780, the rectangular top above a thumb-moulded slant lid opening to a fitted interior with fan-curved and fluted prospect door flanked by document drawers, 39in. wide. (Christie's) £43,120

North Italian marquetry slant-front desk, second quarter 18th century, the top with chevron-banded reserves centring repeating classical urns and dolphins, raised on bracket feet, 46in. wide. (Butterfield & Butterfield) £6,555

A Venetian giltwood and lacquered bureau on stand, the flap and frieze painted in the arte povera style with genre scenes, on slender cabriole legs, 18th century, 110cm. wide.
(Finarte) £12,617

A Queen Anne walnut and feather banded bureau, the sloping flap enclosing an interior of four drawers and pigeonholes above a well, on later bun feet, 3ft. 2in. wide.
(Phillips) £2,800

A Louis XVI walnut cross-banded marquetry and parquetry bureau de dame, the sloping fall of shaped outline inlaid with flowers, 2ft. 11½in. wide.
(Phillips) £2,20(

An early Georgian burr walnut bureau, the top section with rectangular top and hinged flap with reading shelf enclosing a fitted interior with slide and secret drawers, 34in. wide.
(Christie's) £4,400

A Dutch marquetry bombé cylinder bureau, the cylinder opening in conjunction with a pull-out slide revealing fitted interior, 40in. wide.
(Lawrence Fine Art) £6,820

An early 19th century mahogany bureau, the fall front enclosing an interior of drawers and pigeonholes around a removable cupboard inlaid with leafy ovals, 40¼in. wide. (Bonhams) £950

An 18th century Piedmontese walnut and ivory marquetry bureau, of arc en arbelette form, inlaid with putti, grotesques, mythological beasts and trailing flower stems, 4ft. wide.
(Phillips) £18,000

A Chippendale carved mahogany serpentine slant-front desk, Massachusetts, circa 1770, the **rectangular** hinged lid carved with a concave fan flanked by two convex fans, 40in. wide.
(Sotheby's) £4,301

A Chippendale mahogany slant-front desk, New England, 1760–1790, the thumb-moulded slant lid opening to a fitted interior of short drawers over valanced pigeonholes, 41in. wide.
(Christie's) £2,125

A 19th century French lady's bureau, of Louis XV design in kingwood with marquetry panels of flowers, scrollwork and trellis, 2ft. 9in. wide. (Russell Baldwin & Bright) £800

A William and Mary stained burr-elm bureau attributed to Coxed and Woster, inlaid overall with pewter lines and crossbanded with kingwood, on bracket feet, 26in. wide. (Christie's) £7,700

A mid-Georgian green and gilt-lacquer bureau-on-stand, the top and sloping flap and sides decorated with chinoiserie scenes enclosing a fitted interior with a well, 35in. wide. (Christie's) £1,688

Anglo/Indian calamander tambour cylinder desk, first quarter 19th century, tambour top enclosing a fitted interior above a leather lined writing surface, 41¼in. wide. (Skinner Inc.) £3,608

Dutch Neoclassical walnut and marquetry cylinder bureau, second quarter 19th century, scalloped apron on square tapering supports, 34½in. wide. (Butterfield & Butterfield) £1,719

A late Victorian rosewood bureau inlaid with ivory and marquetry panels depicting gryphons, cornucopiae, scrolling arabesques and a falconry hunt, 31in. wide. (Christie's S. Ken) £1,155

A Dutch marquetry mahogany bombé bureau with scrolling foliate and bird motifs, the sloping fall front enclosing fitted interior, 19th century, 40in. wide. (Christie's) £4,840

A Japanese Export ebonised and marquetry cylinder bureau, last quarter 19th century, with a rectangular moulded cornice above a superstructure fitted with pigeonholes, 45¾in. wide. (Christie's East) £5,247

An early 18th century walnut and featherbanded bureau, the rectangular top with a sloping flap enclosing a cupboard, flanked by pillar drawers, on later bracket feet, 3ft. 1in. wide. (Phillips) £1,800

A North Italian walnut, ebonised and bone-inlaid bureau, with rectangular top and hinged flap inlaid with an oval of Leda and the Swan, enclosing a fitted interior with slide, 47in. wide. (Christie's) £11,000

A brass-mounted mahogany bureau à cylindre, the rectangular white-marble top with three-quarter gallery above two drawers and fitted interior with slide above one long drawer, 26in. wide. (Christie's) £3,850

A Veneto olivewood and ebonised bureau with rectangular top and hinged flap enclosing a fitted interior with slide, above three bowfronted graduated long drawers, mid-18th century, possibly Friulano, 49in. wide. (Christie's) £19,800

An 18th century Italian walnut crossbanded and strung bureau, the sloping fall opening to reveal a fitted interior with open centre part, on scrolled bracket feet, 4ft. wide. (Phillips) £9,500

An 18th century South German walnut crossbanded fruitwood and burr maple veneered bureau cabinet, the projecting concave fronted lower part containing three long drawers, on later bracket feet, 4ft. 4in. wide. (Phillips) £8,000

A William and Mary walnut and seaweed marquetry bureau-on-stand with rectangular top and hinged flap enclosing a fitted interior, $30^{1}/_{2}$in. wide. (Christie's) £8,250

A Milanese walnut bureau, banded overall with tulipwood, with stepped rectangular top with a drawer above a hinged flap enclosing a fitted interior on shaped bracket feet, 46in. wide. (Christie's) £27,500

A Victorian walnut-veneered and marquetry lady's bureau inlaid throughout with foliate arabesques and applied with gilt brass mounts, $34^{1}/_{2}$in. wide. (Bearne's) £2,350

A South German walnut, fruitwood and marquetry bureau, the rectangular top and waved flap inlaid with rosebuds, enclosing a fitted interior above two graduated long serpentine drawers, mid 18th century, 44in. wide. (Christie's) £8,800

CABINETS

Cabinets, as pieces of furniture, saw their British beginnings in the 17th century, when, designed basically for either specialised storage or display, they were introduced by craftsmen imported from the continent.

It was during the 18th and 19th centuries, however, that cabinets began to achieve a certain importance when they served to meet the needs of a nation obsessed with learning. Everybody, it would seem, began to collect things; coins, shells, fossils, ores, mineral samples, china – and what was the point of amassing vast collections of these wonders without having the means of displaying them for the enjoyment of family and admiring friends?

Cabinets, then, became indispensable, and although most of the earlier examples were imported from Europe, a few were actually made in Britain.

Handles can be a useful pointer to the age of a piece of furniture, though not infallible, for they were continually swapped around or replaced.

Earliest handles were brass drop loops which were held on to the backplates with brass or iron wire or, after 1700, by the heads of nutted bolts. The heavier brass loop handles began to be used in 1735, and each bolt head is mounted on a separate backplate.

Pierced backplates date from about 1720 and continued to be used, with the addition of ornamental key escutcheons, until about 1750, when sunken escutcheons began to be used.

An ormolu-mounted amboyna, marquetry and parquetry commode after the model by Riesener at Chantilly, with bowed eared carrara marble top, third quarter 19th century, 83in. wide.
(Christie's)   £22,000

A Louis XIV boulle and ebony cabinet en armoire inlaid in contre partie marquetry with brass, pewter and brown tortoiseshell, in two sections, on block feet, the top section with later back, 57in. wide.
(Christie's)   £104,500

A red and gilt-japanned cabinet-on-stand decorated overall with chinoiserie figures in landscapes, the stand with two doors flanking a kneehole drawer on chamfered square legs and block feet, circa 1900, 60in. wide.
(Christie's S. Ken)   £2,750

A mid-Victorian ormolu-mounted burr walnut stained wood and ebonised side cabinet the moulded breakfront top with beaded rim above a foliate frieze, on plinth base, 69¹/₂in. wide.
(Christie's)   £3,520

A George III satinwood and marquetry bombé cabinet, the eared serpentine top above a pair of doors, each inlaid with a rose above a pair of doors simulated as three drawers, 39³/₄in. wide.
(Christie's)   £5,500

A George III harewood, mahogany and marquetry side cabinet banded overall with tulipwood, the two doors with waved apron each inlaid with an oval with ribbon-tied end-cut marquetry foliate wreaths, 38¹/₄in. wide.
(Christie's)   £4,400

Late 16th century Spanish walnut and red-painted cabinet with two frieze drawers, 48in. wide. (Christie's) £20,900

A late George III dwarf mahogany side cabinet of breakfront D shape with one fielded panel door, 40½in. wide. (Lawrence Fine Arts) £2,860

An 18th century Portuguese Colonial rosewood table cabinet, the front with various sized drawers, 13in. wide. £700

A fine Aesthetic Movement ebony and lacquer cabinet, set with lacquered rosewood panels of Japanese landscapes with parquetry borders, stamped Gregory & Co. 212 & 214, Regent St., London 944, 202cm. high. (Christie's) £1,870

An ebony veneered drug cabinet, with gilt brass ormolu mounts and fittings, inscribed *George Henry Rogers M.R.C.S. in grateful rememberance of valuable services Erasmus Wilson May 8th 1871*, 22in. wide. (Christie's) £495

A walnut cabinet with moulded rectangular top inset with a serpentine marble slab, above a panelled door inset with a pietra dura panel inlaid with a flower-vase within an arched niche, the cabinet 17th century, 28in. wide. (Christie's) £5,500

Grain painted pine lawyer's cabinet, the panel doors opening to reveal thirty-eight compartments, New England, circa 1800, 33in. wide. £2,300

One of a pair of early George III rosewood cabinets on stands, each with pierced fretwork gallery, 37in. wide. £27,500

A North Italian walnut cabinet, with marquetry and ivory inlay, 4ft.9in. wide, circa 1700, with later additions. £1,000

French Restoration mahogany and mahogany veneer marble top console cabinet, probably New York, circa 1820, 42in. wide.
(Skinner) £1,154

A French gilt-metal-mounted marquetry side cabinet with breccia marble top, on cabriole legs with gilt sabots, 39in. wide.
(Christie's) £880

A French mahogany purpleheart and walnut D-shaped cabinet with giltmetal mounts and inlaid overall, on gilt toupie feet, 48in. wide.
(Christie's) £3,850

A walnut cabinet in two sections with moulded cornice above central arched glazed compartments flanked by open compartments, mid 19th century, possibly Colonial, 100in. high.
(Christie's) £6,050

A George III mahogany serpentine side cabinet, crossbanded overall in satinwood and inlaid with trails of grapes and vine leaves and with ebonised lines in an interlocking oval pattern, 40½in. wide.
(Christie's) £20,900

A mahogany and black bean panelled cabinet on chest designed by Betty Joel, in two parts, with a pair of inlaid cupboard doors enclosing adjustable shelf, January 1937, 60cm. wide.
(Christie's) £770

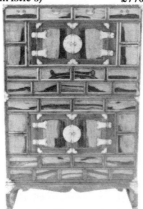

An Arts & Crafts painted cabinet and bookshelves (top missing), the figures drawn by M. Reed, 61cm. wide.
(Phillips) £320

An Italian Renaissance style walnut cabinet on stand, on a scroll cut trestle base, 49½in. high.
(Skinner Inc.) £355

A Korean paulownia wood tansu, 19th century, on bracket feet, brass mounts, (piece missing) 50½in. high.
(Skinner Inc.) £414

A George III mahogany side cabinet with eared rectangular breakfront top above one long central cedar-lined drawer, on turned feet, 62in. wide. (Christie's) £33,000

A French walnut cabinet à deux corps, inset with black-veined marble tablets, in two sections, carved with Leda and the Swan and Diana and a stag, second half 16th century, 40in. wide. (Christie's) £9,900

A Regency brass-inlaid rosewood side cabinet with later white marble top, the frieze with three tablets inlaid with scrolling foliage, on paw feet, 71in. wide. (Christie's) £6,050

A George III green, black and gold japanned cabinet-on-stand mounted with copper hinges and escutcheons in the Japanese style, decorated with chinoiserie scenes, 38$^{1}/_{2}$in. wide. (Christie's) £26,400

A pair of Louis XV black and gilt-japanned and lacquer encoignures, each with later bowed liver marble top above a bowed door incorporating a Chinese lacquer panel, 28in. wide. (Christie's) £9,350

A black and gilt-japanned cabinet-on-stand, decorated overall with chinoiserie scenes of birds and figures in a landscape, the stand with chain pattern frieze on cabriole legs, early 18th century, 40$^{1}/_{2}$in. wide. (Christie's) £4,400

A Flemish silver-mounted parcel-gilt, tortoiseshell, ebony, rosewood and marquetry cabinet-on-stand, the scroll broken cresting carved with the Virgin and Child and Saint John, on shaped giltwood feet, 76in. wide. (Christie's) £71,500

A mid Victorian inlaid walnut credenza with ledged back above a central pair of doors with oval panels of scroll marquetry flanked by column uprights and glazed compartments, 72$^{1}/_{2}$in. wide. (Christie's) £5,500

A Portuguese colonial rosewood and bone-inlaid cabinet with rectangular top and fall-front inlaid with foliate scrolls, the sides with carrying-handles, early 18th century, 23$^{1}/_{2}$in. wide. (Christie's) £4,400

A North Italian cabinet with bone inlay and carrying handles, the ebonised stand with spiral supports, 20in. wide. (Greenslades) £2,450

A 17th century Flemish ebonised, decorated and tortoiseshell cabinet-on-stand, the interior and reverse of the doors, backs and drawer fronts with paintings, 3ft. 2in. wide. (Phillips) £12,500

Shibayama style inlaid lacquer shodana, Meiji period, with an upper section of hinged double-doors, decorated to the front with Genso teaching the flute to Yokihi, 37³/₄ in. high. (Butterfield & Butterfield) £2,541

One of a pair of ormolu-mounted citronnier side cabinets banded overall in amaranth, each with canted rectangular carrara marble top with pierced three-quarter gallery, 35in. wide. (Christie's) £13,200

A red and gilt-lacquer cabinet-on-stand, the cabinet decorated overall with chinoiserie figures, buildings and birds in a landscape, on a giltwood stand, 48in. wide. (Christie's) £6,050

A George III mahogany cabinet banded overall in tulipwood and inlaid with ebonised and boxwood stringing, the bowed top centred by an oval above two bowed doors, 51in. wide. (Christie's) £9,900

A French Provincial mahogany side cabinet with two panelled doors enclosing a shelf flanked by two narrow panelled doors, 18th century, 50in. wide. (Christie's) £4,950

Shibayama style inlaid gold lacquer and wood cabinet, Meiji period, carved in high relief with prunus and songbirds, 48in. wide. (Butterfield & Butterfield) £3,886

A 17th century Milanese ebonised coromandel and ivory inlaid table cabinet, fitted with nine drawers about a central enclosed cupboard with incised and inlaid Classical military figure, fruit, grotesques, flowers and landscapes, 2ft. 1¹/₂in. wide. (Phillips) £4,600

CABINETS

French mahogany and kingwood ormolu mounted encoignure, circa 1860, 2ft.8in. wide.

£850

A good mid Victorian walnut and inlaid side cabinet of broken 'D' shaped outline, the figured top with a broad band of entwined shamrock and leafy tendrils, 65in. wide.
(Tennants) £3,700

A Dutch oak cabinet with moulded arched cornice above a pair of glazed doors, mid 18th century, 89½in. high.
(Christie's) £6,600

A walnut cabinet on stand, the stepped top with moulded cornice and arcaded frieze above two partly glazed panelled doors, on ribbed and fluted naturalistic cluster columns carved with acanthus, 42in. wide. (Christie's London)
£5,280

A Liberty & Co. break-front cabinet, shaped central glazed cupboard doors above rectangular top, flanked on each side with arched and columned open recesses and adjustable shelves, 122.5cm. wide.
(Christie's) £550

An ebonized and painted corner cabinet, designed by Charles Rennie Mackintosh, with painted panels by Margaret Macdonald Mackintosh, the two cupboard doors with pierced hinge plates, circa 1897, 183cm. high.
(Christie's) £13,200

One of a pair of 19th century Continental serpentine-fronted walnut inlaid and crossbanded side cabinets, 26in. wide.
(Giles Haywood) £1,850

A Regency design satinwood and gilt decorated side cabinet of broken D-shaped outline with a rosewood banded top above two frieze drawers with grill doors below, 56in. wide.
(Christie's S. Ken) £4,950

A Regency mahogany side cabinet with a frieze drawer and pair of panelled doors filled with gilt trellis, 25in. wide.
(Christie's) £2,200

An ormolu mounted mahogany cabinet, the base with a pair of shibayama lacquer panel doors, 48¼in. wide. £6,500

A Victorian ebonised and porcelain mounted side cabinet, applied throughout with gilt brass mouldings, 59½in. wide. (Bearne's) £820

A lacquered stacking double cabinet on stand, each pair of doors and the sides painted in polychrome on gilt, 2ft.9in. wide. £1,250

A late 17th century japanned cabinet on contemporary carved giltwood stand, the upper part enclosed by a pair of panel doors decorated with chinoiserie landscapes, 1m. wide.
(Phillips London) £3,200

A fine pair of Regency mahogany dwarf cabinets in the Gillows manner, banded with satinwood and outlined throughout with boxwood and ebony stringing, 31½in. wide.
(Bearne's) £31,000

Flemish baroque style oak cabinet, 19th century, enclosed by two pairs of panelled doors applied with mitred geometric mouldings centred by cherubs' heads, 4ft. 4in. wide.
(Butterfield & Butterfield)
£2,699

A Flemish ivory inlaid ebony and tortoiseshell cabinet-on-stand, the cabinet 17th century, 40in. wide.
(Christie's) £2,860

A George III satinwood and marquetry breakfront side cabinet of coffer form in the style of Mayhew and Ince with rectangular stepped top inlaid with a fan oval centred by a bacchic mask, 55in. wide.
(Christie's) £46,200

An ormolu mounted birch side cabinet, with a door applied with roundels and anthemions, on turned feet, 32in. wide.
(Christie's) £3,080

A late 17th century burr walnut credenza, the moulded front with two arched panelled doors, North Italian, 167cm. wide.
(Finarte) £11,938

An Italian ivory inlaid display cabinet, probably Milan, circa 1880, in 17th century manner, 149cm. wide.
(Sotheby's) £6,380

A French gilt-bronze mounted side cabinet, Napoléon III, Paris, circa 1850, of breakfront form with three panelled cupboard doors, 220cm. wide.
(Sotheby's) £3,080

A Dutch walnut and marquetry bombé display-cabinet inlaid overall with trailing foliage and foliate arabesques, 19th century, 75in. wide.
(Christie's) £9,350

A Korean brass-mounted hardwood table cabinet with a pair of cupboard doors enclosing a fitted interior, on bracket feet, 22in. wide.
(Christie's) £1,100

A pair of purplewood corner cabinets, with two concave arched mirrored doors above three drawers flanked by two cupboards, 218cm. high, Piedmonte, second half 18th century.
(Finarte) £36,731

A French red Boulle side cabinet, Napoléon III, Paris, circa 1855, of breakfront form with a black marble top, 162cm. wide.
(Sotheby's) £3,080

A good Italian ivory-inlaid ebony-veneered cabinet on stand, probably Milan, circa 1860, in Renaissance style, 127cm. wide.
(Sotheby's) £11,000

A tortoiseshell cabinet, Spanish, 19th century, with central door centred by a saint surrounded by numerous small drawers, 70cm. high.
(Sotheby's) £2,860

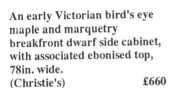

An early Victorian bird's eye maple and marquetry breakfront dwarf side cabinet, with associated ebonised top, 78in. wide.
(Christie's) £660

An early 19th century thuya bedside cabinet with coloured fruitwood inlay of mythological figures and black marble top, French, 91.5cm. high.
(Finarte) £5,739

A good French side cabinet, Napoléon III, Paris, circa 1870, in Louis XVI manner, the white marble top above four painted enamelled panels, 167cm. wide.
(Sotheby's) £7,920

A French Vernis-Martin bombé side cabinet, Paris, circa 1890, with a serpentine breccia marble top above a cupboard door painted with scènes galantes, 87cm. wide.
(Sotheby's) £5,280

A pair of French 'Boulle' small side cabinets, Louis-Philippe, Paris, circa 1845, each with a cupboard door disguised as four drawers, 67cm. wide.
(Sotheby's) £7,920

A good French carved walnut Renaissance Revival cabinet, Napoléon III, Paris, circa 1860, in the manner of Fourdinois, 153cm. wide.
(Sotheby's) £12,100

A Queen Anne lacquered cabinet on stand, painted in polychrome with Chinese figures, on hipped carved cabriole legs and scroll feet, 134cm. wide.
(Finarte) £10,101

One of a pair of French ebony side cabinets, Napoléon III, Paris, circa 1850, each with mottled marble tops, 130cm. wide.
(Sotheby's) £15,400

A 17th century Chinese black lacquer cabinet with engraved and shaped brass hinges, on a late 17th century English silvered and giltwood stand, 41in. wide.
(Bearne's) £6,500

A mid Victorian walnut floral marquetry and ormolu-mounted side cabinet with inlaid glazed panelled door flanked by female mask mounts, 31in. wide. (Christie's) £1,650

A William IV mahogany library cabinet with leather lined articulated rounded rectangular top, the sides with foliate bronze handles, on plinth base, 54in. wide. (Christie's London) £17,600

A Louis XIV walnut cabinet on later oak stand with moulded cornice above foliate carved frieze flanked by cherub heads, 51in. wide. (Christie's) £990

An Edwardian mahogany and marquetry side cabinet inlaid overall with satinwood bands and ebony and boxwood stringing, 30¼in. wide. (Christie's) £1,650

An oak dwarf cabinet with two doors each carved with a grotesque mask, a basket of fruit, a bowl of flowers, a bunch of grapes, a scroll and a sheaf of foliage, 16th century, probably Spanish, 34in. wide. (Christie's London) £4,400

An ormolu mounted marquetry and parquetry side cabinet of Transitional style with moulded and chamfered breakfront rouge marble top, 34in. wide. (Christie's) £1,760

A Federal apple-green painted tulip poplar cabinet with drawers, Pennsylvania, circa 1825, the rectangular top with shaped splashboard, width 42¼in. (Sotheby's) £2,837

A good Victorian porcelain mounted walnut side cabinet of broken shallow D-form, with small floral porcelain ovals, 60in. wide, 39½in. high. (Tennants) £2,800

An ormolu mounted ebony and black lacquer side cabinet, the door decorated with a Chinese landscape, on paw feet, 28in. wide. (Christie's London) £1,870

A gilt-metal mounted rosewood dwarf cabinet with mottled green marbled top above brass grille, first quarter 19th century, 23¹/₂in. wide.
(Christie's) £605

A rosewood breakfront side cabinet with a central trellis-filled pleated silk-backed door enclosing a shelf flanked by rosette-headed pilasters, part early 19th century, 61¹/₄in. wide.
(Christie's) £2,420

An oak gate-leg writing cabinet designed by M. H. Baillie-Scott, rectangular top above fall-flap with pierced steel hinge plates designed by C. A. Voysey, 91.5cm. wide.(Christie's)£3,300

A Regency ormolu-mounted mahogany side cabinet with moulded rectangular top above two doors inlaid with ebonised lines and fitted brass trellis, 38in. wide.
(Christie's) £1,650

A carved wooden wall cabinet, the design attributed to the Workshop of Princess Tenichef in Talachkino, the rectangular overhanging top above two doors carved with the characters 'Tsar Saltan Saltanivich' and 'Solovei the Robber', 40cm. wide.
(Christie's) £385

A Goanese ivory, ebony and hardwood cabinet on stand inlaid with interlaced geometric roundels, on stylised mermaid caryatids upon block and bun feet, 40in. wide.
(Christie's) £27,500

A late Victorian giltmetal-mounted brass-inlaid ebonised and hardstone side cabinet, the triple-mirrored superstructure with waved cresting centred by a ribbon-tied oval, 70in. wide.
(Christie's) £1,980

A French gilt metal mounted mahogany breakfront side cabinet with eared Carrara marble top and frieze applied with riband tied swags of flowers, 75in. wide. (Christie's S. Ken) £2,090

A Regency mahogany side cabinet with pierced Grecian motif brass galleried top above two doors with brass grille panels, 52¹/₂in. wide.
(Christie's S. Ken) £1,210

An inlaid walnut cabinet, circa 1850, the serpentine lower part with inset oval leather panel, a drawer and cabriole legs, 3ft. 2in. wide. (Sotheby's) £2,750

A late Victorian satinwood and marquetry bowfronted side cabinet by Edwards & Roberts, the shaped rectangular top crossbanded with rosewood and inlaid with a central fan medallion, on moulded plinth and turned tapering toupie feet, 79¼in. wide. (Christie's) £4,620

A walnut and marquetry cabinet on stand, inlaid with 17th century Augsburg marquetry panels of stylised architectural and foliate landscapes, 3ft. 4in. wide. (Phillips) £2,400

A satinwood, rosewood and parcel-gilt breakfront side cabinet, the top crossbanded with rosewood and with two curved sides above a pair of panelled doors filled with brass grille and backed with pleated silk, basically late 18th century, 42¼in. wide. (Christie's) £7,150

A Regency rosewood side cabinet, surmounted by a grey veined marble top enclosed by a pair of pleated silk grille doors, 3ft. 7in. wide. (Phillips) £1,400

An ormolu-mounted kingwood and parquetry side cabinet of Louis XV style, with eared serpentine-shaped breche violette marble top above a frieze drawer, late 19th/20th century, 48½in. wide. (Christie's) £6,050

A black and gold japanned chinoiserie double dome cabinet, the concave moulded cornice with gilt finials above a pair of doors with pierced brass lock plates and hinges, parts 18th century, 4ft. 1in. wide. (Phillips) £6,500

A small marquetry side cabinet, London, circa 1855, in the contemporary French manner, the breakfront 'D' shape door inlaid with foliage, 4ft. 3in. wide. (Sotheby's) £2,035

A Regency rosewood dwarf side cabinet inlaid with boxwood lines, the frieze with marquetry panels above a pair of grille doors, backed by pleated silk, 2ft. 4in. wide. (Phillips) £2,000

An ormolu-mounted rosewood, simulated rosewood and parcel-gilt inverted-breakfront side cabinet with shaped channelled rectangular white marble top, part early 19th century, 72¼in. wide.
(Christie's)   £7,150

A Lamb of Manchester walnut carved side cabinet, the design attributed to Bruce J. Talbert, overall with ebonised details, on four turned and carved legs supporting a platform shelf, 100cm. wide. (Christie's) £2,750

A fine marquetry side cabinet, attributed to Cremer of Paris, circa 1860, with two mirrored doors flanking a pair of doors inlaid with musical trophies, 7ft. wide. (Sotheby's)   £8,800

One of a pair of ormolu-mounted, pietra dura and ebonised cabinets, each with a rectangular verde antico marble top, above an egg-and-dart moulding, the frieze with an acanthus and flower stem cast mount, 19th century, 44¾in. wide.
(Christie's) (Two)   £12,100

A pair of Chinese export brass-mounted red and gilt-lacquer cabinets-on-stands decorated overall with chinoiserie landscapes, each with rectangular top above a pair of doors enclosing seven variously-sized decorated drawers, 22in. wide.
(Christie's)   £7,150

A walnut and marquetry cabinet-on-stand inlaid overall with stylised foliate scrolls, the later rectangular cavetto cornice above a long convex-fronted frieze drawer, basically late 17th century, 48in. wide.
(Christie's)   £2,420

A George III satinwood and floral marquetry side cabinet of semi-elliptical form, the top banded with rosewood and centred by a ribbon-tied floral spray of roses, narcissi and other flowers, 26¼in. wide.
(Christie's)   £9,900

A George III satinwood and marquetry table cabinet, crossbanded in tulipwood and inlaid with fan spandrels, the top inlaid with a harewood medallion, 1ft. 4in. wide.
(Phillips)   £900

A Japanese copper-mounted Lac Burgaute black lacquer cabinet-on-stand, decorated overall with flowering trees, the foliate legs headed by putti clasping flowers and joined by an X-shaped stretcher centred by a flowerhead, 32¼in. wide.
(Christie's)   £5,500

A George III mahogany collector's cabinet on stand, fitted with twelve drawers enclosed by a pair of panel doors, 1ft. 9in.
(Phillips) £2,600

Late 18th century Dutch mahogany inlaid dressing cabinet with hinged cover, 46½in. wide. £1,250

A yew and brass mounted cabinet-on-stand surmounted by rectangular rouge marble top above a pair of doors inset with oval Sèvres-style porcelain panels, 41in. wide.
(Christie's) £2,640

A William and Mary walnut, crossbanded and oyster veneered cabinet on stand, crossbanded in acacia, terminating in bun feet, 5ft. 2in. wide. (Phillips) £11,000

A satinwood collectors' cabinet, probably London, circa 1860, the pair of panelled cupboard doors open to reveal ten graduated drawers, with key, 67cm. wide.
(Sotheby's) £2,530

A Goanese hardwood brass mounted and ivory inlaid cabinet, fitted with six drawers above a frieze drawer, on bobbin-turned uprights with bun feet, early 18th century, 28in. wide.
(Christie's) £3,080

A 18th century Continental fruitwood cabinet, the upper part with a moulded cornice and concave sides flanking a pair of doors with a later lattice, 6ft. 1in. wide.
(Phillips) £22,000

A French kingwood and parquetry side cabinet, the oval mirror back with gilt metal cresting centred by a ribbon tied Sèvres style plaque, 72in. wide. (Bonhams) £3,600

A Regency rosewood side cabinet, the upper section with plain frieze applied with a gilt metal spray of flowers and leaves, 5ft. 9in. high.
(Spencer's) £1,000

Ceylonese carved rosewood four door cabinet made for the English market, second quarter 19th century, raised on tapering ring-turned feet, 47¾in. wide. (Butterfield & Butterfield) £1,215

One of a pair of Regency mahogany side cabinets, each with a rectangular banded top with brass border above two frieze drawers and brass grill doors, 40in. wide. (Christie's S. Ken) (Two) £3,300

A Chinese Export black and gilt lacquer cabinet, fitted with two doors and decorated overall with rocky landscapes, 18th century, 32in. wide. (Christie's) £893

A black and gilt lacquer cabinet, the front fitted with doors and with engraved brass hinges and lock plate, 18th century European, possibly Irish, 38in. wide. (Christie's) £1,787

A fine mahogany slide cabinet of twenty-one drawers with bone handles, containing a large number of professional and amateur slide preparations, 19th century, 14½in. high. (Christie's) £935

A Flemish and ebonised cabinet on stand, the moulded cornice above eight drawers each with pietra paesina marble panel, late 17th century, 46in. wide. (Christie's) £3,850

Empire style mahogany and ormolu mounted cabinet last quarter 19th century, moulded cornice above a pair of cabinet doors, 37in. wide. (Skinner Inc) £1,038

A William III walnut veneered cabinet on stand, the moulded frieze fitted with two drawers. £3,600

A late Victorian ebonised and amboyna large salon cabinet, the stepped superstructure with balustraded frieze over a horizontal rectangular miror plate, 6ft. 1in. wide. (Spencer's) £1,800

An important 17th century Italian tortoiseshell, ivory, ebony and gilt bronze mounted architectural cabinet of impressive proportions and accentuated perspective, the whole inset with gilt metal classical relief panels, 6ft. 4in. wide.
(Phillips)   £290,000

An 18th century South German walnut and marquetry cabinet on stand, inlaid with lines and panels of flower sprays, on a walnut veneered and beechwood stand, 2ft. 10in. wide.
(Phillips)   £1,300

A mid Victorian burr-walnut, tulipwood banded and ormolu-mounted credenza, the serpentine and eared top above two shaped panelled doors, flanked by open shelves, 76¼in. wide.
(Christie's)   £4,950

A mid-Victorian mother-of-pearl-inlaid black and gilt-japanned side cabinet, decorated overall with floral bouquets within gilt scrolls, on plinth base, 45in. wide.
(Christie's)   £4,180

One of a pair of early Victorian giltmetal-mounted table-cabinets, crossbanded in kingwood, on tapering acanthus-cast feet, 31in. wide.
(Christie's)   (Two)   £4,180

A 'Dieppe ivory' architectural cabinet on stand, carved and engraved all over, the cabinet surmounted by a crenellated cornice and eight tapering finials, fitted with seven concealed drawers, second half 19th century, the cabinet 25¼in. wide. (Christie's)   £19,250

A Regency ormolu-mounted ebonised, parcel-gilt and Chinese lacquer side-cabinet, the two panelled doors each inset with a panel of 18th century Somada-style Chinese lacquer, 57¾in. wide.
(Christie's)   £16,500

An ormolu-mounted brass, brown tortoiseshell and ebony boulle side cabinet in the manner of A-C Boulle with moulded rectangular breakfront top, late 19th century, 71in. wide.
(Christie's)   £3,300

A mid-Victorian ormolu-mounted burr walnut and Sèvres-style porcelain side cabinet banded overall in amaranth and inlaid with boxwood stringing, 66in. wide.
(Christie's)   £3,300

A Napoleon III ormolu-mounted brass-inlaid ebony and simulated tortoiseshell side cabinet, the breakfront black marble top above an acanthus-cast frieze, 66in. wide.
(Christie's) £3,520

A Viennese ebonised and polychrome enamel table cabinet, mounted all over with plaques depicting mythological scenes, late 19th/early 20th century, 13$\frac{1}{2}$in. wide.
(Christie's) £4,400

A tortoiseshell, ivory and mahogany cabinet with a panelled fall-front enclosing six variously-sized mahogany-lined drawers, the interior and panels Colonial, 18th century, in a William IV exterior, 11$\frac{1}{2}$in. wide.
(Christie's) £1,210

A rare late 17th century Iberian tortoiseshell and mother of pearl two-tier cabinet on stand of trapezoidal form, on octagonal section fluted knopped and ring turned legs, 5ft. 6in. wide.
(Phillips) £10,500

A pair of side cabinets, rectangular overhanging moulded top above single banded cupboard door with brass drop handles, on baluster turned legs, 34.7cm. wide.
(Christie's) £5,500

A late 18th century North Italian walnut, fruitwood, tulipwood crossbanded and marquetry side cabinet, in the manner of Maggiolini, on square tapered legs, 1ft. 10in. wide.
(Phillips) £5,000

One of a pair of Napoleon III ormolu-mounted tulipwood and rosewood wall-cabinets each with two shaped mirror-backed glass shelves, 24in. high.
(Christie's) (Two) £1,760

Fine Regency rosewood, parcel-gilt and gilt-brass side cabinet, circa 1810, with an orange scagliola top surmounted by a galleried three-division mirrored back superstructure, 5ft. 11$\frac{3}{4}$in. wide.
(Butterfield & Butterfield) £5,781

A Charles II black japanned and chinoiserie decorated cabinet on a contemporary carved and silvered stand, the upper part containing eleven drawers, 5ft. high.
(Phillips) £8,000

An unusual Edwardian mahogany drinks cabinet, the fall front opening to reveal a suspended shelf retaining three cut glass decanters, 31in. wide. (Tennants) £850

A Regency rosewood serpentine side cabinet with brass acanthus leaf borders to the top and base, 51in. wide. (Lawrence Fine Arts) £2,200

A 1930s English Art Deco burr birch cocktail cabinet, in two parts, the upper arm of drum form, mirror-backed and with shaped shelves, 43in. wide. (Tennants) £600

Pair of Louis XIV style marquetry cabinets, third quarter 19th century, each polished slate rectangular top with outset rectangular corners above a frieze drawer over a cupboard door enclosing a shelf, 29in. wide. (Butterfield & Butterfield) £5,358

An Art Nouveau music cabinet, in mahogany, the central door with copper plaque embossed with stylised flower and quotation *If music be the food of love play on*, 1.50m. high. (Phillips) £820

A J.P. White oak inlaid dwarf cabinet designed by M.H. Baillie-Scott, with pewter and fruitwood inlay of stylised flowers and flanked on one side by open recess with fitted shelf, circa 1904, 50.8cm. wide. (Christie's) £1,540

A fine 18th century Vigiza-patan padouk and ivory inlaid collector's cabinet with engraved foliate borders, 57cm. wide. (Phillips) £12,000

A Regency Irish brass-inlaid satinwood and ebony side cabinet by J. Dooly & Sons with breakfront D-shaped top with reeded edge above a glazed door enclosing two shelves, 36$\frac{1}{2}$in. wide. (Christie's) £8,250

An Art Deco wrought iron and zebra wood cabinet, carved signature J. Cayette, Nancy, circa 1925, 115cm. high. £1,850

An early Victorian ormolu mounted ebony and pietra dura side cabinet, 43in. wide. £6,000

Victorian rosewood smoker's cabinet in the form of a chiffonier, shaped back piece, squat ogee formed feet, 14 x 8½in.
(G. A. Key) £120

A Brainerd & Armstrong Co. spool cabinet with twelve glass front drawers over one oak drawer, circa 1900, 37in. high. £500

Fine Louis XV style gilt-bronze-mounted mahogany side cabinet, circa 1900, the cupboard door mounted with a canvas panel painted with a scene depicting an 18th century couple in a pastoral setting, 36in. wide.
(Butterfield & Butterfield) £2,049

A late 17th/early 18th century japanned and decorated cabinet on carved and silvered stand, 1.18m. wide, 1.65m. high.
(Phillips) £6,000

A neo-gothic carved and inlaid oak hanging cabinet, the central section comprising three open galleries with panelled mirrored and marquetry interiors, 104cm. wide.
(Christie's) £3,080

Regency satinwood and ebony collector's cabinet, the ebony handles with ivory centres, 38in. wide. £13,250

A George III mahogany side cabinet inlaid overall with a rosewood band, the serpentine top with foliate-inlaid corners and gadrooned edge above a pair of doors, 39in. wide.
(Christie's) £6,600

A Sue et Mare rosewood, ebonised and marquetry music cabinet on elongated ebonised legs, 95.2cm. wide. £4,000

A mid-Georgian lacquered brass-mounted black and gilt-japanned cabinet-on-stand decorated overall with flowers, foliage, birds and landscapes, with repository label, 40½in. wide.
(Christie's) £2,750

A Milanese ebonised cabinet decorated overall with carved and pierced ivory and bone arabesque panels, on inverted plinth base, mid 19th century, 43¾in. wide.
(Christie's) £8,250

A William and Mary polychrome and white-japanned cabinet-on-stand, with giltmetal escutcheon, hinges and corners, fitted with a pair of doors decorated with a Japanese-style panoramic scene of figures, possibly Dutch, 43¾in. wide.
(Christie's) £40,700

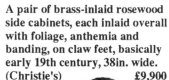

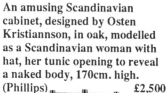

An amusing Scandinavian cabinet on stand, designed by Osten Kristiannson, in oak, modelled as an army officer, his flies opening to reveal a mechanical curiosity, 169cm. high.
(Phillips) £4,000

A pair of brass-inlaid rosewood side cabinets, each inlaid overall with foliage, anthemia and banding, on claw feet, basically early 19th century, 38in. wide.
(Christie's) £9,900

An amusing Scandinavian cabinet, designed by Osten Kristiannson, in oak, modelled as a Scandinavian woman with hat, her tunic opening to reveal a naked body, 170cm. high.
(Phillips) £2,500

A mid Victorian harewood, marquetry and giltmetal mounted credenza of broken D-shaped outline, inlaid overall with a dot-trellis, 48in. wide.
(Christie's) £2,750

A Dutch walnut and marquetry cabinet, decorated overall with birds and flower filled urns, on hairy paw feet, damage to cornice, mid 18th century, 85½in. wide.
(Christie's) £13,200

An ebonised and painted corner cabinet, designed by Charles Rennie Mackintosh, with painted panels by Margaret Macdonald Mackintosh, the two cupboard doors with pierced hinge plates, circa 1897, 183cm. high. (Christie's) £13,200

A Spanish gilt-metal mounted walnut vargueno, the interior with twelve drawers and a central door enclosing three further drawers, 43in. wide.
(Christie's) £5,280

A fine mid-Victorian ebonised and brass inlaid side cabinet with gilt bronze and hardstone mounts, with turned and fluted projecting column supports above a shaped apron on disc feet, 79in. wide.
(Tennants) £2,200

Fine Napoleon III gilt-bronze and Sèvres porcelain mounted tulipwood serre à bijoux, third quarter 19th century, mounted with Sèvres porcelain plaques, 16³⁄₄in. wide.
(Butterfield & Butterfield) £7,066

Extremely fine Italian Renaissance style hardstone, marble and bronze-mounted ebonised cabinet, Florence, circa 1860, the cupboard doors opening to an architectural interior with an arrangement of drawers enclosing secret drawers, 4ft. wide.
(Butterfield & Butterfield) £53,582

A pair of French ormolu and porcelain mounted mahogany corner cabinets, the drawer mounted with two shaped Sèvres style porcelain plaques painted with flowers, 27in. wide.
(Christie's) £4,400

One of a pair of black-japanned and simulated bamboo side cabinets of Regency style, each with a rectangular eared and concave-fronted verde antico marble top, 20th century, 25¹⁄₄in. wide.
(Christie's) £3,850

An 18th century German oak fruitwood banded and marquetry buffet in two parts, decorated with roundels and green stain heightened foliate vases and birds, 4ft. 2in. wide.
(Phillips) £5,000

Fine Italian late Renaissance carved walnut cabinet of large size, circa 1600, the upper part enclosed by a pair of doors inset with wrought-iron scrollwork, 6ft. 9in. wide.
(Butterfield & Butterfield) £12,204

A late 18th century Dutch walnut and marquetry strung display cabinet, decorated with foliate scrolls, floral stems, masks and urns of flowers with birds and butterflies, 6ft. 6in. wide.
(Phillips) £16,000

CANTERBURYS

Originally designed to hold sheet music, this particular item could just as well have been called the Archbishop since, according to Sheraton, it was named after the Archbishop of Canterbury, who was among the first to place an order for one. Most of the original, late 18th century, varieties were rectangular in shape and were made with a drawer in the base.

Regency canterburys are of mahogany or rosewood; the later Victorian examples are generally of burr walnut with flamboyantly fretted partitions or barley twist supports.

A mid-Victorian walnut three section canterbury with pierced fret-carved divisions and frieze drawer, on turned tapering legs, 21¹/₂in. wide.
(Christie's) £880

A rare Federal mahogany canterbury, Boston or New York, circa 1815, the four turned uprights centring scrolled transverses, 20in. wide.
(Sotheby's) £1,820

A mahogany gothic canterbury, the dished rectangular top with gothic arches, panelled pillar-angles, five divisions and a scrolled carrying handle, 19th century, 19¹/₂in. wide.
(Christie's) £1,760

A Victorian burr-walnut upright canterbury, the rectangular top with a pierced three-quarter brass gallery and long frieze drawer, 23¹/₂in. wide.
(Christie's S. Ken) £990

A Regency mahogany four-division canterbury with flattened baluster slats, containing an ebony strung drawer, on ring turned feet, 1ft. 8in. wide.
(Phillips) £1,700

A Regency mahogany canterbury with dished rectangular top and turned baluster spindles to the sides, with giltmetal paw feet, 21in. wide. (Christie's) £13,200

A George III satinwood canterbury, the hinged top with three-quarter gallery.
£9,900

A William IV rosewood canterbury, the laurel carved four division slatted rectangular top above a base drawer on turned legs, 22in. wide.
(Christie's S. Ken) £1,540

A Victorian burr walnut music canterbury of three divisions with spindle turned columns, 1ft.9in. wide. £500

A Victorian rosewood three division canterbury, 20¼in. wide. £700

A late George III mahogany canterbury, the four divisioned slatted top above a drawer on square tapered legs, 18in. wide. (Christie's) £1,980

A Victorian walnut music canterbury, by Gillows, the rectangular galleried shelf with rounded corners, supported on turned uprights, with a panelled base and two open compartments, second half 19th century, 25¼in. wide. (Christie's) £1,430

An Edwardian mahogany five division canterbury with boxwood and bone inlaid mask shell and scrolling foliage decorations to the front and rear, 21½in. wide. (Christie's) £935

A mid Victorian walnut library buffet and canterbury combined, carried on turned legs with brass castors, 42in. wide. (Locke & England) £900

Victorian walnut canterbury, the three section top on turned spindle supports, two drawers to base with brass handles. (G.A. Key) £380

A Victorian rosewood canterbury, the upper section with Prince of Wales' feathers decoration above a frieze drawer, on baluster turned legs. (Bonhams) £950

A George IV mahogany four division canterbury, on ring turned tapered legs terminating in brass cappings and castors. 1ft. 6in. wide. (Phillips) £1,600

DINING CHAIRS

The Hepplewhite style is renowned for its flowing curves, shield, oval and heart-shaped backs and straight lines broken by carved or painted wheat ears and corn husks, all of which Hepplewhite adapted from the work of Robert Adam, the distinguished architect/designer and published in his famous guide: *The Cabinet Maker and Upholsterer*.

Another distinctive Hepplewhite design incorporated the three feathers crest of the Prince of Wales in the backs of chairs.

Though his designs have much in common with those of Hepplewhite, Thomas Sheraton (1751–1806), a drawing master from Stockton on Tees, much preferred straight lines to the curves favoured by Hepplewhite, his chairs achieving their feminine delicacy with their fine turning and slender frames.

Sheraton served his apprenticeship as a cabinet maker but he never actually manufactured furniture himself, concentrating on creating designs which he published in his *Cabinet Maker's and Upholsterer's Drawing Book (1791–1794)*.

Thomas Chippendale designed and made furniture for the wealthy in his premises in St. Martin's Lane, London, establishing styles of his own rather than copying and adapting those of others. Like Sheraton and Hepplewhite, Chippendale published his designs, which were used by cabinet makers throughout the country, with the result that a considerable number of 'Chippendale' chairs were produced in a variety of qualities and a medley of styles.

A pair of Queen Anne maple side chairs, attributed to William Savery, Philadelphia, 1730–1750, on creased cabriole front legs with trifid feet, 45in. high.
(Christie's) £17,160

A black-painted Cromwellian side-chair with padded rectangular back and seat over block and ball-turned legs, 37¾in. high.
(Christie's) £1,065

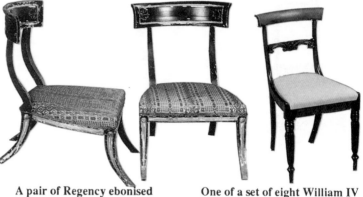

A pair of Regency ebonised chairs, of klismos design, with gilt reeded decoration, on short sabre front and rear legs.
(Phillips) £2,800

One of a set of eight William IV mahogany dining chairs, probably by John Kendell of Leeds, including two open armchairs.
(Christie's) (Eight) £3,080

Two of a set of eight Regency mahogany dining-chairs including a pair of open armchairs, each with tablet back above a horizontal splat centred by an ebonised roundel.
(Christie's) £8,250

A very fine Chippendale carved mahogany side chair, Philadelphia, circa 1770, the moulded seat rail on acanthus-carved cabriole legs ending in claw-and-ball feet.
(Sotheby's) £32,155

DINING CHAIRS

One of an assembled set of four William and Mary crown side-chairs, Fairfield County, Connecticut, 1735–1755, each with shaped and heart-pierced crest.
(Christie's) **(Four)** £3,924

Two of a set of eight Regency cork mahogany and boxwood and ebony-lined dining chairs, including two armchairs, on turned legs.
(Christie's) (Eight) £14,891

A fine and rare Chippendale carved mahogany side chair, Philadelphia, circa 1770, on acanthus- and flowerhead-carved cabriole legs ending in claw-and-ball feet.
(Sotheby's) £102,961

One of a pair of walnut side chairs with spreading rectangular seat covered in crimson velvet, the elaborately pierced splat with scrolling foliate C-scrolls , second quarter 19th century.
(Christie's) (Two) £1,540

Two of a set of eight George III mahogany dining chairs, the backs with reeded uprights, reeded and tablet centred top rails and 'X'-shaped splats.
(Phillips) **(Eight)** £4,500

One of a set of eight mahogany dining-chairs, including two open armchairs, each with waved toprail with acanthus-carved angles centred by a foliate spray.
(Christie's) (Eight) £15,400

One of a pair of George III mahogany side chairs in the French manner, each with oval padded back and shield-shaped seat covered in floral-patterned material.
(Christie's) £2,200

Two of eight birchwood music chairs with gilt carving, the backs lyre shaped, and on tapering reeded legs, Russian, early 19th century.
(Finarte) (Eight) £7,117

One of a set of eight George III mahogany dining chairs in the Sheraton taste with moulded curved bar top rails and curved 'X'-splats, on reeded tapered legs.
(Phillips) (Eight) £4,600

A pine side chair, after a design by A. W. Pugin, made by C. R. Light, circa 1875, the 'C' shaped back with solid dish seat and slab sides.
(Sotheby's) £1,540

Two of a set of eight painted and decorated rush-seat dining chairs, New York State or New England, circa 1820.
(Sotheby's) £1,654

German walnut Black Forest chair, late 19th century, the shaped upholstered back and circular seat within a naturalistic frame, 37in. high.
(Skinner Inc.) £438

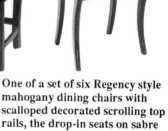

One of a set of six Victorian rosewood chairs, each with a dished top rail above stylised scroll splat, lift-off seat and turned front supports.
(Lawrence Fine Art) (Six) £1,100

Two of a set of twenty mahogany dining chairs of George III style, including two armchairs and five side chairs of late 18th century date, one labelled Coutts & Findlater Ltd., Sunderland. (Christie's) £8,250

One of a set of six Regency style mahogany dining chairs with scalloped decorated scrolling top rails, the drop-in seats on sabre front legs.
(Lawrence Fine Art) (Six) £935

One of a set of six oak side chairs designed by A.W.N. Pugin, on turned and chamfered legs joined by chamfered stretchers.
(Christie's) (Six) £1,320

A pair of early 19th century Dutch mahogany floral marquetry and brass strung music chairs, with bar top rails and lyre shaped splats.
(Phillips) £600

One of a set of six Regency mahogany dining chairs, the reeded frames with scrollover finials, and sabre front supports.
(Lawrence Fine Art)(Six) £1,595

DINING CHAIRS

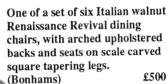

One of a set of four oak side chairs, slightly arched rectangular backs with carved shaped finials and vertical carved slats.
(Christie's)   £462

A pair of late George III mahogany dining chairs, each with a pierced lattice back and padded seat on turned tapered reeded legs. (Christie's S. Ken)   £935

One of a set of six Italian walnut Renaissance Revival dining chairs, with arched upholstered backs and seats on scale carved square tapering legs.
(Bonhams)   £500

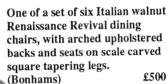

One of a set of nine early Victorian mahogany dining chairs with solid curved top rails, lift-off seats and lobed front supports.
(Lawrence Fine Art)   £1,155

One of a set of six late 18th/early 19th century German carved walnut dining chairs, in the Louis XV taste, on cabriole legs with cabochon incised decorated feet.
(Phillips)   £1,800

One of a pair of Edwardian mahogany salon chairs, each with boxwood and bone inlaid foliate scrolling toprail and splat with waisted back.
(Christie's)   £715

One of a set of six Victorian walnut dining chairs with shaped and moulded balloon backs, conforming crossbars, and on moulded cabriole legs.
(Bearne's)   £1,000

Two of an attractive set of four Regency beech stained as rosewood salon chairs, with rope twist carved slightly arched cresting rails.
(Spencer's)   £380

Greene and Greene mahogany chair, executed in the workshop of Peter Hall for the D.B. Gamble House, Pasadena, California, circa 1908.
(Skinner)   £5,077

One of a set of nine French ormolu-mounted mahogany dining-chairs, each with pierced rectangular back with lyre-shaped splat, late 19th century. (Christie's) (Ten) £7,700

One of a set of fourteen early Victorian oak dining chairs, including two open armchairs. (Christie's S. Ken) £4,620

One of a set of four Hepplewhite period carved mahogany wheelback chairs, the circular backs with vase-shaped radiating splats with central roundels. (Phillips) £950

One of a pair of fine early 18th century Chinese carved hardwood dining chairs in the Queen Anne style, the balloon-shaped backs with solid vase splats decorated in relief with interlaced strapwork. (Phillips)(Two) £36,000

One of a set of four Italian Empire grey-painted and parcel-gilt side chairs, the toprail carved with anthemia on monopodia legs headed by anthemia, and lotus leaves, on paw feet, first quarter 19th century. (Christie's) £9,900

One of a set of six Dutch elm and walnut marquetry dining chairs, each inlaid with a bird perched amongst flowers, the uprights and shaped seat frames inlaid with trailing flowers. (Bearne's) £7,500

One of a pair of early George III Irish mahogany dining chairs, the backs with pierced X-centred splats carved with C-scrolls and foliage to the clasped ends of the top rails. (Phillips) £1,000

One of a pair of George III mahogany side chairs, each with waved rectangular back and serpentine seat covered in associated 18th century close-nailed gros and petit point needlework. £2,420

One of a set of six George III mahogany dining chairs in the Hepplewhite taste, with shield shaped backs with husks and scrolled end top rails, and two elbow chairs of a later date. (Phillips) £1,900

DINING CHAIRS

One of a set of four George IV hall chairs by Gillows of Lancaster, each with cartouche shaped back carved with C-scrolls and centred by a coat-of-arms with a bugle horn.
(Christie's)   £3,190

One of a set of eight George III rosewood dining chairs, including two armchairs, after a design by George Hepplewhite, the shield-shaped backs carved with husk chains.
(Bonhams)   £3,800

One of a set of ten mahogany dining-chairs, each with curved panelled horizontal toprail and pierced arcaded splat, on square tapering fluted legs.
(Christie's)   £5,500

One of a set of six George III mahogany dining-chairs, each with waved toprail and pierced vase-shaped splat, on square chamfered legs joined by stretchers.
(Christie's)   £3,350

One of a set of sixteen mahogany dining chairs of George II design, the concave arched back with pierced interlaced splat above green leather upholstered seats, on cabriole legs with claw-and-ball feet.
(Christie's S. Ken)   £19,250

One of a pair of Italian Empire giltwood side chairs, each with panelled toprail carved with foliage and splat in the form of crossed arrows centred by a flowered roundel, on turned tapering legs. (Christie's)
£3,520

One of a pair of George I carved red walnut dining chairs, the balloon shaped backs with paper scroll crestings and solid vase splats.
(Phillips) (Two)   £2,200

One of a pair of George III mahogany dining-chairs, each with arched back and pierced vase-shaped splat with a patera, on square chamfered legs.
(Christie's)   £935

One of a set of six George III mahogany dining-chairs, each with arched toprail and pierced vase-shaped splat, and an open armchair but of later date.
(Christie's)   £4,620

One of a set of ten mahogany ladder back dining chairs, with cabriole front supports with pad feet. (Lawrence Fine Arts) £1,760

Two of a set of four George III mahogany dining chairs, the oval backs carved and pierced with floret filled wheel splats. (Phillips) £500

One of a set of six Regency ebonised and parcel gilt dining chairs with split cane seats and buttoned squabs. £11,250

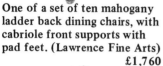

One of a matched set of six ash and fruitwood 'ear' spindle back rush seat chairs, early 19th century, North West Region, attributed to Lancashire or Cheshire. (Lawrence Fine Art) (Six) £1,012

Two of a set of six George III style mahogany dining chairs, each with eared foliate scroll carved toprail and pierced interlaced vase splat above serpentine drop-in seat. (Christie's) (Six) £1,320

One of a set of six Regency mahogany dining-chairs each with curved panelled toprail with brass roundel terminals, the padded drop-in seats covered in brown leather. (Christie's) (Six) £3,740

One of a set of six Louis Philippe walnut dining chairs, each with cartouche-shaped back and bowed cane-filled seat. (Christie's) £715

Two of a set of four Japanese bamboo and lacquer sidechairs, late 19th century, each with a rounded-arched top. (Butterfield & Butterfield) £2,569

A George II walnut dining chair with shaped uprights flanking a solid vase shape splat carved with birds' heads. (Lawrence Fine Arts) £1,595

One of a set of six Louis Philippe carved giltwood and gesso salon chairs in the manner of Fournier. (Phillips) £5,000

A pair of Morris & Co. ebonised side chairs, each with turned treble bar top rails and cross splat. (Christie's) £1,155

One of a composite set of eight ash ladder back chairs, including two with arms, early 19th century. (Lawrence Fine Arts) £1,870

One of a set of six Edwardian painted satinwood dining chairs, each with stepped and finialled toprail above a pierced lattice lower rail, on square tapering sabre legs. (Christie's) £3,520

Pair of Italian neoclassical carved walnut side chairs, circa 1800, each with a broad bowed crestrail centred by a floral medallion above a pierced urn-form splat. (Butterfield & Butterfield) £405

One of a set of six mahogany dining-chairs each with arched toprail flanked by flowerheads and with pierced vase-shaped splat centred by a lobed wheel above a compass. (Christie's) £3,300

One of a set of three Dutch 19th century floral marquetry side chairs, the arcaded top rails with barley twist central supports. (Tennants) £500

Two of a set of six mahogany and parcel gilt side chairs in the manner of Robert Man-waring, on cabriole legs carved with cabochons. (Christie's) £176,000

One of a set of five late 18th/ early 19th century Dutch carved elm dining chairs, the oval backs with riband crestings and pierced splats. (Phillips) (Five) £950

One of a set of twelve mahogany hall chairs by Seddon, Sons & Shackleton, the moulded oval backs painted with the crest of Richard Hall Clarke.
(Bearne's) (Twelve)   £23,000

Two of a set of six George II mahogany dining chairs, each with a paper-scroll serpentine toprail.
(Bearne's) (Six)   £5,400

One of a pair of oak side chairs, designed by Peter Behrens, the slightly tapering backs with broad central splats flanked by three intersecting cross bars, on waisted square section legs, 100cm. high.
(Christie's) (Two)   £3,300

One of a set of four George IV rosewood dining-chairs, each with curved scrolled rectangular toprail above a pierced lotus-carved foliate splat centred by a horizontal bar mounted by three balls. (Christie's) (Four)   £2,750

Two of a set of ten mahogany dining chairs, including two armchairs, of George III design, each with an arched moulded and yoked toprail.
(Christie's) (Ten)   £13,898

A Chippendale walnut side-chair, Philadelphia or Pennsylvania, 1740–1760, the incised serpentine crest flanked by shaped ears above a solid vase-shaped splat over a trapezoidal slip-seat, $39\frac{1}{2}$in. high. (Christie's)   £2,631

One of a pair of Regency mahogany hall chairs, each with shield-shaped back crowned by eagle-heads flanking a paper-scroll, with central oval sunken panel.
(Christie's) (Two)   £2,640

Two of a set of six early George III mahogany dining chairs, the waved pounced toprails carved with scallop shells and acanthus foliage and a pair of later date.
(Christie's)   £12,906

One of a set of twelve William IV rosewood and parcel-gilt dining-chairs each with arched waisted back, with flowerhead-centred tablet toprail flanked by leaf-carving.
(Christie's) (Twelve)   £7,150

A Federal mahogany klismos chair, New York, 1790–1810, the carved tablet crest centring intertwined cornucopiae over a lyre splat flanked by scrolled and reeded stiles, 23¹/₂in. high. (Christie's) £3,157

A very fine pair of Queen Anne carved walnut balloon-seat side chairs, Newport, Rhode Island, circa 1755, on shell volute and bellflower-carved cabriole legs. (Sotheby's) £43,008

A rare William and Mary turned and joined walnut wainscot side chair, Southeastern Pennsylvania, 1700–30. (Sotheby's) £14,556

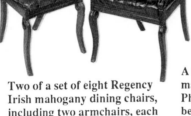

One of a set of thirteen George III dining-chairs, each with panelled curved toprail and trellis-filled splat, with bowed padded seat covered in beige cotton, on square tapering legs and spade feet. (Christie's) (Thirteen) £14,300

Two of a set of eight Regency Irish mahogany dining chairs, including two armchairs, each with a curved panelled and reeded top rail, on grooved sabre legs. (Christie's) (Eight) £11,913

A Chippendale carved mahogany side-chair, Philadelphia, 1765–1785, with bead-moulded shaped crestrail centring a carved pendent leaf flanked by carved scrolled ears above a pierced and scroll-carved splat over a trapezoidal slip seat, 38in. high. (Christie's) £3,617

One of a set of ten ebonised, parcel-gilt and red-painted dining-chairs including a pair of open armchairs and four Regency single chairs, each with scrolled bowed toprail. (Christie's) (Ten) £4,950

A fine and rare pair of Queen Anne carved mahogany side-chairs, Newport, Rhode Island, 1750–1770, each with shaped crest centring a carved shell above a vase-shaped splat flanked by tapering stiles over a balloon seat, 38³/₄in. high. (Christie's) £62,481

A Chippendale mahogany side-chair, Newport, Rhode Island, 1765–1785, the serpentine crest with central carving flanked by moulded scrolled ears over a pierced interscrolling vase-shaped splat, 38in. high. (Christie's) £4,275

A Federal carved curly maple side chair, New York, early 19th century, on sabre legs ending in carved paw feet.
(Sotheby's)   £1,489

Two of a composite set of eight early 19th century spindle back dining chairs of Lanca-shire type. (Tennants)
(Eight)   £3,600

A George III carved maho-gany hall chair of grotto design with pierced shell shaped back and solid seat.
(Phillips)   £5,500

One of a set of three English oak side chairs, each with shaped raised cresting centred by a flowerhead, with 19th century patched-needlework squab cushions.
(Christie's)   (Three)   £770

One of an unusual pair of Regency carved mahogany hall chairs, the wide oval panel backs with radiating reeded ornament, having solid seats, on turned tapered legs.
(Phillips)   (Two)   £1,300

One of a set of four mid Victorian mahogany Gothic Revival side chairs, after a design by Charles Bevan, each with red leather upholstered outswept back.
(Christies)   (Four)   £990

One of a set of six George III style mahogany dining chairs, the arched toprails above pierced splats centred by paterae, on square chamfered legs, late 19th century.
(Bonhams)   (Six)   £700

A pair of chairs designed by A.W. Pugin, oak with upholstered seats, the curving back legs continuing to form vertical supports joined at the top by curved back legs.
(Christie's)   £3,080

One of a set of four ebonised side chairs, attributed to Bruce J. Talbert, bobbin-filled, pierced and moulded rectangular backs, above padded seats.
(Christie's)   (Four)   £880

DINING CHAIRS

A D. C. W. birch plywood chair designed by Charles Eames for Evans Products Company, 68cm. high.
(Bonhams)   £620

One of a set of six Regency beechwood, simulated rosewood and rosewood brass inlaid dining chairs, on sabre legs.
(Phillips) (Six)   £1,600

'Military chair' by Gerrit Rietvel the white painted rectangular back and seat on black painted bar frame, on rectangular section legs. (Christie's)   £11,000

One of a pair of oak side chairs, designed by J.P. Seddon, the chamfered curving legs supported by carved brackets, joined by chamfered stretcher, upholstered backs and seats.
(Christie's) (Two)   £1,760

A pair of Italian rococo carved walnut side chairs, third quarter 18th century, each with floral-carved serpentine crestrail centred by a carved flowerhead.
(Butterfield & Butterfield)
                           £1,114

One of a set of seven Windsor scroll back small chairs, including one with arms, in beech, fruitwood and elm, each with triple baluster spindles, 19th century.
(Lawrence Fine Art)
(Seven)   £1,265

One of a set of seven oak dining chairs, designed by A. W. Pugin and made by Gillows of Lancaster, circa 1860, on square chamfered legs.
(Sotheby's)   (Seven) £1,815

A pair of important oak arm chairs designed by C. F. A. Voysey, each with a slatted back rest with tapering square section supports, carved arms, above rush seats with shaped apron.
(Christie's)   £19,800

One of a pair of laminated walnut side chairs by Thonet, each with curved bar toprail, pierced splat, caned seat and incurved legs, 19th century.
(Christie's)   (Two)   £550

One of a set of eight Italian walnut dining-chairs including an associated armchair, on turned tapering fluted legs and pointed feet, early 19th century.
(Christie's)   (Eight)   £8,250

One of a pair o 18th century Venetian decorated and parcel gilt salon chairs, in the Louis XV taste, on cabriole legs with shell carved knees and scroll feet.
(Phillips)   £1,400

One of a set of eighteen George IV mahogany dining-chairs attributed to Gillows of Lancaster, each with a semi-balloon back, on turned and reeded tapering legs.
(Christie's)   (Eighteen) £20,900

One of a pair of George I walnut chairs with slightly curved backs and solid baluster splats carved with foliage and rosettes, the crestings centred by shells framed by foliate scrolls, 40³/₄in. high.
(Christie's)   (Two)   £52,800

A painted Windsor fan-back side-chair, New England, 1780–1800, the serpentine bowed crestrail with shaped ears above seven spindles flanked by baluster-turned stiles, 37¹/₄in. high.
(Christie's)   £574

One of a set of eight George III mahogany dining-chairs with lobed shield-shaped backs carved with flowerheads and foliage with foliate lunette bases, 37³/₄in. high.
(Christie's)   (Eight)   £18,700

One of a fine set of six antique American Federal mahogany scrollback dining chairs in the manner of Duncan Phyfe, on reeded splayed legs, probably New York, circa 1810.
(Selkirk's)   (Six)   £2,881

A fine early 18th century walnut and burr walnut chair, the back with inscrolled uprights and cresting carved in high relief with rocaille rockwork and leaf scrolls, possibly Dutch, or North German.
(Phillips)   £750

One of a set of eighteen George IV oak dining-chairs, the padded seat covered in close-nailed striped material on turned tapering reeded legs.
(Christie's)   (Eighteen) £12,100

One of a set of eight walnut dining-chairs, each with waved toprail, on cabriole legs headed by scallop-shells and claw-and-ball feet, part-18th century.
(Christie's) (Eight) £12,100

One of a set of four late George II mahogany hall chairs, the shaped solid seats on cabriole legs joined by turned stretchers, 36in. high.
(Christie's) (Four) £14,300

One of a set of eight George III Scottish mahogany dining chairs, including two open armchairs, each with shield-shaped back with pierced vase-shaped splat.
(Christie's) (Eight) £6,050

One of a set of fourteen early Victorian oak dining-chairs by Holland & Sons, and designed by A.W.N. Pugin, each with padded rectangular back and seat covered in nailed red leather.
(Christie's) (Fourteen) £12,650

One of a set of three Queen Anne walnut and marquetry dining chairs, on tapered legs united by turned and curved stretchers terminating in pad feet.
(Phillips) (Three) £4,500

A Chippendale mahogany side-chair, Newport, 1760–1780, the serpentine crestrail centred by diapering flanked by moulded scrolling ears over a scrolling, pierced vase-shaped splat, 37$\frac{1}{4}$in. high.
(Christie's) £2,552

One of a set of six George III mahogany dining-chairs each with rectangular back with pierced vertical-railed splat and leafy capitals.
(Christie's) (Six) £4,950

One of a set of eight William IV rosewood dining-chairs, on turned tapering acanthus-carved legs and turned feet.
(Christie's) (Eight) £6,600

One of two black-painted Queen Anne side-chairs, New York, late 18th century, each with yoked crestrail over a vase-shaped splat, 41$\frac{1}{2}$in. high.
(Christie's) (Two) £986

DINING CHAIRS

One of a set of ten Regency green-painted and parcel gilt dining chairs.
(Christie's) **£15,400**

Two of a set of eleven George III mahogany dining chairs, including an open armchair. **£16,750**

A French Art Nouveau oak dining chair, designed by C. Plumet and A. Selmersheim.
(Phillips) **£340**

One of a set of six Regency mahogany dining chairs, the scroll tablet top rails above bar splats and overstuffed seats, on sabre legs.
(Bonhams) (Six) **£1,500**

A set of four Regency mahogany dining chairs, including an elbow chair, the curved, panelled top rails scrolled at each end above carved tablet crossbars.
(Phillips) **£450**

One of a set of seven William IV mahogany dining chairs, including two with arms, with solid curved cresting rails above turned horizontal splats.
(Lawrence Fine Art)
(Seven) **£2,200**

One of a set of seven George III mahogany dining chairs, including two with arms, repairs and restorations.
(Lawrence Fine Arts)
(Seven) **£3,190**

Two of a set of twelve George I style mahogany dining chairs including two open armchairs on shell headed cabriole legs.
(Christie's) (Twelve) **£2,860**

A Chippendale carved mahogany side chair, Philadelphia, circa 1770, on cabriole legs ending on claw-and-ball feet.
(Sotheby's) **£1,059**

One of a set of four George III mahogany side chairs with moulded oval pierced 'umbrella' backs. (Four)   £6,500

Two of a set of six painted ash bamboo fancy chairs, New England, 1800–15.   £2,200

One of a set of six Scottish Regency period mahogany side chairs, seats covered in striped material.   £3,350

An oak side chair, the design attributed to A. W. Pugin, on chamfered bracket trestle ends forming pointed arches, joined by chamfered stretchers with metal sabots.
(Christie's)   £1,100

Two of a set of eleven late Victorian oak dining chairs, each with a classical pierced foliate carved cresting above a padded back and seat.
(Christie's S. Ken) (Eleven) £990

One of a pair of ormolu mounted mahogany side chairs of Empire style, on griffin monopodia with paw feet, third quarter 19th century.
(Christie's) (Two)   £1,870

One of six Hepplewhite period carved mahogany dining chairs, the slightly balloon shaped backs with arched top rails and pierced vase splats.
(Phillips) (Six)   £1,400

Two of a set of eight Regency period mahogany dining chairs, the backs with oval paterae to the horizontal rails.
(Woolley & Wallis)
(Eight)   £1,700

One of a pair of Italian ebony children's chairs with foliate incised ivory panels, on spiral-twist legs joined by stretchers, 19th century.
(Christie's)   £1,210

An 18th century Italian carved giltwood chair, the arched padded cartouche back with pierced 'C'-scroll cresting, overscrolled leaf and mask, the sides with grotesques and foliage, probably Venetian.
(Phillips) £1,400

A Regency bronzed and parcel-gilt mahogany klismos tub armchair, the panelled back applied with rosettes, covered in close-nailed buttoned green leather.
(Christie's) £4,180

A Chippendale carved mahogany side chair, Philadelphia, 1760–1780, on cabriole legs with ball-and-claw feet, 37³/₄in. high.
(Christie's) £5,720

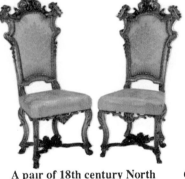

A carved mahogany 'riband back' dining chair, after a design by Thomas Chippendale, on cabriole legs with 'C'-scroll decorated trailing ornament terminating in scroll and pad feet. (Phillips) £1,800

A pair of 18th century North Italian giltwood chairs, the padded cartouche backs within channelled frames carved with scrolls, foliage and leafy crestings, possibly Venetian.
(Phillips) £3,600

One of a set of six Empire walnut, maple and mahogany dining chairs, the scoop shaped backs with curved overscrolled top rails and solid tulip shaped splats, possibly Danish.
(Phillips) (Six) £4,500

One of two George II side chairs each with padded rectangular back and seat covered in chinoiserie blue silk brocade, on cabriole legs.
(Christie's) (Two) £3,080

One of a fine and large pair of American modern gothic walnut and oak parlour chairs, attributed to Daniel Pabst, the design attributed to Frank Furness, circa 1877.
(Butterfield & Butterfield) £1,114

One of a pair of George III mahogany dining-chairs in the manner of Robert Manwaring, each with waved toprail carved with acanthus and centred by an acanthus-spray.
(Christie's) (Two) £1,760

Wing chairs have been made since the 17th century, this being one of the few designs to have remained virtually unchanged since its conception, only the legs changing shape according to the dictates of fashion.

The Queen Anne wing chairs had high cabriole legs canted from the corners which demanded extra stretchers for strength. The legs were later straightened and squared off with the inside legs chamfered, before the Georgian influence saw a return of the cabriole legs, but shorter this time and terminating in ball and claw feet.

The armchair by Thomas Chippendale is one of the best chairs ever made. Beautifully constructed to a superbly elegant design, it is strong, graceful and comfortable; a truly classic example of everything a chair should be.

The strong rectangle of the back is softened by the flow of the humped top rail and the arm supports, moulded and richly carved with feathers, terminate in cabochon ornament above the graceful acanthus carved cabriole legs with claw and ball feet.

The mid Victorian period abounds with furniture showing the exaggerated curves and floral and leaf carving which clearly reflect the Louis XV rococo influence and beautifully designed chairs of this period simply cry out to be sat in.

Earlier examples had filled-in arms and rather plain frames of mahogany or rosewood but, within a few years, they developed open arms and grandly flamboyant lines.

A Regency mahogany tub bergère with curved arched reeded backrail, the padded back and bowed seat covered in close-nailed green velvet.
(Christie's)   £2,090

An early Victorian oak open armchair after a design by A.W.N. Pugin, on channelled downswept legs and carved foliate feet.
(Christie's)   £3,850

A very fine **pair of Regency white painted and parcel gilt bergère chairs in the manner of Morel and Hughes, the curved top rails with fluted guilloche ornament with acanthus leaf and rosette terminals.**
(Phillips)   (Two) £16,000

One of a set of four George III cream painted and parcel gilt armchairs, in the Louis XV manner, on cabriole legs with leaf carved feet.
(Bonhams)   (Four) £6,000

A Queen Anne carved walnut wing armchair with stuffover back, outswept padded scroll arm supports and bowed seat, on cabriole legs.
(Phillips)   £7,000

A Regency rosewood library open armchair, on X-frame support and brass caps, one cap stamped *COPES PATENT*, lacking reading stand.
(Christie's)   £3,960

An early Victorian mahogany open armchair, on X-frame supports, with Buckingham Palace inventory mark VR BP No 361 1866.
(Christie's)   £2,200

Chinese export bamboo re-clining armchair, early 19th century, with extending caned foot rest, on wheels, 62in. long extended. (Skinner Inc.) £1,125

A Regency simulated rosewood bergère chair with a rectangular cane filled back, the ring-turned spreading arm supports on turned legs, castors.
(Phillips)   £600

One of a pair of Louis XV walnut fauteuils, each with padded cartouche-shaped back, arms and serpentine seat, on cabriole legs headed by flowerheads.
(Christie's) (Two)   £5,500

A George IV brass-inlaid rosewood bergère with rectangular padded back, scrolled arms and padded squab cushion, the padded seat covered in close-nailed pale brown material.
(Christie's)   £2,860

One of a pair of George III later decorated open armchairs, in the French taste, having padded scroll arm supports and stuffover seats with palmette decorated seat rails, on cabriole legs.
(Phillips)   (Two)   £3,200

A late Victorian mahogany and leather campaign chair, the folding rectangular back with ring-turned side supports, on turned baluster legs and brass caps.
(Christie's)   £880

Louis XV carved giltwood chauffeuse, third quarter 18th century, the slightly rounded channel moulded back carved with a cresting of a bouquet of flowers.
(Butterfield & Butterfield) £809

A Victorian tub bergère by Lenygon & Morant, on turned tapering legs and casters, with its chintz loose cover with exotic birds and flowers on an ivory ground.
(Christie's)   £1,870

A late Regency mahogany bergère with caned slightly bowed panel back, arms and seat within a reeded frame, on turned legs and castors.
(Christie's) £4,180

A 'Napoleon' chair, made by the firm of Aldam Heaton, the upholstered rounded angular back-rest with low scroll leg support.
(Christie's) £3,740

One of a pair of Louis XV style needlepoint-upholstered painted bergères, mid-19th century, raised on cabriole legs.
(Butterfield & Butterfield) £2,521

One of a pair of Directoire white painted and gilt heightened fauteuils, the rectangular padded backs, open arms and bowed stuffover seat with anthemion and rosette decoration.
(Phillips) (Two) £3,800

A William IV mahogany reclining open armchair, on ring-turned tapering legs and brass caps, stamped twice *R Colvil* at the base of the arms, the slide front possibly reveneered.
(Christie's) £1,540

One of a pair of mahogany and parcel-gilt open armchairs of George II style, the arm terminals with ormolu tips, the eared cabriole legs carved with acanthus and flower-heads, on hairy paw feet, 19th century.
(Christie's) (Two) £16,500

One of a pair of late Victorian oak and floral upholstered easy armchairs, each with button upholstered outswept back and arms.
(Christie's) (Two) £1,980

A good early George III mahogany 'Gainsborough' armchair, the arm supports carved with crisp outscrolling and continuing to the moulded square front legs.
(Tennants) £5,500

One of a pair of mid-Victorian ebonised spoon-back chairs, each with padded buttoned arch back and seat covered in yellow damask.
(Christie's) (Two) £3,520

One of a pair of Empire mahogany fauteuils with rectangular padded backs, the downwardly curving arms with reeded and floral carved decoration.
(Phillips) (Two) £1,600

A gilt-silver and green-painted grotto rocking chair with back and seat in the form of a scallop shell, with scrolling dolphin arms, supported by seahorses riding on the backs of sea serpents.(Christie's) £2,420

One of a pair of Louis XV style giltwood fauteuils, branded *Jean Mocqué, à Paris*, each with cartouche-shaped over-upholstered back.
(Christie's East) £2,449

One of a matched pair of Louis XV giltwood bergères, each with outward-scrolling channelled arm-terminals and cabriole legs headed by shells, re-gilded, stamped *I. POTHIER*.
(Christie's) £12,650
(Two)

One of a pair of Louis XVI giltwood fauteuils à la reine, the channelled frame with foliate finials, the arms with scrolled terminals on stop-fluted supports, on turned tapering stop-fluted legs.
(Christie's) £7,150

One of a pair of Louis XVI white-painted fauteuils à la reine, the channelled arms with scrolling terminals on turned tapering fluted legs headed by paterae, each stamped *G. IACOB*. (Christie's) £5,500

One of a pair of Louis XV beechwood chaises basses en ottomane by Nicolas Heurtaut, the scrolling high backs and shaped seats upholstered in yellow silk velvet.
(Christie's) £17,600

One of a pair of Empire giltwood fauteuils, the toprails carved with halved flowerheads and dolphins above flowerhead and acanthus sprays. (Christie's) £15,400

One of a pair of George III mahogany open armchairs, on channelled cabriole legs headed by anthemia on scrolled feet, both with repairs to front legs.
(Christie's) £3,080

A Russian ormolu-mounted mahogany bergère, the reeded armrests with arched rectangular terminals supported by winged female masks, early 19th century.
(Christie's) £37,400

A Venetian giltwood throne chair with padded cartouche-shaped back, the moulded frame carved with acanthus, the backrail centred by a vase of pomegranates, 19th century.
(Christie's) £2,200

One of a pair of Louis XVI giltwood fauteuils à la reine, the channelled frame carved with oak leaves and acorns, the back with pomegranate finials.
(Christie's) £8,800

One of a pair of Louis XVI fauteuils, the moulded frame carved with guilloche on turned tapering fluted legs headed by paterae.(Christie's) £7,150

A Louis XVI giltwood tabouret de pieds attributed to Jean-Baptiste-Claude Sené, possibly supplied for royal use at Versailles. (Christie's) £23,100

One of a set of ten Italian ebonised and parcel-gilt armchairs, on square legs with flat stretchers and paw feet, basically 19th century, 60in. high. (Christie's) £20,900

One of a pair of Empire white-painted and parcel-gilt fauteuils, the arms with tapering sphinx-headed supports, the tapering turned legs headed by long leaves, stamped *CRESSENT*.
(Christie's) £16,500

One of a set of three Louis XV walnut fauteuils, each with cartouche-shaped back, padded arms and bowed seat covered in close-nailed floral cut-brown velvet. (Christie's) £7,700

An olivewood and certosina X-frame open armchair, on X-frame supports and block feet, 17th/18th century, possibly Syrian or Hispano-Moresque.
(Christie's) £1,540

A Regency mahogany reading chair with deeply buttoned green leather upholstery and yoke shaped toprail. **£725**

One of a pair of William and Mary scarlet and gold lacquer X-frame open armchairs, 26½in. wide. **£35,000**

One of a pair of early Victorian rosewood armchairs, each with a spoon-shaped back and serpentine seat, on cabriole legs. **£4,100**

A George IV mahogany bergère, the arms carved with anthemia, on ring turned tapering legs headed by paterae and brass caps.
(Christie's)   **£990**

One of two George III mahogany open armchairs, each with an arched cartouche shaped padded back, on cabriole legs.
(Christie's)   **£82,500**

A Morris and Company ebonised oak reclining chair, after a design by Philip Webb, circa 1870, with bobbin turned legs and stretchers.
(Sotheby's)   **£1,485**

A Victorian mahogany armchair the scrolling arms and seat upholstered in figured brocatelle, on cabriole legs with knob feet. (Christie's S. Ken)   **£715**

An early Victorian mahogany reclining chair with buttoned panel back and adjustable seat, on curved legs. (Christie's S. Ken)   **£715**

An inlaid rosewood curule-type armchair, attributed to Pottier and Stymus, circa 1870, 34in. high, 31in. wide.   **£1,000**

A parcel gilt and beechwood fauteuil of neo-classical design, on spirally-turned tapering legs. £1,900

A Regency mahogany tub bergère, with cane-filled back and button drop-in seat, stamped HW. £2,000

A Louis XVI stained beechwood bergère, the back, seat and squab covered in plum velvet. £1,750

A mid 18th century Venetian parcel gilt and aquamarine open armchair, the padded back and seat upholstered in point d'hongerie velvet. £1,450

Empire style mahogany and gilt-metal mounted armchair, late 19th century, supported by winged sphinxes raised on winged griffins, 39in. high. (Skinner Inc.) £1,298

A Victorian walnut armchair, with needlework upholstery, the top rail curving down into arms with carved scrolled supports on cabriole legs. (Bonhams) £400

A 17th century beechwood X-framed open armchair covered in fragments of contemporary associated tapestry. £5,750

A Victorian walnut nursing chair with original Berlin woolwork upholstery, on cabriole legs. (Bearne's) £630

A Regénce style walnut fauteuil à l'oreilles, the padded back and arms within a rocaille carved frame, on cabriole legs. (Bonhams) £420

A George III mahogany open armchair in the French taste, the padded arm supports with moulded scroll terminals on cabriole legs.
(Phillips) £5,500

An oak panel-back armchair in the gothic style, with rectangular back centred by a blind strapwork panel below a pierced foliage and ogee-carved cresting, 19th century.
(Christie's) £2,530

A Queen Anne walnut wing armchair, Massachusetts, circa 1750, the back with arched crest and shaped wings.
(Sotheby's) £11,579

A George III mahogany open armchair, in the French Hepplewhite taste, the cartouche-shaped back, arms and serpentine seat close nailed and upholstered in red-brown leather. (Phillips) £3,200

One of a pair of George I gilt-gesso open armchairs, each with rounded rectangular padded back and seat covered in green velvet, the channelled downswept scrolling arms upon acanthus-carved supports, on cabriole legs.
(Christie's)(Two) £57,200

An 18th century Spanish mahogany armchair, with brass label on the back: *This chair was used by Napoleon Buonaparte in his cabin on board H.M.S. "Northumberland" en route for St Helena 1815.*
(Phillips) £4,800

One of a pair of George III mahogany library open armchairs with rectangular padded back, seat and arms upholstered in ivory trellis-patterned material, on square legs joined by stretchers.
(Christie's) (Two) £6,050

A mahogany wing armchair, the rectangular padded back, scrolled arms and squab cushion covered in bargello pattern material, on cabriole legs headed by acanthus sprays, part 18th century. (Christie's) £1,100

A Chippendale carved mahogany easy chair, New York, 1760–1780, on cabriole legs with foliate carved knees and ball-and-claw feet, 44¼in. high.
(Christie's) £2,145

A George II mahogany wing armchair, with padded back, on cabriole legs with claw and ball feet.
(Phillips)   £1,600

A George III mahogany armchair, in the gothic taste, the cartouche-shaped back, on octagonal legs joined by cross stretchers and castors.
(Phillips)   £800

A fine Queen Anne carved walnut wing armchair, Newport, Rhode Island, circa 1765, the arched upholstered back flanked by ogival wings.
(Sotheby's)   £18,158

One of a pair of George III mahogany library open armchairs, each with arched padded back, armrests and serpentine seat covered in trellis-pattern green and ivory cotton, the legs possibly later carved.
(Christie's)   (Two)   £9,900

An Empire mahogany and parcel-gilt bergère, the sides decorated with anthemia, on square tapering legs headed by Roman masks, on paw feet, lacking mounts, possibly North European.
(Christie's)   £7,700

One of a pair of William IV rosewood tub bergères, each with deeply-curved arched padded back, sides and seat covered in close-nailed green leather, with downswept scroll arms and lotus leaf-carved sabre legs on brass caps.
(Christie's)   (Two)   £4,620

A George I walnut wing armchair with arched rectangular padded back, sides and squab cushion covered in associated floral needlework on a brown ground.
(Christie's)   £4,180

One of a pair of Regency mahogany bergères, each with rectangular padded back, arms, buttoned back-cushion and squab seat cushion covered in ivory silk damask, on square tapering front legs.
(Christie's) (Two)   £5,280

An important Chippendale carved mahogany wing armchair, Philadelphia, circa 1770, the arched upholstered back flanked by ogival wings.
(Sotheby's)   £211,513

LIBRARY CHAIRS

George III mahogany library chair, third quarter 18th century, blind fret and floral carved arms, raised on blind fret-carved square legs. (Skinner Inc.) £324

One of a pair of William IV mahogany library armchairs, each with buttoned crested bow back with three pierced tear drop splats. (Christie's) (Two) £1,760

A William IV mahogany bow-back library armchair, the scrolling acanthus carved back and arms above a bowed seat on reeded tapering legs. (Christie's) £770

An early George III mahogany library armchair, of Gainsborough design, with carved moulded downswept arm supports and moulded chamfered square legs joined by stretchers. (Phillips) £1,000

One of a pair of George IV rosewood spoonback library open armchairs with arched curved padded back, bowed seats and padded arms covered in close-nailed brown suede. (Christie's) (Two) £8,250

An early George III mahogany library chair, the downswept arm supports and square section legs with flower and lattice ornament terminating in castors. (Phillips) £800

A George III mahogany library armchair, the back and seat upholstered in green floral silk. £5,000

A Regency mahogany library bergère upholstered in buttoned pale green leather. £2,000

One of a pair of George III mahogany library armchairs upholstered in pale grey floral silk. £30,000

LIBRARY CHAIRS

A William IV mahogany library armchair with cane filled back, arms and seat, with leather squab cushions. £1,450

A George III library open armchair with arched padded back, arms and seat covered in red leather, on channelled square legs.
(Christie's) £2,200

A George III mahogany library armchair, the padded back and seat covered in red leather. (Christie's) £5,280

A Regency mahogany library open armchair with stuffover button-down back, upholstered in red leather, on square tapered legs terminating in brass cappings and casters.
(Phillips) £1,000

One of a pair of George II mahogany library armchairs, the curved padded arms ending in out-turned realistically carved dolphins' heads, 41in. high.
(Christie's) (Two) £286,000

A William IV mahogany library bergère, with scroll-topped rectangular back with channelled scrolled and leaf-carved sides, the padded back, sides and squab cushion covered in black leather.
(Christie's) £1,430

A William IV library armchair, the back, arms and seat upholstered in pale green leather. £650

A late George II mahogany library armchair with serpentine back, circa 1750. £5,500

One of a pair of mid Georgian mahogany library armchairs with padded backs, armrests and seats. £20,000

A Liberty & Co. throne armchair, circa 1900, oak, leather back panel and seat cushion, 44in. high. (Sotheby's) £1,870

Two of a set of four 17th century armchairs with scrolling arms and turned legs joined by upper and lower stretchers, North Italian. (Finarte) (Four) £11,109

A George III giltwood armchair in the manner of John Linnell, the frame carved with entrelac, supported by foliate-enriched and spirally-carved stiles. (Christie's) £1,100

A Queen Anne walnut armchair with arched padded back and swollen shaped padded seat upholstered in associated mid-18th century floral crewel-work on an ivory ground. (Christie's) £13,200

One of a pair of Anglo-Indian rosewood open armchairs, each with shaped toprail carved with anthemion lunettes, the tapering rectangular padded back, arm-rests and drop-in seat upholstered in green and white floral material, second quarter 19th century. (Christie's) (Two) £1,650

A carved walnut armchair, circa 1850, the back with an arched padded panel above a carved armorial, with padded serpentine seat and the legs with lion heads and paw feet. (Sotheby's) £2,530

A George IV mahogany adjustable open armchair by Robert Daws, with rectangular padded back, lotus-enriched scrolled arms and seat covered in close-nailed green leather. (Christie's) £2,090

An unusual English walnut armchair, circa 1860, the padded arched back on a pair of massive wing-like scrolls, on down-curved legs with hoof-like feet. (Sotheby's) £2,640

A George II mahogany armchair with slightly-arched padded wing-back, outscrolled arms and seat covered in pink velvet, on cabriole legs headed by an acanthus-carved cabochon. (Christie's) £2,970

A George IV mahogany library bergère with later adjustable reading-slope, the reeded scrolling top rail above a caned rectangular back, seat and sides with green velvet squab cushions. (Christie's)   £6,050

One of a pair of William IV library bergères, each with dished deeply-curved padded back, sides and seat covered in crimson velvet, on turned tapering legs and brass caps. (Christie's) (Two)   £3,960

One of a pair Egyptian Revival parcel-gilt walnut armchairs, circa 1880, almost certainly retailed by Christopher Dresser's 'Art Furnishers Alliance'. (Sotheby's)   £15,400

A Regency brass-mounted ebonized and parcel-gilt bergère, the padded scroll back, sides and squab cushions covered in green and white floral cotton, on panelled sabre legs and brass paw feet. (Christie's)   £3,520

A Regency brass-mounted mahogany library open armchair with scrolled cane-filled back, on turned legs and ribbed brass caps. (Christie's)   £2,750

One of a pair of Regency bamboo bergères, each with deeply curved arched pierced back filled with vertical rails and pierced fretwork, with squab cushion covered in green silk. (Christie's)   £6,160

An early George III giltwood open armchair in the manner of John Cobb, the arched cartouche-shaped gadrooned back, scrolled arms and serpentine padded seat covered in associated petit point needlework. (Christie's)   £4,400

A Regency mahogany library bergère with caned scrolled back and sides, buttoned green-leather covered drop-in seat and close-nailed padded arms above a panelled frieze on tapering channelled sabre legs. (Christie's)   £3,850

One of a set of four George III giltwood open armchairs, each with oval padded back, armrests and seat upholstered in peach silk, the frame with guilloche moulding. (Christie's)   (Four)   £16,500

WING CHAIRS

George I walnut frame wing easy chair with floral pattern upholstery and loose cushion. (Hobbs & Chambers) £2,000

A Queen Anne style easy chair, upholstered in a red, white and blue bargello patterned fabric. £1,350

A fine Queen Anne leather-upholstered turned walnut and maple wing armchair, Boston, Massachusetts, circa 1760. (Sotheby's) £41,353

A walnut wing armchair of Queen Anne design, scrolling arms and seat upholstered in figured brocade, on cabriole legs with pad feet. (Christie's S. Ken) £1,650

A George III mahogany wing armchair, the padded rectangular back, arms and seat covered in close-nailed green leather, on square chamfered legs. (Christie's) £3,740

An early George III mahogany wing armchair, with stuffover shaped undulating back, outscrolled padded arm supports and seat with a cushion. (Phillips) £3,290

A George II mahogany wing armchair, the rectangular back, outscrolled arms, seat and cushion upholstered in stuffover green velvet, on cabriole legs. (Phillips) £2,200

A Queen Anne walnut and maple easy chair, probably Massachusetts, circa 1760, on cabriole legs ending in pad feet. (Skinner Inc.) £23,863

A walnut wing armchair of William and Mary style with rectangular back, padded arms and loose cushion in green cotton. (Christie's London) £880

WING CHAIRS

An early Georgian walnut wing armchair, the back and out-scrolled arms and bowed seat upholstered in floral moquette. £3.250

A mid Georgian elm wing armchair with arched back and leather upholstery. £3,150

A George I mahogany easy chair on cabriole legs with slipper feet, 1720-30. £2,850

A Georgian mahogany frame wing armchair, the back, scroll arms and stuffover seat upholstered in 18th century hookstitch and gros point needlework. (Phillips) £3,200

A George II mahogany wing armchair, the padded seat, squab back and outscrolled arms upholstered in red damask, on shell carved cabriole legs. (Phillips) £7,000

A Queen Anne walnut wing armchair covered in later yellow and purple patterned needlework on cabriole legs joined by a turned H-shaped stretcher. (Christie's) £1,980

A George I walnut framed wing armchair upholstered in lozenge pattern needlework, on lappet-headed cabriole legs. (Bearne's) £17,000

A William and Mary stained wing armchair, English, 18th century, ring-turned legs with scrolled Spanish feet joined by a moulded X-stretcher, 32in. wide. (Christie's) £3,924

A Queen Anne walnut wing armchair with padded back, outscrolled arms, bowed seat and squab cushion covered in gros-point needlework. (Christie's) £8,800

One of a pair of mahogany library open armchairs of George III style, each with padded waved rectangular back, on cabriole legs carved with acanthus and claw-and-ball feet. (Christie's) Two **£5,500**

'Piamio', a laminated birch armchair designed by Alvar Aalto, the black painted back and seat formed from a single piece. (Christie's) **£1,650**

A George III later painted and carved elbow chair, attributable to the workshop of Thomas Chippendale, the oval upholstered panel back with pierced riband and laurel swag cresting. (Phillips) **£22,500**

A George III carved beechwood open armchair, in the Adam manner, the reeded husk entwined frame with a padded serpentine seat and oval padded back.
(Phillips) **£6,900**

An Empire ormolu-mounted mahogany fauteuil and chaise, each with padded rectangular back and bowed seat covered in patterned close-nailed red silk, on sabre legs headed by lotus leaves and paterae on paw feet. (Christie's) **£3,300**

One of a pair of Venetian giltwood open armchairs, each with padded cartouche-shaped back, the moulded frame carved with S-scrolls and centred by rockwork, on cabriole legs, re-gilt. (Christie's) (Two) **£2,860**

A Regency mahogany bergère with rectangular padded back, on square tapering legs and brass caps, partially rerailed; and another en suite of later date.
(Christie's) (Two) **£2,640**

A Charles X ormolu-mounted mahogany tub bergère, the seat-rail applied with anthemia and stars, on sabre legs headed by paterae, later blocks, minor restorations. (Christie's) **£990**

A George II carved walnut open armchair of Gainsborough design, with a stuffover rectangular back and seat, on cabriole legs with pad feet. (Phillips) **£6,000**

ELBOW CHAIRS

Possibly the greatest problem confronting a designer of chairs has always been that of creating a style robust enough to survive while retaining a degree of elegance.

Very few designers achieved this happy blend, most coming down on the side of strong practicality and a few, such Sheraton and Hepplewhite, concentrating on a fashionable delicacy at the expense of strength. Chippendale was the man who came closest to combining the two elements and it is this which has made chairs based on his designs among the most popular ever made.

Beside the elegance of his designs, Hepplewhite is to be remembered for the explicit instructions given in his book regarding the materials to be used for the purpose of covering his chairs: for japanned chairs with cane seats, cushions covered in linen; for dining chairs, horse hair material which may be either plain or striped; for upholstered chairs, red or blue morocco leather tied with silk tassels.

While most surviving Sheraton chairs are made of mahogany, they can also be found in satinwood, painted white or gold or even japanned.

The delicacy of his designs demands that a fine fabric be used to cover the upholstery, green silk or satin being generally considered the most suitable.

More suited to the parlour than the dining room, his chairs must be treated with the utmost delicacy for, not being a manufacturer himself, Sheraton concerned himself more with the aesthetics of design than with the practicalities of use.

A Napoleon III rosewood prayer seat with hinged padded back and seat covered in patterned neddlework, on X-shaped support.
(Christie's)   £660

One of a set of eight   George III mahogany dining chairs, the backs with horizontal curved bar top rails and horizontal ebony strung splats. (Phillips)   £3,500

An English walnut open arm chair designed by Sir Edwin Lutyens, on turned legs incorporating the characteristic Lutyens 'Delhi Bell' motif, with stool en suite.
(Christie's)   £7,150

A set of ten George III style mahogany 'ribbon back' dining chairs in the manner of Thomas Chippendale, including two armchairs.
(Christie's East) (Ten)   £20,988

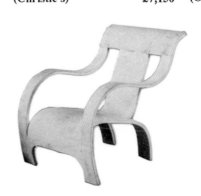

A Makers of Simple Furniture laminated birch armchair designed by Gerald Summers, cut and shaped to form a curved top rail with central splat and curved arms extending into plank legs. (Christie's)   £5,500

One of a set of fourteen elm ladder back chairs, including three open armchairs, with rush seats on turned legs joined by turned stretchers, late 18th/early 19th century.
(Christie's)   £6,050

One of a pair of Heal & Sons oak open arm chairs, each turned base with curved and vertical back rails, with linking spheres, above rush seat, circa 1915.
(Christie's) (Two)   £495

An unusual pair of branch-form laurel 'Centennial' armchairs, signed by *W. L. Carter*, Marietta, Pennsylvania, circa 1876.
(Sotheby's)   £4,632

One of a pair of George III mahogany elbow chairs, with loop backs, pierced and fluted splats, on square, tapering and chamfered legs joined by stretchers.
(Phillips)   (Two)   £500

A 19th century mahogany 'curule' open armchair after the design of Thomas Hope, the wide top rail with tapered finials and carved with a central roundel.
(Tennants)   £1,600

A pair of Clisset Highback ash armchairs designed by Ernest Gimson, with ladder backs above rush seats.
(Christie's)   £660

One of a pair of Regency ebonised and parcel-gilt open armchairs, on ring-turned tapering legs, re-decorated, minor differences in seat rail construction and proportions.
(Christie's)   (Two)   £1,760

One of a set of six mahogany dining chairs, of mid Georgian design, with a drop-in seat, on square chamfered legs joined by stretchers.
(Christie's)   (Six)   £2,200

A pair of George III mahogany open armchairs, each with a shield shaped curved back with five reeded splats. (Christie's)   £41,800

A Charles X mahogany fauteuil de bureau, the tub-shaped back with scrolling toprail and scrolling arms above a caned seat, on cabriole legs.
(Christie's S. Ken)   £1,650

A Regency painted open armchair, the back with curved top rail, and lion head tablet centred crossbar, the carved tapering seat with buttoned squab cushion.
(Phillips) £350

Two of a set of four Eastlake Victorian parlour chairs in walnut, one gentleman's chair and three lady's chairs, all with arms.
(Eldred's)   (Four)   £410

'Chair 24', one of a set of eight beechwood open armchairs designed by Hans Wegner, 1950, the horseshoe armrest of each with 'V' splat above shaped seat.
(Christie's) (Eight)   £1,210

One of a pair of late George III grained and parcel-gilt open armchairs, each with arched caned back and ball decorated splat above bowed caned seat.
(Christie's)   (Two)   £3,300

A pair of open armchairs, designed by Ernest Gimson, with shaped arms above turned legs and turned double stretchers. (Christie's)   £880

One of a set of twelve George III style stained mahogany dining chairs, including six open armchairs, on fluted tapering legs.
(Christie's) (Twelve)   £2,200

A late Elizabethan oak X-frame chair carved with scrolling foliage within a double-guilloche arch, with moulded sides, hipped scrolling arms and planked seat.
(Christie's)   £4,180

Two of four satinwood dining-chairs including two open armchairs, each with pierced shield-shaped back painted with an oval.
(Christie's)   £2,530

A Regency mahogany library reading-chair in the manner of Morgan & Saunders, the deeply curved back with scroll terminals and adjustable sliding reading-slope.
(Christie's)   £3,740

A very fine Queen Anne walnut armchair, Philadelphia, 1740–60, with removable slip seat enclosing a pewter basin, the basin probably Philadelphia, 18th century.
(Sotheby's) £9,500

An unusual and early Elizabethan Revival hall seat, in the manner of Richard Bridgens, circa 1840, the back carved to simulate Mannerist strapwork and centred upon a cabochon, 126cm. wide.
(Sotheby's) £4,400

A very fine painted and turned Windsor brace-back armchair, Rhode Island, circa 1780, the incised bowed crest above nine baluster-turned and tapered spindles. (Sotheby's) £5,624

A black-painted banister-back child's high-chair, New England, 19th century, the ring and baluster-turned stiles framing a scalloped crestrail above three banisters over a rush seat, $36\frac{1}{2}$in. high. (Christie's) £1,121

A pair of Regency painted open armchairs, in the manner of George Smith, the backs with curved top rails decorated with Greek key pattern around a tablet.
(Phillips) £4,600

An extremely rare Chippendale carved walnut armchair, Philadelphia, 1760–1780, on cabriole legs with stocking trifid feet, appears to be original leather-upholstered seat, $39\frac{3}{4}$in. high. (Christie's) £30,030

A William and Mary crown great-chair attributed to the shop of Thomas Salmon, Stratford, Connecticut, 1725–1735, on turned legs joined by double turned stretchers, 43in. high.
(Christie's) £4,484

One of a pair of late 19th century mahogany open armchairs in the Adam style, the frames carved with overlapping leaves, the oval backs fitted with a carved anthemion.
(Phillips)(Two) £2,600

A William and Mary banister-back crown great-chair possibly by Nathaniel Street, Norwalk area, 1725–1745, with scrolled crown and quadruple heart-pierced crest, $48\frac{7}{8}$in. high.
(Christie's) £11,210

ELBOW CHAIRS

One of a pair of Regency brass-nlaid open armchairs, each with curved toprail and horizontal splat with ebonised balls, on sabre legs.
(Christie's) (Two) £4,950

A George III mahogany open armchair, with pierced vase-shaped splat, on square tapering legs joined by H-shaped stretchers, on block feet.
(Christie's) £3,300

A George III mahogany open armchair, the bowed padded seat on beaded tapering legs headed by paterae.
(Phillips) £2,200

One of a pair of mahogany open armchairs of Chinese Chippendale style, each with padded rectangular seat upholstered in a needlework panel depicting wooing birds, the pierced splat with serpentine top rail centred by a pagoda.
(Christie's)(Two) £2,420

A pair of early 19th century Russian Empire 'tiger-wood' or tiger-birch open armchairs, on sabre legs.
Phillips) £7,000

One of a matched composite set of ten Flemish and English oak side or dining chairs, including two open armchairs, one walnut, each with padded back covered in a fragment of close-nailed 17th century Brussels tapestry.
(Christie's) (Ten) £3,080

A turned maple great-chair, Massachusetts, late 17th/early 18th century, with spool-turned crest rail above a further turned crest rail over three turned vertical splats, 40in. high.
(Christie's) £2,803

One of a set of six George II mahogany dining chairs with moulded scroll, paterae and rocaille decoration, the backs with undulating toprails and pierced vase splats, possibly Irish.
(Phillips) (Six) £3,600

A George III mahogany elbow chair, of 'Cockpen' design, with lattice back and stuffover saddle seat on moulded splayed legs.
(Phillips) £1,200

A Bohemian satin birch armchair, with downcurved arms, on scrolling supports, with upholstered seat, on square section tapered legs. (Bonhams) £280

One of a set of twelve parcel gilt and black-painted open armchairs of Regency style with cane-filled backs and seats, redecorated. (Christie's) £15,400

A George III mahogany elbow chair, the back formed of Chinese lattice-work with undulating top-rail. (Phillips) £1,500

A George III satinwood and decorated elbow chair in the manner of Seddon, the shield-shaped back with interlaced pierced splat. (Phillips) £1,800

A painted and turned maple double-back conversation 'Courting' chair, New England, 1780–1810, painted brown with yellow highlights, length 43in. (Sotheby's) £4,918

A George III mahogany ladder back armchair with pierced waved back, padded needlework seat and square chamfered legs joined by stretchers. (Christie's) £396

A George III carved mahogany elbow chair, the cartouche shaped back with paterae decorated pierced vase splats. (Phillips) £2,300

A Régence carved beechwood fauteuil, with cartouche cane back and rocaille scroll cresting with trailing flowers, on cabriole legs and scroll feet. (Phillips) £950

A George III mahogany spindle back desk chair, decorated with paterae, garya husks and foliate moulding with a curved toprail and arm supports. (Phillips) £1,500

One of a set of seven Regency mahogany dining chairs, with outscrolled bar top-rails, on channelled sabre legs. (Christie's) (Seven) £990

A Regency rosewood library chair with bow back, twisted stick back on turned front and rear splay supports. (Russell Baldwin & Bright) £580

A George III yewwood and elm Windsor comb-back armchair with waved top-rail and spindle-filled back, the dished seat on cabriole legs. (Christie's) £825

One of a pair of American hickory open armchairs, on simple turned legs, stamped 'Old Hickory, Artinsvill, Indiana'. (Bearne's) Two £390

A Queen Anne carved walnut balloon-seat corner chair, Newport, Rhode Island, 1740–65, the U-shaped back ending in scrolled handholds. (Sotheby's) £10,592

Gustav Stickley armchair, no. 366, circa 1907, straight crest rail over three vertical slats, flat arms with front corbels, 26in. wide. (Skinner) £169

A George III mahogany open armchair, the shield-shaped back centred by a beaded circular medallion enclosing the Prince-of-Wales' feathers. (Christie's) £1,320

A Georgian bergère armchair, the mahogany frame with reeded top rail, supported upon fluted tapering legs ending in brass castors. (Spencer's) £1,200

A George III mahogany open armchair with eared scroll carved toprail and pierced vase splat above padded seat, on square chamfered legs. (Christie's) £462

ELBOW CHAIRS

One of a set of four Regency white painted and gilt decorated elbow chairs, the cane seats with horsehair cushion squabs on sabre legs.
(Phillips)   (Four) £3,600

One of a pair of late George III Irish mahogany hall seats, each with waisted rectangular back and waved toprail centred by an anthemion amidst acanthus-scrolls with flowerhead terminals and finials, 33¹/₂in. wide.
(Christie's) (Two)   £55,000

A George II mahogany open armchair, the arched tapering back centred by a shell cresting with pierced interlaced knot-pattern splat headed by rosettes, 37¹/₂in. high.
(Christie's)   £39,600

A Federal white-painted and parcel-gilt armchair, Philadelphia, circa 1790, the arching moulded crestrail decorated with acorns amid oak leaves over a padded tapering back flanked by reeded baluster-turned stiles, 36in. high.(Christie's)   £30,600

Two of a set of six Regency black and gilt-japanned dining-chairs, and two similar open armchairs, each with scrolled back and shaped toprail painted with eagle-masks.
(Christie's)   (Six)   £6,050

One of a pair of George II mahogany open armchairs with arched tapering heart-shaped backs, moulded and beaded toprails and crestings carved with fruiting vines issuing from flowerheads, 36in. high.
(Christie's)   (Two)   £275,000

A James I oak open armchair, the rectangular back with waved scrolled cresting and pointed finials above a band of stylised flowerhead-filled guilloche.
(Christie's)   £5,500

One of a set of eight Regency mahogany dining chairs, the backs with curved bar top rails and rope twist horizontal splats.
(Phillips)   £2,800

A walnut open armchair with rectangular padded back and seat covered in associated petit-point foliate needlework, third quarter 17th century, one back foot spliced.
(Christie's)   £1,760

A mahogany open armchair, the arms with lion-mask terminals, on cabriole legs carved with acanthus issuing from a lion-mask on claw-and-ball feet.
(Christie's) £4,070

One of a set of eight Regency blue-painted and parcel-gilt open armchairs in the manner of Henry Holland, each with channelled toprail.
(Christie's) (Eight) £71,500

A George I walnut and burr walnut open armchair, the arched back with tablet cresting centred by a scallop shell and vase-shaped splat.
(Christie's) £36,300

A blue-painted Windsor sack-back armchair, New England, late 18th century, the arching crestrail above seven spindles and shaped arms over baluster-turned supports and a shaped plank seat, retains 19th century paint, 43$\frac{1}{2}$in. high.
(Christie's) £6,000

Two of a set of fourteen William IV mahogany dining-chairs including two open armchairs, with moulded seat-rail on channelled sabre legs, later blocks. (Christie's) (Fourteen) £9,350

A George II mahogany open armchair with arched back, rockwork and foliage cresting, solid vase-shaped splat, shepherd's crook arms and drop in grospoint needlework seat, 41$\frac{1}{4}$in. high.
(Christie's) £19,800

A George II mahogany open armchair with waved foliate toprail, and pierced vase-shaped splat carved with interlaced tiered C-scrolls and foliage, on cabriole legs carved with acanthus sprays, 38$\frac{1}{2}$in. high.
(Christie's) £57,200

One of a pair of George II black and gilt-japanned open armchairs by William and John Linnell, each with stepped rectangular back filled with black and gold Chinese paling.
(Christie's) £165,000

One of a pair of George III mahogany Gothic open armchairs in the manner of Robert Manwaring, the rectangular crenellated back carved with a pierced cusped rose centred by spandrels.
(Christie's) £10,450

113

ELBOW CHAIRS

A Regency painted elbow chair, the horizontally railed back with arched and pierced top rail and 'X'-crossbar.
(Phillips) £400

A pair of Directoire style parcel-gilt and carved walnut fauteuils, late 19th century, the downswept arms above urn-form supports.
(Butterfield & Butterfield) £1,576

A Lancashire mahogany spindle back armchair with slightly bowed arms, on square legs, circa 1790.
(Bonhams) £35

One of six Regency painted elbow chairs, the beech frames with rectangular and canted openwork backs and cane seats. £4,500

Pair of neoclassical style parcel-gilt and cream-painted armchairs, 19th century, the rectangular arms above a caned seat, raised on tapering square legs.
(Butterfield & Butterfield) £1,576

Twig armchair, 20th century, shaped arms and back comprised of Southern woods, 49in. high.
(Skinner Inc.) £2

One of a pair of 19th century hardwood elbow chairs with marble inset panel splats and cane seats, (Phillips) £1,900

A pair of red-painted and parcel-gilt open armchairs of Regency style decorated overall with foliage, on turned tapering legs.
(Christie's) £1,870

One of a set of eight Regency mahogany dining chairs, including two elbow chairs with stuffover seats.
(Phillips) £4,800

A George III carved mahogany elbow chair, in the Hepplewhite taste, on square tapered legs united by stretchers.
(Phillips) £850

Two of six "Linear" chairs, attributed to Luigi Tagliabue, Italy, two armchairs, four side curved plank-back, 27in. high.
(Skinner Inc.) £1,333

One of a pair of George III cream and green painted open armchairs, with bowed cane-filled seats.
£1,600

An Egyptian hardwood X-framed armchair inlaid throughout in ivory with geometric motifs.
(Bearne's) £360

A pair of Robert 'Mouseman' Thompson oak armchairs, each with horseshoe arms and back, carved with two cats' heads and shaped terminals, dated 1928.
(Christie's) £1,980

A walnut open armchair with flat spirally twisted arms supported on female busts, third quarter of the 17th century.
(Christie's) £3,080

A George III mahogany open arm elbow chair in the Sheraton taste, the rectangular back with turned uprights.
(Phillips) £1,400

A pair of Gordon Russell turned yew armchairs, the spindle filled back with two tall bun finials, on turned legs with bar stretchers.
(Christie's) £990

A George III mahogany 'cockpen' armchair, with chinoiserie fretwork back, on square chamfered legs.
(Bonhams) £500

One of a set of seven George III carved mahogany dining chairs in the Hepplewhite taste, the slightly balloon shaped backs with trefoil top rails, on moulded square tapered legs. (Phillips) £4,200

One of a pair of walnut fauteuils, the channelled toprail carved with acanthus and rockwork, on cabriole legs headed by cabochon-encrusted rockwork on scrolling feet. (Christie's) £7,260

One of a matched pair of yew and elm Windsor Gothic ope armchairs, with shaped sadd seat, the cabriole legs joined bowed stretchers, on pad feet 18th century. (Christie's) £2,7.

A mahogany open armchair with waved eared toprail centred by rockwork with pierced interlaced splat, on square chamfered fluted legs. (Christie's) £495

One of a pair of ebonised and parcel-gilt open armchairs each with a double-caned panelled back, the arm supports and sabre legs carved in the form of a leopard monopodia with wings. (Christie's) £3,300

One of a set of ten Hepplewhite period carved mahogany dinin chairs, the shaped balloon arched backs with anthemion crestings, and another pair of dining chairs of a later date. (Phillips) (Twelve) £20,00

One of a set of ten ash and elm dining-chairs including two open armchairs, on turned legs joined by turned stretchers and pad feet, first half 19th century, Lancashire/Cheshire. (Christie's) £3,080

A North Italian simulated rosewood and parcel-gilt klismos armchair, on turned reeded tapering legs, first quarter 19th century. (Christie's) £6,820

A Charles II oak child's chair with rectangular panelled back carved with a lozenge, the solid seat on turned legs joined by square stretchers, lacking finia (Christie's) £4,40

One of a pair of George III mahogany open armchairs each with panelled bowed toprail, the reed-shaped arms terminated by a floral rosette.
(Christie's)　　(Two)　£4,180

A Regency mahogany metamorphic library step chair, after a patent by Morgan & Saunders, the padded seat folding out to form four steps on sabre legs. (Phillips)　£3,000

A Regency ebonised and parcel-gilt open armchair in the manner of Henry Holland, with rectangular padded back and seat covered in close-nailed green leather.
(Christie's)　£1,375

One of a pair of George II black and gilt japanned open armchairs by William and John Linnell, each with stepped rectangular back filled with black and gold Chinese paling, 40¾in. high. (Two)
(Christie's)　£110,000

A Cromwellian oak open armchair, the panelled back with scrolled tablet cresting carved *THOMAS CORBETT 1657* flanked by two lions, on turned legs joined by stretchers.
(Christie's)　£3,080

One of a pair of George III mahogany armchairs in the manner of John Cobb, each with deeply curved back, railed splat and downscrolled arms, on cabriole legs headed by floral carving.
(Christie's)　£14,300

One of a set of five George III later white painted and gilt decorated elbow chairs, in the Sheraton taste, with column splats having padded arm supports and stuffover seats.
(Phillips)　(Five)　£2,800

A Regency simulated rosewood klismos chair, the deeply curved padded toprail, splat and seat covered in red wool, on sabre legs with brass caps.
(Christie's)　£1,100

An Aesthetic Movement ebonised and inlaid open armchair, rectangular padded back with ivory and gilded inlay of various geometric and stylised floral motifs, circa 1870.
(Christie's)　£1,760

A Carlo Bugatti ebonised and inlaid open armchair, the seat-rail covered in beaten copper, above carved supports inlaid with pewter and bone.
(Christie's)   £2,420

Harden & Co. armchair, circa 1910, wide straight crest rail over three vertical back slats, flat arms over three wide vertical slats.
(Skinner)   £197

One of a set of eight George III style mahogany shield-backed dining chairs, on square section tapered legs.
(Bonhams)   (Eight)   £800

One of a set of nine late George III mahogany dining chairs, with rectangular bowed toprail and horizontal splats between reeded arms, on square tapering legs.
(Christie's)   (Nine)   £4,400

One of a pair of Regency simulated bamboo bergères, each with caned back, sides and seat, on turned tapering legs joined by an H-shaped stretcher, decoration refreshed.
(Christie's) (Two)   £6,380

One of a set of eight black japanned and grisaille-painted dining chairs, each with a bar back and central oval panel depicting a cherub driven in a chariot.
(Christie's S. Ken) (Eight) £2,200

Late 18th century German carved oak lug armchair, the seatrail carved with stylised leaves and lions' heads, on cabriole legs. (Kunsthaus am Museum)   £559

One of a pair of Liberty and Co. large oak armchairs, with rectangular upholstered red leather backs and seats, the wings carved with mythical beasts.
(Christie's) (Two)   £2,200

A James II oak open armchair, the panelled rectangular back carved with strapwork, the toprail carved 1686 flanked by animal scrolls.
(Christie's)   £2,090

CHESTS OF DRAWERS

Throughout the transitional period from coffer to chest of drawers, there were a great many variations on the basic theme but, eventually, a practical and attractive formula emerged about 1670. Not slow to respond to the demand, cabinet makers produced vast quantities of chests of drawers, employing, as a rule, the familiar native wood, oak, for the purpose.

Architectural geometric mouldings proved popular as decoration and these were glued and bradded in position – a practice which continues to the present day.

As taste developed, there arose a need for more sophisticated chests in more exotic woods such as figured walnut, which was put on to an oak or pine carcass.

The use of veneers made the manufacture of moulded drawer fronts impractical and, consequently, more emphasis was placed on the figuring of the veneers as a decorative feature. The oyster design was particularly popular and results from careful cutting of the veneer from a tree bough. This is glued vertically on to the drawer front, the figuring being meticulously matched, and it is crossbanded on the edges, often with an intermediate herringbone inlay.

The drawers are now found to slide on the horizontal partitions which separate them and they are finely dovetailed, where earlier they were more crudely jointed or even nailed together.

Walnut continued as the most favoured wood for chests of drawers until the middle of the 18th century, when it gave way to Spanish mahogany.

A George III mahogany serpentine chest, the eared top crossbanded in kingwood, above three graduated long drawers and on splayed bracket feet, 43³/₄in. wide.
(Christie's) £3,300

A George III mahogany bachelor's chest, the rectangular fold-over top with draw-out lopers, and with four long graduated drawers below, 2ft. 5in. wide.
(Spencer's) £1,400

A William and Mary oyster-veneered walnut chest, banded overall with fruitwood, the moulded rectangular top inlaid with concentric circles and geometric pattern, on later bun feet, 37¹/₄in. wide.
(Christie's) £7,480

A Georgian mahogany serpentine front chest with rosewood moulded crossbanded top with boxwood lines, containing four long drawers between reeded stiles, on swept bracket feet, 3ft. 1in. wide.
(Phillips) £3,200

Dutch rococo style oak chest of drawers, 19th century, with a scalloped edge above a bombé front fitted with three drawers flanked by buttress stiles, 33¹/₂in. wide.
(Butterfield & Butterfield) £1,349

George II burl walnut chest of drawers, second quarter 18th century, the rectangular top with moulded edge and notched front corners, raised on bracket feet, 32in. wide.
(Butterfield & Butterfield) £3,467

A late 18th century Continental walnut and inlaid chest of bowed outline, the top, front and sides veneered with panels with geometric and key inlay, on ring turned tapered feet, possibly Spanish or Italian, 4ft. (Phillips) £7,200

A George II padoukwood bachelor's chest, the rounded rectangular hinged top above four graduated long drawers, on shaped bracket feet, 30¼in. wide. (Christie's) £3,960

A late 18th century Continental sycamore, walnut crossbanded and marquetry rectangular chest, the top and sides with stellar inlay framed by interlaced husks, on bracket feet, possibly Italian or Danish. (Phillips) £2,000

A George III mahogany serpentine chest with moulded top above four long drawers, the top drawer with velvet-lined slide enclosing compartments and a drawer, on bracket feet, 36in. wide. (Christie's) £6,820

A pair of Regency mahogany, boxwood strung and partridgewood fronted chests of small size, each containing two short and three long graduated drawers, 1ft. 11in. wide. (Phillips) £7,500

A George III mahogany and marquetry serpentine chest inlaid overall with fruitwood lines, the top with an oval medallion with an urn, with waved apron and splayed bracket feet, 41½in. wide. (Christie's) £3,960

A Regency mahogany chest with bowed rectangular top above two short and three graduated long drawers with waved apron and splayed bracket feet, 43in. wide. (Christie's) £990

A William and Mary walnut oyster veneer and acacia banded chest, the top inlaid with geometric lines, on later bun feet, 3ft. 2in. wide. (Phillips) £9,200

A William and Mary burr-yew chest inlaid with geometric lines, moulded rectangular top above two short and three long drawers, on later bun feet, 37¼in. wide. (Christie's) £5,500

An 18th century Italian walnut crossbanded and penwork marquetry serpentine chest, the top centred by an architectural roundel with a goddess in a chariot flanked by foliate grotesques, 4ft. 4¹/₂in. wide.
(Phillips) **£14,000**

An early Georgian walnut chest with rectangular top above a slide and four graduated long drawers, on bracket feet, 33in. wide.
(Christie's) **£5,500**

An early 18th century walnut and feather banded chest, containing eight short and a long drawer, having brass carrying handles to the sides, on bracket feet, 3ft. 9in. wide.
(Phillips) **£2,200**

A Regency mahogany serpentine chest inlaid overall with fruitwood lines, with eared top and three graduated long drawers with waved apron, on sabre legs, 42in. wide.
(Christie's) **£3,080**

A mahogany chest with rectangular top above four graduated long drawers, on bracket feet, basically 18th century, 29¹/₂in. wide.
(Christie's) **£1,980**

A Dutch fruitwood chest with eared rectangular moulded top above four long drawers between keeled angles with waved apron, late 18th century, 35in. wide.
(Christie's) **£1,980**

A fine Charles II oyster veneered olivewood chest, the concentrically veneered top outlined with boxwood stringing above two short and three long drawers, 38in. wide.
(Bonhams) **£9,000**

A George III mahogany chest with moulded rectangular top above a slide and two short and three graduated long drawers, on bracket feet, 36in. wide.
(Christie's) **£2,420**

A late 18th century neo-Classical Italian walnut crossbanded and marquetry chest, in the manner of Maggiolini, the top with a quatrefoil border and central oval medallion depicting a seated figure, on square tapered legs, 4ft. wide. (Phillips) **£12,000**

A mahogany and ormolu mounted chest, with rectangular marble top above a frieze drawer and three large drawers under, first half 19th century, 14cm. wide.
(Finarte) £2,388

Rare William and Mary grain painted spice chest, Massachusetts, early 18th century, 18³/₄in. wide.
(Skinner) £6,451

A Federal curly maple-inlaid birchwood chest of drawers, New England, circa 1820, the rectangular top above four cockbeaded graduated drawers, width 41in.
(Sotheby's) £1,740

A rare William and Mary walnut chest of drawers, Pennsylvania, probably Chester County, early 18th century, the moulded base continuing to ball feet, 41³/₄in. wide.
(Sotheby's) £4,962

A William and Mary walnut oyster veneered and acacia banded chest, the rectangular moulded top with geometric panels, on later bracket feet, 3ft. 1in. wide.
(Phillips) £3,400

A William and Mary grain-painted blanket-chest, Connecticut, 1725–1735, the case with applied moulding with two sham and two long drawers, 41¹/₂in. wide.
(Christie's) £1,682

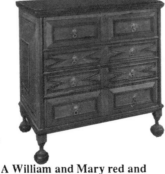

A fine Federal inlaid mahogany chest of drawers, Boston area, Massachusetts, circa 1805, the shaped skirt continuing to reeded legs, on brass casters, 41in. wide.
(Sotheby's) £5,293

A William and Mary red and black-painted chest-of-drawers decorated with geometric mouldings in imitation of pairs of short drawers, on turned feet, 39in. wide.
(Christie's) £5,045

A good Chippendale mahogany serpentine-front chest of drawers, Massachusetts, circa 1780, the moulded base continuing to ball and claw feet, 38³/₄in. wide.
(Sotheby's) £6,286

A George III mahogany chest with moulded eared serpentine top with slide and four graduated mahogany-lined drawers, on shaped bracket feet, 38in. wide.
(Christie's) £8,800

A Dutch walnut and marquetry small bombé chest of three long drawers with waved edge to the top, shell apron and ball and claw feet, 34in. wide.
(Lawrence Fine Art) £3,850

A walnut and marquetry chest, with two short and three long similarly inlaid drawers, on bracket feet, early 18th century, the marquetry later, 28in. wide. (Christie's London) £3,850

A fine Queen Anne mahogany block-front chest of drawers, Boston, Massachusetts, circa 1765, the moulded base with shaped pendant continuing to bracket feet, width 35½in.
(Sotheby's) £39,638

A William and Mary blue, black and red painted chest with rectangular top naively painted with a black speckled panel on a cream ground, 41in. wide.
(Christie's London) £24,200

A William and Mary walnut-veneered chest, with crossbanding and ebony stringing, ovolo carcase mouldings and on later bun feet, 39in. wide.
(Bearne's) £580

A mahogany chest with moulded serpentine top carved with flower-applied entrelac above a green leather-lined slide and four graduated long drawers, on ogee bracket feet, 39in. wide.
(Christie's) £9,900

A Dutch walnut small bombé chest of four drawers with waved top and projecting angles, on carved paw feet, 18th century, 35in. wide.
(Lawrence Fine Art) £1,485

A George III small mahogany chest of four graduated drawers surmounted by a slide with moulded top and base and on bracket feet, 33½in. wide.
(Lawrence Fine Art) £1,100

A fine Chippendale carved mahogany block front chest of drawers, Massachusetts, 1760–1780, with four graduated long drawers over conforming base moulding above a shell-carved pendant, on ogee bracket feet, 37³/₈in. wide. (Christie's) £11,220

A Federal inlaid and flame birch veneered mahogany chest of drawers, Portsmouth, New Hampshire, 1790–1810, the rectangular top with bowed front edged with crossbanding and stringing, on French feet, 40in. wide. (Christie's) £14,025

A Queen Anne walnut high chest of drawers, Pennsylvania, 1740–1760, the upper section with coved cornice above three short and three long thumb-moulded drawers, 41¹/₂in. wide. (Christie's) £8,415

A black and gold-japanned chest decorated overall with chinoiserie figures, birds and landscapes, on bracket feet, basically early 18th century, 38in. wide. (Christie's) £1,980

The important Gilbert family matching Queen Anne walnut high chest of drawers and dressing table, Salem, Massachusetts, 1750–1770, on cabriole legs with pad feet, 38in. wide. (Christie's) £84,150

A fine Chippendale mahogany reverse serpentine chest of drawers, Massachusetts, 1760–1780, with four graduated long drawers with cockbead surrounds over a conforming base moulding, on ogee bracket feet, 37in. wide. (Christie's) £10,659

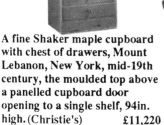

A fine George III mahogany serpentine chest, containing four long cockbeaded drawers, having a shaped apron, on slender splayed feet, 4ft. 6in. wide. (Phillips) £8,500

A fine Shaker maple cupboard with chest of drawers, Mount Lebanon, New York, mid-19th century, the moulded top above a panelled cupboard door opening to a single shelf, 94in. high. (Christie's) £11,220

A Chippendale carved mahogany reverse-serpentine chest of drawers, Massachusetts, 1775–1790, with moulded edge reverse-serpentine front above a conforming case, 41in. wide. (Christie's) £4,208

A George III mahogany serpentine chest, with a slide above two short and four graduated mahogany-lined long drawers on angled bracket feet, 40in. wide.
(Christie's) £5,500

A mahogany chest of American Queen Anne Boston style with moulded waved rectangular top, the block front with four graduated long drawers, on cabriole legs and claw-and-ball feet, 32½in. wide.
(Christie's) £2,750

A good late 17th century walnut and burr walnut chest, of mellow golden colour, on bracket feet, the drawers retaining some contemporary patterned lining paper, 38¼in. wide.
(Tennants) £4,000

A George III mahogany serpentine chest, the eared top inlaid with chevron banding above four graduated long drawers, on splayed bracket feet, 42½in. wide. (Christie's) £9,900

A kingwood and tulipwood semainier inlaid with fruitwood lines, the moulded D-shaped mottled grey marble top above six short drawers, 12¼in. wide.
(Christie's) £6,050

A mid-Georgian mahogany bachelor's chest with moulded folding top above two short and three long drawers, on bracket feet, 33¾in. wide.
(Christie's) £14,850

A mid-Georgian mahogany bachelor's chest, the rectangular moulded folding top with re-entrant corners above four graduated drawers, the sides with carrying-handles, 32¾in. wide.
(Christie's) £8,250

A mid-Georgian mahogany upright chest, the rectangular top above two short and four graduated long drawers on bracket feet, 16in. wide.
(Christie's) £12,650

A George III mahogany chest with moulded eared serpentine top above a slide and four graduated mahogany-lined drawers, 41in. wide.
(Christie's) £9,350

A George III mahogany chest, the top with a moulded edge, containing a brushing slide and four graduated drawers, on bracket feet, 3ft.
(Phillips)   £1,300

A George III mahogany serpentine chest with eared top above four graduated long drawers and on later shaped bracket feet, 39¼in. wide.
(Christie's)   £1,760

A Charles II oyster walnut and floral marquetry chest of drawers, the top inlaid with birds and a flower filled urn, 36½in. wide.
(Lawrence)   £9,900

An Aesthetic Movement burr-maple chest of drawers, the rectangular top above two short and four long drawers with ebonised stringing, 96cm. wide.
(Christie's)   £1,210

A bone-inlaid oak and fruitwood chest in two sections with moulded rectangular top, on bun feet, basically 17th century, 44in. wide.
(Christie's)   £1,980

An attractive mahogany serpentine front chest in the Georgian style, the top with thumb moulded edge, 2ft. 11in. wide.
(Spencer's)   £980

19th century brass bound military chest in two sections, with brass inset handles, on turned feet, 35½in. long.
(Phillips Manchester)   £900

An early 18th century walnut and boxwood strung chest, the crossbanded top decorated with geometric inlay, on bun feet, 3ft. 2in. wide.
(Phillips)   £2,800

A Chippendale carved walnut chest of drawers, Pennsylvania, circa 1780, with four graduated moulded long drawers, quarter-columns flanking, on ogee bracket feet, 35in. wide.
(Sotheby's)   £6,617

George III mahogany bow-front chest of drawers, early 19th century, on a scrolled drawers skirt, raised on splayed feet, 41in. wide. (Skinner Inc.) £452

Biedermeier inlaid walnut and parcel ebonised chest of drawers, circa 1820, raised on tapering square feet, 47in. wide. (Butterfield & Butterfield) £1,856

A Robert 'Mouseman' Thompson oak chest of drawers, the rectangular, moulded and chamfered top above two short and three long drawers, 91.5cm. wide. (Christie's) £1,210

A 19th century camphorwood campaign chest with ebonised stringing, two deep drawers above three long drawers and on turned feet, 37³/₄in. wide. (Bearne's) £900

A very fine Federal flame birch and ivory-inlaid mahogany bow-front chest of drawers, Portsmouth, New Hampshire, circa 1805, 41¹/₄in. wide. (Sotheby's) £17,203

An 18th century Danish walnut crossbanded and parcel gilt serpentine chest with simulated black marble top and incised gesso frieze, 2ft. 7in. wide. (Phillips) £4,000

William and Mary oak chest of drawers, fitted with two short over three geometrically fronted drawers, on bracket feet, 40in. wide. (Butterfield & Butterfield) £964

A late George III mahogany bow front chest, the boxwood strung caddy top above four graduated long drawers on splayed legs, 3ft. 1in. wide. (Phillips) £823

A George III oak chest crossbanded overall, the retangular top above two short and three graduated long drawers, on later bracket feet, 37in. wide. (Christie's) £660

A tortoiseshell and bone-inlaid chest, the rectangular top and sides inlaid with a lozenge-pattern, above five cedar-lined drawers, the central drawer with arched recess, 26³/₄in. wide.
(Christie's) £2,420

A Goanese rosewood, teak and bone-inlaid cabinet-on-stand inlaid overall with stars on concentric circles, the cabinet with eight short drawers and two deep short drawers, late 17th century, 36in. wide.
(Christie's) £26,400

A Spanish walnut vargueno in two sections, the iron-bound top section with rectangular top and fall-front enclosing a fitted gilt and arcaded interior of twelve drawers around a cupboard.
(Christie's) £12,100

A Dutch ebony and bone-inlaid cabinet-on-stand with moulded rectangular top above two doors with geometrical inlay enclosing a fitted interior with ten panelled drawers around a pillared door, second half 17th century, 36in. wide. (Christie's) £5,280

A Louis XV lacquered-brass mounted, rosewood and tulipwood chiffonier with moulded rounded rectangular brown and grey mottled marble top above six drawers, 23¹/₂in. wide. (Christie's) £4,180

A William and Mary walnut and oyster-veneered cabinet-on-stand, banded overall with fruitwood and moulded rectangular cornice, above two doors enclosing eleven drawers around a central cupboard, 43in. wide. (Christie's) £17,600

A William and Mary walnut secrétaire-on-chest with moulded cornice, one long drawer and a fall-front with fitted interior, 42in. wide.
(Christie's) £7,150

A George III mahogany secrétaire chest with moulded rectangular top above a panelled secrétaire drawer enclosing a fitted interior, 34in. wide.
(Christie's) £1,980

A Queen Anne burr walnut secrétaire-on-chest with moulded rectangular top above one long drawer and fall-front enclosing a fitted interior, 42in. wide.
(Christie's) £5,500

CHESTS ON CHESTS

In the early 18th century, the tallboy, or chest on a chest, began to replace the chest on a stand and, by about 1725, had virtually superseded it.

Tallboys are made in two parts, the upper chest being slightly narrower than the lower and, although they are inclined to be bulky, this is often minimised visually by means of canted corners.

Early examples were veneered in finely grained burr walnut and often sport a sunburst decoration of boxwood and holly at the base, which usually has the fashionable bracket feet.

As an added bonus, buyers of these superb pieces of furniture often get a secret drawer in the frieze as well as the brushing slide fitted above the oak lined drawers in the lower section.

Despite the obvious difficulty in reaching the top drawers and the competition from wardrobes and clothes presses, tallboys were made in vast quantities throughout the second half of the 18th century. So common were they, in fact, that George Smith, in his *Household Furniture* observed that the tallboy was an article "... of such general use that it does not stand in need of a description".

As a rule, tallboys were made of mahogany and ranged in quality from rather plain, monolithic but functional pieces to magnificent, cathedral-like specimens with elaborate cornices, fluted pillars flanking the upper drawers, low relief carving on the frieze and fine ogee feet.

Their popularity lasted until about 1820 when the linen press, with cupboard doors to the upper section, proved to be more practical.

A George III mahogany chest-on-chest, circa 1760, 3ft.8in. wide. £2,500

An 18th century Continental mahogany chest-on-chest, 43in. wide. £3,000

Early 18th century walnut chest on bracket feet, 28in. wide. (Chancellors Hollingsworths) £1,650

A George II walnut chest-on-chest, moulded cornice and three short drawers, over six long drawers, 69¾in. high. (Skinner) £3,770

A George I walnut chest on chest, the drawer front inlaid with narrow bands, the sides varnished pine and on later replaced bracket feet, 90cm. wide. (Lawrence Fine Arts) £1,100

Late George III mahogany chest-on-chest, first quarter 19th century, the top drawer of the lower section fitted with a later leather-inset writing slide, 40¼in. wide. (Butterfield & Butterfield) £1,687

CHESTS ON CHESTS

A George III mahogany chest-on-chest, 3ft.7½in. wide, circa 1765. £1,400

A Chippendale maple chest-on-chest, in two parts, probably New Hampshire, 1760-90, 38½in. wide. £10,000

Georgian mahogany chest-on-chest, 1790. £1,750

A George III mahogany chest on chest with two short and three long drawers, the lower part with a slide above three long drawers, on bracket feet pierced with scrolls, 43in. wide. (Lawrence Fine Art) £2,970

An important Federal carved and figured mahogany serpentine-front chest-on-chest, the carving attributed to Samuel McIntire, Salem, Massachusetts, circa 1795, 45¼in. wide. (Sotheby's) £218,346

A George II walnut chest on chest with a cavetto cornice above three short and three long drawers, with oak sides and bracket feet, restored, 101cm. wide. (Lawrence Fine Arts) £3,520

A Chippendale carved cherrywood chest-on-chest on frame, Connecticut, probably Woodbury, circa 1770, on C-scroll carved frontal cabriole legs, 39¾in. wide. (Sotheby's) £6,286

A fine Chippendale carved mahogany scroll-top chest-on-chest, Philadelphia, circa 1770, in three parts, on a moulded base and ogee bracket feet, 47in. wide. (Sotheby's) £7,940

A George III mahogany chest on chest with a concave cornice above three short and three long drawers flanked by fluted canted angles, 41in. wide. (Lawrence Fine Art) £1,210

A George III mahogany chest-on-chest, circa 1770, 3ft.6in. wide.   £1,550

A Chippendale walnut chest-on-chest on ogee bracket feet, 44in. wide, 1760-90.
£28,500

A George III mahogany secretaire chest-on-chest, 3ft.7½in. wide, circa 1760.   £1,750

A George III mahogany chest-on-chest, the serpentine front with two short and seven graduated long drawers divided by reeded bands, on short cabriole legs ending in scrolled feet, 47¼in. wide.
(Christie's)   £44,000

A mid-18th century mahogany chest-on-chest of small proportions, with two short and two long drawers to the upper section, three graduated long drawers below, 27½in. wide.
(Bearne's)   £620

A George III Welsh oak chest on chest, the upper part with moulded cornice and flute moulded frieze above, the whole raised on bracket feet, 41in. wide.
(Spencer's)   £900

George III mahogony chest on chest, last-quarter 18th century, Greek key cornice above two short and three long graduated drawers, 71in. high.
(Skinner Inc)   £2,272

A mid-George III mahogany chest-on-chest with a moulded dentil cornice above three short and six graduated long drawers, on bracket feet, 46in. wide.
(Christie's S. Ken)   £4,400

George III mahogany chest-on-chest, late 18th century, with a cavetto-moulded cornice, on ogee bracket feet, 40¼in. wide.
(Butterfield & Butterfield)
£2,699

A Georgian inlaid mahogany double chest of six long and two short drawers, 6ft.8in. high. (Anderson & Garland) £650

A James Bartram Chippendale mahogany chest-on-chest, in two sections, circa 1750–70, 44½in. wide. £80,000

A Georgian oak chest on chest with a cavetto cornice, two plain quarter round pilasters, on ogee bracket feet, 39in. wide. (Lawrence Fine Arts) £1,760

A George III mahogany chest on chest, the lower part with three long drawers, all oak lined with brass loop handles, and on bracket feet, 45in. wide. (Lawrence Fine Arts) £2,530

An early 18th century walnut chest on chest, the upper part with a moulded cornice above three short and three long graduated drawers between reeded angles, on bracket feet, 3ft. 4in. wide. (Phillips) £9,000

A George III mahogany chest on chest, the dentil moulded cornice above two short and three long graduated drawers, the lower section with three long graduated drawers, on bracket feet, 44in. wide. (Bonhams) £1,050

A George II walnut chest on chest with ogee moulded cornice, on later bracket feet, restored, 68½in. high. (Lawrence Fine Arts) £3,080

A fine Chippendale carved mahogany block-front bonnet-top chest-on-chest, Boston, Massachusetts, circa 1770, 42in. wide. (Sotheby's) £31,429

A George III mahogany chest on chest, the lower part with a slide above three long drawers, on bracket feet, 115cm. wide. (Lawrence Fine Arts) £2,860

Towards the end of the 17th century, many chests were raised on stands, often with an extra drawer in the lower section. The reason for this may have been to create a sense of fit proportion between furniture and the high ceilinged rooms of the period, or it may have reflected the stiff backed deportment which was considered proper at that time, raising furniture to a height at which the operative parts could be reached without stooping or bending in an unfashionable manner.

Legs of stands were either turned or barley twist, and were braced with shaped stretchers ending in bun feet.

There were a few pieces made of oak but most, if we are to judge by the survivors, were made of pine with walnut veneer and oak lined drawers. Some sport fine arabesque marquetry decoration, their tops having an oval design in the centre and triangular corner pieces. There are half round mouldings between drawers which, with the ovolo lip on the top of the stand, are characteristic of pieces of this period.

It is not uncommon to find later bases under these pieces for, although they were generally pretty well made, when full they were inclined to be just that bit too heavy for the rather delicate stands on which they originally stood.

Although of delicate constitution, the chest on stand continued to be made in the early part of the 18th century but, instead of the barley twist legs with shaped stretchers, we find that the later pieces have flowing cabriole legs with ball and claw feet.

A William and Mary walnut chest-on-stand with two short and three long graduated drawers, 38½in. wide. £1,750

A Queen Anne walnut chest-on-stand with two short and three graduated long drawers, 40in. wide. £7,850

A William & Mary burr elm chest-on-stand crossbanded overall in walnut, the quarter-veneered rectangular top inset with an oval, above two drawers, 40½in. wide. (Christie's) £3,300

A Queen Anne style walnut chest on stand, of shaped bow front form, on cabriole supports with shell carved knees and pad feet, 3ft. wide. (Russell Baldwin & Bright) £1,450

A figured walnut foliate marquetry and penwork chest on stand, decorated throughout with flower swag panels, 40in. wide, late 17th century. (Christie's) £2,420

A Japanese parquetry chest on 17th century style walnut stand, the two doors enclosing eight small drawers, 54¼in. high. (Bearne's) £900

133

A Chippendale cherrywood high chest-of-drawers, probably New London County, Connecticut, 1760–1780, in two sections, on cabriole legs with pad feet, 82¼in. high, 38¾in. wide. (Christie's) £39,462

A Queen Anne walnut and feather-banded chest-on-stand with moulded cornice above three short and three graduated long drawers, 44in. wide. (Christie's) £2,860

A Chippendale carved walnut high chest-of-drawers, Salem, Massachusetts, 1760–1780, on cabriole legs with pad-and-disc feet, 84in. high, 40in. wide. (Christie's) £36,173

A Queen Anne walnut high chest-of-drawers, in two sections, the lower section with two short drawers above one long drawer over a scalloped apron and cabriole legs, 40in. wide. (Christie's) £2,429

An early George III mahogany chest-on-stand, the sides with carrying handles, 30¾in. wide. (Christie's) £5,500

An oak chest on stand, the chest with four geometrically panelled drawers, the stand with a drawer and arcaded apron, late 17th century, the stand later, 40in. wide. (Christie's London) £1,760

A William and Mary walnut oyster veneered and marquetry chest on stand, having oak veneered sides, on later turned legs, stretchers and bun feet, 3ft. 1in. wide. (Phillips) £2,600

A William and Mary black and gilt-japanned chest-on-stand, decorated with birds, figures and buildings within chinoiserie landscapes, the base part late 17th century, 40in. wide. (Christie's) £3,850

A William and Mary oak high chest-of-drawers, English, late 17th century, on six spiral-turned legs joined by shaped stretchers with compressed ball feet, 38½in. wide. (Christie's) £1,848

Late 17th century oak chest-on-stand with four long graduated drawers with brass furniture, 3ft.2in. wide. (Hobbs & Chambers) £1,000

A Queen Anne tiger maple high chest of drawers, North Shore, Massachusetts, 1740–1760, in two sections, on cabriole legs with pad feet, 38in. wide. (Christie's) £4,934

William and Mary design walnut veneered chest-on-stand, the drawers with brass drop handles. (Worsfolds) £800

A walnut and marquetry chest-on-stand crossbanded and inlaid overall with floral panels and boxwood and ebonised lines, on spirally-turned legs joined by waved stretchers, late 17th century, 38¹/₂in. wide. (Christie's) £4,620

An early Georgian figured and pollard oak chest-on-stand, 43in. wide. (Christie's) £4,180

A William and Mary black-painted high chest-of-drawers, Pennsylvania, 1720–1740, the upper section with rectangular moulded cornice over two short drawers and three graduated long drawers, 39in. wide. (Christie's) £7,847

A William and Mary oyster-veneered walnut chest-on-stand inlaid overall with sycamore, the rectangular top with circles and scrolls, on later barley-twist legs, 41in. wide. (Christie's) £3,740

An early 18th century walnut, burr elm veneered featherstrung chest on stand, the base with a long drawer and shaped apron, on cabriole legs, pad feet, 3ft. 2in. wide. (Phillips) £2,000

A walnut and feather-banded chest-on-stand with moulded cornice, three short and three long drawers between reeded canted angles, early 18th century, 43in. wide. (Christie's) £880

A Queen Anne walnut chest-on-stand inlaid with fruitwood compass medallions, 42in. wide. £2,150

A walnut chest-on-stand, the base with six various sized drawers, 42in. wide. £2,900

Spanish Colonial painted chest-on-stand, Mexican/New Mexican, 38in. wide. (Skinner Inc.) £1,011

A Queen Anne oak chest on stand, with shaped apron and cabriole supports with scrolls at the knees, 36½in. wide. (Lawrence Fine Arts) £2,750

A William and Mary walnut chest on later stand, crossbanded and herringbone inlaid with walnut and rosewood, 102cm. wide. (Lacy Scott) £1,250

A Queen Anne walnut high chest of drawers, Massachusetts, 1740-1760, on cabriole legs with pad feet, the rear legs of maple, 41½in. wide. (Christie's New York) £6,226

A Queen Anne burr walnut chest-on-stand with feather banded top, 40¾in. wide. £3,250

A William and Mary walnut and marquetry chest-on-stand, 38½in. wide. £3,500

A William and Mary kingwood oyster veneered and rosewood banded chest-on-stand, the stand circa 1840, 49½in. wide. £4,400

This delightful piece first put in an appearance around 1800 when it achieved instant popularity. The name is from the French chiffonier, defined as 'a piece of furniture with drawers in which women put away their needlework'.

It was designed, possibly as an alternative for the large sideboards of the period, or as a replacement for the commode, whose flowing lines and profuse decoration were not to the taste of the leaders of Regency fashion.

Whatever its parentage, the chiffonier was made, often in pairs, with a glass fronted cabinet in the lower part and, usually, shelves above, which were frequently constructed with lyre or fine scroll shaped supports.

Earlier pieces were made usually of rosewood and, occasionally, of satinwood, while those of later manufacture were of either of those woods and mahogany. In Loudon's *Encyclopaedia of Furniture*, the virtues of the chiffonier are extolled as follows: 'A most useful object for families who cannot afford to go to the expense of a pier or console table.'

A William IV rosewood corner chiffonier with spindle turned shelved gallery, 46in. wide. (Christie's) £2,090

A fine Victorian mahogany chiffonier, the arched superstructure with a single shelf on scroll supports, 44in. wide. (Bonhams) £850

A George IV brass-mounted rosewood chiffonier with mirror-backed two-tier superstructure, the upper level edged with bead-and-reel and with three-quarter pierced scrolled gallery, on ribbed bun feet, 60in. wide. (Christie's) £2,970

A Regency mahogany and ebonised secrétaire à abattant with inverted breakfront top above a flowerhead-mounted frieze with mahogany-lined drawers and a panelled fall-front with green leather-lined writing-surface, 36¼in. wide. (Christie's) £4,950

A Regency brass-mounted red ebony chiffonier with three-quarter scroll-galleried rectangular top above a shaped shelf, 33in. wide. (Christie's) £3,850

A William IV rosewood chiffonier, the mirrored back carved with lotus, acanthus and scrolls, on a concave plinth base, 54in. wide. (Bearne's) £980

A Regency simulated rosewood and brass inlaid secrétaire chiffonier, with shelved super-structure and drop-front drawer, 36in. wide. (Christie's) £1,320

A George IV rosewood chiffonier, the shelved back inset with a mirror plate, 44in. wide. **£1,150**

A Regency giltmetal-mounted brass-inlaid rosewood and simulated rosewood bonheur-du-jour in the manner of John McLean, 32³/₄in. wide. (Christie's) **£7,150**

A Regency period mahogany chiffonier, the drawers with brass knob handles, 3ft.3in. wide. **£2,450**

A Regency rosewood and banded chiffonier, the rectangular brass three-quarter galleried mirrored ledged back top with turned supports, 36³/₄in. wide. (Christie's) **£1,320**

A Regency rosewood chiffonier, the frieze decorated with brass moulded lozenges, paterae and laurel wreaths with a pair of brass trellis doors, 2ft. 9in. wide. (Phillips) **£2,500**

A Regency rosewood, satinwood crossbanded and brass inlaid secretaire, having a shelved superstructure with pierced gallery and turned uprights, 3ft. 4in. wide. (Phillips) **£4,200**

A George IV brass inlaid rosewood chiffonier, the super-structure with galleried shelf above three drawers inlaid with foliage, 36½in. wide. (Christie's London) **£4,950**

One of a pair of Regency rosewood chiffoniers with brass galleries and mirrored doors, 47in. wide. (Worsfolds) **£3,900**

A William IV mahogany chiffonier, the single shelf superstructure on turned front supports, on a plinth base, 41¹/₂in. wide. (Bonhams) **£1,000**

A Regency ebonised maple-wood and bois clair chiff-onier with two open shelves, 34in. wide. £3,750

Early 19th century rosewood chiffonier, with fielded panels and applied scrolls to the side pilasters, 3ft. 6in. wide. (G. A. Key) £1,200

A Regency rosewood secre-taire chiffonier with shelf and mirror superstructure, 27in. wide. £850

A Regency rosewood chiffonier, the shelved superstructure with a pierced brass gallery above a beaded frieze and a pair of upholstered panelled doors, 33in. wide.
(Christie's S. Ken) £1,870

An Empire carved mahogany chiffonier, the shelved superstructure with foliate scroll crestings and lion mask scroll uprights with flowerheads and foliage, 4ft. 2in. wide. (Phillips) £4,000

One of a pair of George III satinwood open bookcases, one painted with roses, the other with pansies, on square tapering legs and brass caps, restoration to legs, 24in. wide. (Christie's) (Two) £35,200

Regency rosewood chiffonier, early 19th century, the top with a three quarter pierced brass gallery, on a rectangular base, 29¾in. long.
(Skinner Inc.) £3,681

A Regency brass-inlaid rosewood side cabinet, 45in. wide. (Christie's) £5,940

A Dutch mahogany side buffet, the hinged rectangular lid en-closing folding shelves, on square tapering legs, 19th century, 42in. wide. (Christie's S. Ken) £825

CHIFFONIERS

19th century rosewood chiffonier with satinwood inlay, double glazed doors, and raised gallery top, with mirror, 36in. wide. (Jacobs & Hunt) £680

A William IV rosewood and parcel gilt breakfront chiffonier, the doors filled with lime-green silk pleats, 70in. wide. £3,750

One of a pair of late Victorian ebonised chiffoniers banded with amboyna, 35¾in. wide. £3,000

A Regency mahogany secrétaire-chiffonier, the associated two-tier superstructure of pedimented form with brass-supports above a sliding mahogany-lined fitted drawer, 52½in. high. (Christie's) £1,320

A pair of Regency mahogany dwarf chiffoniers, the open shelved superstructure with graduated shelves and pierced Vitruvian scrolled cresting and sides, 3ft. wide. (Phillips) £5,400

A simulated rosewood and marblised chiffonier with shelved superstructure on scroll supports above two simulated grille doors, early 19th century, 38in. wide. (Christie's S. Ken.) £2,420

A Regency mahogany chiffonier with reeded uprights and graduated shelves, slight restoration, 31in. wide. (Christie's S. Ken.) £1,540

A Regency rosewood, ebonised and parcel-gilt chiffonier, the raised superstructure with brass three-quarter gallery on column supports, the lower section with galleried rectangular top above a cupboard door, 36in. wide. (Christie's) £3,300

A Regency mahogany chiffonier, the two-tiered superstructure with baluster supports and gallery, 24in. wide. £2,350

CLOTHES PRESSES

These were the earliest form of wardrobe, with which they became synonymous in the 18th century. They were essentially cupboards for storing clothes, the lower section usually with drawers, and the upper with doors concealing either shelves, sliding trays, or hanging space.

Early examples were generally of oak, and decoration was mainly confined to carving, though occasional examples are found with friezes picked out in colour.

Chippendale and his contemporaries produced a number of patterns for clothes presses, some interesting ones with bombé, commode-style lower sections.

The evolution of the clothes press is closely allied to changes in the style of the clothes they had to contain, as, for example, padded trunk hose, doublets and farthingales gave way to thinner materials, which could be folded and laid away.

A George III mahogany breakfront clothes press, 6ft.6in. wide, circa 1770, later pediments. £2,950

A George II mahogany clothes press, the cornice with foliate and egg-and-dart border, 53in. wide. £28,500

An Anglo-Indian vizagapatam padouk-wood and engraved ivory clothes-press decorated overall with scrolling foliage and flowerheads, the dentilled cornice with broken pediment, late 18th century, 56in. wide. (Christie's) £68,200

A Regency mahogany clothes press inlaid with ebony lines with shaped pediment flanked by akrotiri inlaid with anthemions above a moulded cornice, on splayed bracket feet, 48in. wide. (Christie's London) £2,200

A George III satinwood clothes press, the cupboard doors enclosing five slides, 49½in. wide. £5,200

An early George III mahogany clothes press on panelled bracket feet, 49½in. wide, 79in. high. (Christie's) £3,960

A George III mahogany clothes press on bracket feet, 50in. wide, 71in. high. £1,300

A George III mahogany clothes cupboard with a fluted frieze above two fielded panel doors, 52in. wide. (Lawrence Fine Arts) £1,155

A George III satinwood clothes press, the sides cross-banded with rosewood, 51½in. wide, 77¼in. high. £17,000

A George III oak clothes press with two doors, each with two fielded panels, two short and two long drawers below, 63½in. wide. (Bearne's) £1,250

An early-Victorian cast-iron-mounted oak gothic clothes-press designed by A.W.N. Pugin, the cabinet-work by Gillows, the metal-work by Hardman and Iliffe, 47½in. wide. (Christie's) £7,150

A George III mahogany clothes-press, the upper section with rectangular cavetto cornice above a pair of panelled doors enclosing five blue paper-lined slides, 49½in. wide. (Christie's) £2,530

A mid-Victorian bird's-eye maple and mahogany clothes-press by C. Hindley and Sons, the rectangular eared top above a moulded cornice and panelled frieze flanked by flowerheads, 65in. wide. (Christie's) £2,420

A George III mahogany clothes press, the pediment with Gothic arches above a pair of panelled doors crossbanded with rose-wood, on splayed feet, 48in. wide. (Christie's S. Ken) £1,980

A George III mahogany bow-fronted clothes press, the upper section with arched panelled cresting above two panelled doors, the base with two short and two long mahogany-lined drawers, 50in. wide. (Christie's) £3,080

A George III mahogany clothes-press with moulded cornice above a pair of oval panelled doors, the base with two short and two graduated drawers, 52½in. wide. (Christie's) £1,886

The name commode was first used in France, where it served to describe diverse pieces of furniture. Some took the form of a heavy table with drawers below, while others resembled sarcophagus-shaped coffers with lids, but the most widely accepted use of the term refers to those elaborate and ornate chests of drawers destined for the drawing room.

Most early French commodes had their basic rectangularity softened by subtle curves in the rococo manner – a popular style from the accession of Louis XV in 1715. Good examples are often beautifully inlaid with birds, garlands of flowers and musical instruments besides having superb ormolu mounts and handles made by such masters as Cressent, Gouthière and Caffieris.

By the 1780's, many commodes appeared with fine decoration after the styles of Angelica Kaufmann and Pergolisi – often painted in the form of cupids set in ovals surrounded by painted flowers and scrolls. Another style, particularly favoured by Adam, was that of a white ground on which were coloured urns set amid wreaths and surrounded by friezes of gilt moulding. Toward the end of the century, however, the commode slipped somewhat from its former importance in fashionable drawing rooms and the quality took a predictably downward turn.

Early in the 19th century, commodes lost their flamboyance altogether, returning to a rectangular form and resembling more the chiffonier.

One of a pair of George III kingwood commodes in the French style, 50in. wide.
£110,000

An ormolu mounted king-wood commode of Louis XV-style with serpentine breccia marble top, 48in. wide.
£2,650

A giltmetal-mounted rosewood and kingwood miniature commode, feather-banded overall, the canted rectangular top above three long drawers on cabriole legs, 12½ in. wide. (Christie's) £1,760

A Dutch walnut and marquetry bombé commode inlaid throughout with vases of flowers, birds, insects and foliage, on scroll feet, 33¾in. wide, mid-18th century. (Bearne's) £4,200

An 18th century palisander veneered and fruitwood inlaid commode, the top in grey marble, on outswept legs with gilt sabots, Genoa, 121cm. wide. (Finarte) £53,738

A North Italian walnut bombe commode, the sides with cup-boards, on cabriole legs carved with flowerheads and trefoil feet, 41in. wide. (Christie's London) £4,180

COMMODE CHESTS

An early Louis XV kingwood, crossbanded and ormolu mounted bombé commode, surmounted by a moulded rance marble top with rounded re-entrant corners, 1.32m. wide, stamped *G. Schwingkens.*
(Phillips London) **£7,200**

A good French marble-topped marquetry commode, by Paul Sormani of Paris, circa 1890, in Louis XV/XVI Transitional style, with moulded mottled rust and beige marble top, 146cm. wide.
(Sotheby's) **£7,150**

A fine George III mahogany serpentine commode, in the French taste and in the manner of Thomas Chippendale, with a moulded overhanging top, 4¹/₂in. wide.
(Phillips) **£22,000**

Louis XV tulipwood and kingwood commode, stamped *Schlichtig, JME,* circa 1770, the rectangular mottled grey, brown and white marble top with rounded edge, 30in. wide.
(Butterfield & Butterfield) **£3,933**

Régence gilt-bronze-mounted inlaid kingwood galbé commode, stamped *J.M. Chevalier,* mid-18th century, surmounted by a brèche marble top with a moulded edge, 36¹/₄in. wide.
(Butterfield & Butterfield) **£9,448**

A late 18th century Baltic mahogany commode of small size, the rectangular top above a frieze drawer applied with a band of raised dots interspersed with foliate clasps, 2ft. 10in. wide.
(Phillips) **£2,000**

A Régence rosewood, crossbanded and brass mounted serpentine commode of small size, veneered à quatre faces and applied with gilt metal cartouche key plate and handle, 3ft. wide. (Phillips) **£3,400**

A Louis XV rosewood and kingwood crossbanded parquetry bombé commode en tombeau surmounted by a moulded grey marble top, containing two short and two long drawers, 4ft. 4in. wide.
(Phillips) **£9,000**

A Dutch mahogany and marquetry commode inlaid throughout with fan medallions and stringing, on a plinth base, 39in. wide, early/mid-19th century.
(Bearne's) **£1,350**

A Louis XV kingwood and ormolu mounted bombé commode en tombeau, by B. Péridiez, quarter veneered and crossbanded with ormolu mounts, 4ft. 10in. wide. (Phillips) **£10,000**

An ormolu mounted king-wood and marquetry commode of Louis XVI design, with breakfront Carrara marble top, stamped five times Wassmus, 50in. wide. **£4,700**

An 18th century crossbanded Dutch mahogany and later marquetry bombé chest, the serpentine top with central musical trophy and others to the corners, 4ft. 4½in. wide. (Phillips) **£4,200**

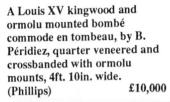

Italian rococo painted commode, third quarter 18th century, decorated with Oriental figures and pavilions in landscape setting and tones of red, yellow, green, blue and brown on a pale yellow ground, 4ft. 3in. wide. (Butterfield & Butterfield) **£11,347**

One of a pair of George II mahogany commodes of serpentine outline, each fitted with three graduated long drawers mounted with foliate rococo gilt-lacquered brass handles and lock-plates, 31¼in. wide. (Christie's) (Two) **£253,000**

Louis XV Provincial carved walnut commode, third quarter 18th century, the later rectangular top with moulded edge over three bow-fronted drawers, a scalloped apron below, 4ft. ½in. wide. (Butterfield & Butterfield) **£2,049**

A Louis XV-style kingwood and marquetry bombé commode, the pink veined marble serpentine top above drawers inlaid sans travers with scrolling foliage and flowers. (Bearne's) **£920**

A George III harewood and satinwood banded commode of serpentine outline, fitted with three mahogany lined drawers between slightly bombé keeled angles, 37½in. wide. (Christie's) **£8,800**

A Continental small walnut commode of three long drawers with moulded decorations, on short supports with shells and ball and claw feet, late 18th/19th century, 34½in. wide. (Lawrence Fine Art) **£1,210**

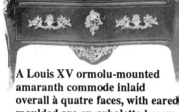

An ormolu-mounted kingwood, tulipwood, parquetry and marquetry commode in the manner of BVRB, the eared moulded serpentine brèche d'Alep marble top above two long drawers, late 19th/early 20th century, 61in. wide.
(Christie's) £7,480

A French Provincial oak commode, on foliate headed cabriole legs with scroll feet, late 18th/early 19th century, possibly adapted, 26in. wide.
(Christie's) £550

A Louis XV ormolu-mounted amaranth commode inlaid overall à quatre faces, with eared moulded arc-en-arbalette brown fossil marble top above two short and one long drawer, 51½in. wide.
(Christie's) £7,700

A Louis XV kingwood bombé commode banded in tulipwood with later serpentine grey and orange fossil marble top, above two long drawers with waved apron mounted with C-scrolls and acanthus, stamped *L BOUDIN JME*, 38½in. wide.
(Christie's) £5,500

A 19th century North Italian walnut, fruitwood and ivory marquetry bombé commode, inlaid with hunting scenes between canted angles, on splayed legs, 2ft. 10in. wide.
(Phillips) £2,600

A Transitional giltmetal-mounted mahogany, amboyna and fruitwood commode by J. Caumont with moulded breakfront mottled grey marble top above three long drawers, stamped *J. CAUMONT*, 35¼in. wide.
(Christie's) £6,05

A South German walnut and fruitwood commode, inlaid overall with satinwood lines and scrolls with eared serpentine top above three graduated long drawers with waved apron, mid-18th century, 48½in. wide.
(Christie's) £14,850

An 18th century Continental rosewood and marquetry bombé petite commode, surmounted by a contemporary moulded serpentine top containing two drawers inlaid à travers with a bucket of flowers, 2ft. wide.
(Phillips) £2,200

A Regency lacquered brass-mounted kingwood bombé commode with associated serpentine liver marble top above two short drawers divided by a concealed drawer above two long drawers, stamped *A CRIAERD JME*, 50in. wide.
(Christie's) £9,350

An ormolu-mounted amaranth, parquetry and marquetry commode after J.H. Riesener, with partridgewood panels and inlaid overall with boxwood and ebonised lines, late 19th century, 64¹/₂in. wide.
(Christie's)   £8,250

A Louis XV kingwood commode, by Jean Charles Saunier, of serpentine bombé shape with a moulded brêche d'Alep marble top, 2ft. 5in. wide.
(Phillips)   £15,000

A fine 18th century Italian carved walnut and tulipwood crossbanded commode of serpentine undulating outline and tapering form, the top with a moulded edge and rounded corners, on moulded cabriole legs, 4ft. 11in. wide.
(Phillips)   £98,000

A Louis XV ormolu-mounted tulipwood and kingwood commode with associated moulded serpentine mottled grey marble top above two short and two long drawers, on angled bracket feet, 38¹/₂in. wide.
(Christie's)   £6,600

A Louis XV style ormolu-mounted kingwood and Vernis Martin meuble d'appui, late 19th century, with a serpentine-moulded liver and grey marble top, 43in. wide.
(Christie's East)   £2,624

A harewood, mahogany-banded, marquetry and gilt metal-mounted demi-lune commode in the style of Mayhew and Ince, on foliate moulded brass feet, 43in. wide.
(Christie's S. Ken)   £38,500

An 18th century South German walnut, crossbanded and inlaid commode of undulating outline, the top veneered with two crossbanded squares, having a moulded edge, on bun feet, 3ft. 1in. (Phillips)   £4,200

A fine Louis XV style ormolu-mounted mahogany and marquetry commode, third quarter 19th century, twice stamped *G. Durand*, with a serpentine brèche d'Alep marble top, 34³/₄in. wide.
(Christie's East)   £4,081

An 18th century French Provincial carved fruitwood, walnut and oak bowfront commode of small size, surmounted by a Sicilian jasper moulded top, containing three long drawers, 2ft. 10in. wide.
(Phillips)   £2,400

A Dutch burr walnut bombé commode with eared serpentine quarter veneered top, with keeled angles and scroll feet, mid-18th century, 38in. wide. (Christie's London) £3,850

One of a pair of ormolu mounted mahogany bombé commodes, each with a serpentine marble top above two drawers inlaid sans travers, 50½in. wide. (Christie's S. Ken) Two £6,600

Swedish rococo elmwood and ormolu mounted commode, mid 18th century, the serpentine moulded top above bombé case with three drawers, 41½in. wide. (Skinner Inc.) £4,384

An Italian walnut and parquetry commode with overall zig-zag inlay within banded borders, the rectangular top above two short and two graduated long drawers, 48in. wide. (Christie's S. Ken) £3,740

A George III mahogany commode with eared moulded serpentine top above four graduated long drawers flanked by scrolled canted angles carved with acanthus, possibly 19th century, 45in. wide. (Christie's) £9,350

An ormolu mounted marquetry mahogany and harewood commode after Leleu with rounded rectangular mottled top, the panelled frieze applied with scrolling foliage, 34in. wide. (Christie's London) £1,870

A Louis XV style kingwood commode, inlaid with marquetry and rosewood bands in boxwood line borders, on splayed legs with sabots, 42in. wide. (Christie's) £1,540

A George III harewood, rosewood and marquetry commode, the banded eared serpentine top inlaid with a bird eating at a basket of fruit, on splayed feet, 49½in. wide. (Christie's) £17,050

A French Provincial fruitwood commode of arc en arbalette outline, the top with moulded edge, on scrolled feet, mid-18th century, 51¾in. wide. (Christie's London) £4,400

Commodes made an appearance in Britain as early as the 16th century, when Henry VIII possessed one. It was covered in black velvet, garnished with ribbons and fringes and studded with over 2,000 gilt nails. Seat and arms were covered in white fustian filled with down and it came complete with lock and key, which Henry kept about his person to prevent illicit use.

Britain, however, was for a long time sadly lacking in examples of the plumber's art for, as late as the sixteenth century, it was deemed sufficient to retire a mere 'bowshot away'.

A George II mahogany corner commode chair with leather covered padded horseshoe toprail, on squat cabriole legs. (Bearne's) £580

A George III mahogany night commode, the pull out pot holder with a brass swan neck handle, and serpentine edge to square pull out legs, 20in. wide. (Woolley & Wallis) £1,300

Georgian mahogany commode with rising top, two door front and fitted interior, 2ft. wide. (G. A. Key) £200

A Regency mahogany step commode with three leather lined treads, the pull out middle with porcelain bowl on six turned legs, 22in. wide. (Christie's London) £825

A George III mahogany bedside cupboard with rectangular tray top, on shaped bracket feet, 24½in. wide. £1,750

A Regency mahogany bedside cupboard with tray-top, the concave front with a tambour shutter, on square legs, 18in. wide. £1,500

A Victorian Marriott portable water closet, painted in black with floral spandrels and borders, 55cm. wide. (Henry Spencer) £360

A George III mahogany bedside commode, the sides pierced with carrying-handles, above a pull-out-section with later green leather-lined top and waved apron, 21in. wide. (Christie's) £825

COMMODES

A George III mahogany bedside commode with a sliding drawer enclosing a glazed ware bowl, 23in. wide.
(Christie's S. Ken.)   £1,430

Chippendale cherry roundabout commode chair, refinished, 32¾in. high.
(Skinner Inc.)   £1,058

A George III mahogany tray to night commode.
(Dreweatt Neate)   £65◦

A George IV mahogany commode armchair, the solid hinged seat with brass recessed handle to the right above two panelled doors, with buttoned green leather cushion, 25in. wide. (Christie's London) £660

A set of George III mahogany bed-steps with three-quarter galleried columnar top step above tambour shutter slide, the sliding middle step with hinged lid enclosing a fitted interior with later removable lid and white porcelain pot, 18in. wide.
(Christie's)   £1,100

A Regency mahogany bedside commode by Gillows of Lancaster, with a drawer and a door and a pull-out section on legs enclosing a bidet, on turned reeded legs, 20in. wide.
(Christie's)   £2,42◦

A George III mahogany bedside commode, the rounded rectangular galleried top above a pair of cupboard doors, 21in. wide.
(Christie's)   £2,990

A 19th century cherrywood veneer commode, in the form of an octagonal marble topped column upon a square base, on ebonised bun feet, 113cm. high.
(Finarte)   £1,102

One of a pair of late 18th early 19th century Italian walnut bedside commode 16¼in. wide.
(Christie's)   £3,08◦

A George III mahogany serpentine-fronted bedside cabinet with shaped tray top, tambour shutters, 23½in. wide. (Bearne's) £1,650

An antique French Provincial carved walnut bidet in the Louis XV taste, with raised padded end with hinged compartment. (Phillips) £950

One of a pair of late 18th century North Italian, Milanese, walnut and ivory bedside commodes, 24¼in. wide. £12,000

A George III mahogany serpentine-fronted bedside commode, the part-galleried hinged top and panelled sides above a hinged flap enclosing a well, on square legs, 22½in. wide. (Christie's) £1,430

An Irish mahogany bedside commode with waved gallery and pierced frieze above a drawer, a door and a sliding base, retaining ceramic pot, 17in. wide. (Christie's) £596

An early George III mahogany tray top commode, with a shaped three-quarter gallery and pierced carrying handles above a pair of cupboard doors and fitted pull-out commode drawer, 1ft. 9in. wide. (Phillips) £1,300

A George III mahogany bedside commode, the shaped tray top above a pair of doors and an adapted drawer below on square moulded legs, 1ft. 11in. wide. (Phillips) £380

An Italian walnut and parquetry bedside commode inlaid overall with geometric banding, on square tapering legs, late 18th/early 19th century, 18in. wide. (Christie's) £3,740

An unusual George III pollard oak bedside cabinet with rectangular tray top, 21in. wide. (Christie's) £2,420

151

A George III mahogany bowfront bedside commode, 21in. wide. £1,200

A set of late Regency mahogany library commode steps, with two hinged treads and a lower tread, on turned tapered legs, 20in. £2,000

An early George III mahogany bedside cupboard, 22in. wide. £1,750

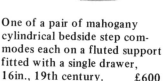

Early 19th century Shaker pine commode with hinged slant lid opening to reveal a shelf interior, 18in. wide. £3,000

A George III gentleman's mahogany toilet commode with box top, fitted interior with mirror, 28in. wide. (Andrew Hartley) £1,050

One of a pair of mahogany cylindrical bedside step commodes each on a fluted support fitted with a single drawer, 16in., 19th century. £600

A George III mahogany converted commode on square legs, 19½in. wide. (Christie's S. Ken) £385

A Georgian mahogany enclosed washstand/commode with fold-over top, rising mirror and fitted compartments and basin, 18in. wide. £800

George II walnut commode table, mid 18th century, raised on cabriole legs ending in pad feet, 25¾in. high. (Skinner Inc) £2,100

Broadly speaking, there are three basic types of corner cupboards and, of these, the earliest was the hanging variety. This was followed, in early Georgian days, by the free standing corner cupboard or cupboard-on-stand and, later and less successfully, by the low-level standing cupboard.

The earliest examples of hanging corner cupboards to be found are usually japanned in the Oriental style.

By the mid 18th century, as architectural styling of furniture became popular, many corner cabinets sported fine pediments whose details reflected the fashionable variations of the period.

Broken-arch pediments were featured on many of the more sophisticated pieces – often in the swan-neck style with a centre entablature – but hanging corner cabinets were largely neglected by the major designers at this time.

Most of the antique corner cupboards found today date from the last quarter of the eighteenth century – the period during which the greatest number were produced, and those of the best quality made.

Bow-fronted models were popular, made of mahogany, with double doors about twelve inches across.

Decoration was usually kept to a minimum, most of the good pieces relying on the figuring of the wood, but some were embellished with satinwood stringing or an inlaid conch shell motif on the door.

Broken pediments continued to be used to some extent, together with dentil cornices and pear-drop mouldings.

A Dutch mahogany and floral marquetry corner cupboard, the breakfront top above a pair of doors, 19th century, 24in. wide. (Christie's) £935

A Dutch polychrome-painted and parcel-gilt bow-fronted corner cupboard, painted with a kneeling woman offering bread to a group of soldiers, second half 18th century, 45¹/₂in. high. (Christie's) £990

A Louis XV period fruitwood, purpleheart and ormolu mounted encoignure, in the style of Adrian Delorme, on shaped bracket feet, 2ft. 6¹/₂in. wide. (Phillips) £2,000

A 19th century flame mahogany corner cupboard, with galleried top, the beaded door with drawer under, 131cm. high. (Finarte) £918

A George III fruitwood corner cupboard in two sections, with moulded cornice above a dentil moulding and two panelled doors enclosing an arched blue-painted interior, 57in. wide. (Christie's) £4,950

A George II carved mahogany hanging corner cupboard with swan neck pediment, rosette terminal and dentil cornice, 4ft. 4in. high. (Phillips) £1,300

CORNER CUPBOARDS

A Country Federal cherry corner cupboard, Penn., circa 1820, 56½in. wide. £1,100

An 18th century black lacquered two-door hanging corner cupboard, 21in. wide. (G. A. Key) £310

A Dutch walnut standing corner cabinet with a domed cornice, 4ft.3in. wide, circa 1740. £3,350

A Dutch walnut and marquetry serpentine-fronted corner cabinet, profusely inlaid with vases and baskets of flowers, cherubs and birds perched amongst foliage, 52in. wide. (Bearne's) £6,200

A pair of Dutch tulipwood, amaranth-banded and marquetry corner cupboards, each with mottled red marble top, early 19th century, each 26in. wide. (Christie's) £1,980

A late 18th/early 19th century Dutch carved mahogany, marquetry and chequer strung serpentine upright corner cupboard with canted angles, on ogee bracket feet, 3ft. 7in. wide. (Phillips) £3,200

A Georgian mahogany hanging corner cabinet with wide canted angles flanking a glazed door, 42½in. high. (Lawrence Fine Arts) £1,012

A green painted bow-fronted standing corner cabinet, painted with an oval medallion of a flower girl, lover and spaniel, 28¼in. wide. (Christie's) £1,100

George III mahogany bow-fronted corner wall cupboard, 27½in. wide. (Prudential Fine Art) £900

CORNER CUPBOARDS

A Chippendale pine hanging corner cupboard, Penn., 1760-85, 46in. high, 26½in. wide. £1,350

Grain painted pine and poplar corner cupboard, possibly Pennsylvania, circa 1830, 83in. high, 55½in. wide. £2,900

A Chippendale pine corner cupboard, 1760-90, 78½in. high. £4,750

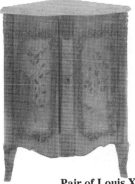

A standing mahogany corner cupboard, inlaid with narrow kingwood bands in geometric patterns, the door with a central oval floral motif, 239cm. high. (Lawrence Fine Arts) £1,980

Pair of Louis XV style marquetry encoignures, stamped *Nogaret a Lyon*, third quarter 19th century, raised on shaped cross-banded feet ending in cast hoof-form sabots, 28¹/₂in. wide. (Butterfield & Butterfield) £1,072

A George III mahogany corner cabinet, with flowerhead terminals and dentilled frieze above two panelled doors enclosing a green-painted interior, 37in. wide. (Christie's) £1,870

One of a pair of Directoire fruitwood corner cabinets with mottled black marble tops, 30½in. wide. (Christie's) £1,650

Georgian bowfronted oak and crossbanded two-door hanging corner cupboard, 37in. high, 28in. wide. (J. M. Welch & Son) £360

A 19th century serpentined boulle dwarf corner cabinet, brass inlaid into red tortoiseshell, 2ft.6in. wide. (Lots Road Chelsea Auction Galleries) £750

A Regency mahogany corner cupboard with blind fret carved frieze above four panel-ed doors, on plinth, 45½in. (Christie's S. Ken) £990

A Louis Philippe ormolu mounted kingwood and tulip-wood corner cabinet of serpen-tine outline with two quarter veneered doors, 37½in. high. (Christie's London) £550

Late Federal two-part cherry corner cupboard, probably North Carolina, circa 1800, 46in. high. (Skinner) £3,056

A Louis XV ormolu mounted Chinese black lacquer encoignure with waved moulded brêche d'Alep top above a bowed cupboard door, reconstructed, 29in. wide. (Christie's London) £1,650

A Queen Anne walnut hanging corner cupboard, the broken arched pediment above an arched fielded panel cupboard door, 33in. wide. (Bonhams) £2,300

George III pine corner cupboard, last quarter 18th century, with a stepped and dentilled cornice above an arched aperture disclosing a blue painted interior, 4ft. 2½in. wide. (Butterfield & Butterfield) £2,025

A George III mahogany veneered bow front corner cupboard, the moulded cornice above a banded frieze, 28in. wide. (Woolley & Wallis) £850

A good Federal pine corner cupboard, American, probably Delaware River Valley, first quarter 19th century, 52¼in. wide. (Sotheby's) £3,308

A Biedermeier mahogany corner cabinet, with a drawer over a door flanked by carved spiral and turned columns, 157cm. high. (Herholdt Jensen) £517

Walnut corner cabinet, in the rococo style, with swan neck pediment, some older parts, 140cm. wide. (Auktionshaus Arnold) £2,867

A mid 18th century Continental kingwood and walnut serpentine corner cupboard of arc en arbalette outline enclosed by a pair of parquetry doors, 1ft. 10in., German or Scandinavian. (Phillips) £1,100

A George III mahogany standing corner cupboard with a bolection moulded cornice above a pair of fielded arched doors, 48in. wide. (Christie's S. Ken) £2,420

A Louis XV rosewood, tulipwood and marquetry encoignure, the grey moulded Brescia marble top above a door inlaid with a spray of flowers, 2ft. wide.
(Phillips) £1,600

An attractive George III mahogany bow front hanging corner cupboard, with swept moulded cornice over a frieze inlaid with a stylised swan, 2ft. 8in. wide.
(Spencer's) £650

A mahogany, ebonised and parquetry corner cabinet, having a door with parquetry panels of maize motifs and painted with a butterfly and flowers, 78.3cm. high.
(Phillips London) £320

A fine Edwardian mahogany and satinwood inlaid double corner cupboard, the moulded overhanging cornice with sunburst frieze, 89cm. wide.
(Phillips) £1,900

A Chippendale painted and carved pine corner cupboard, New Jersey, 1750–1770, the elaborately moulded cornice above two fielded panels, 51in. wide.
(Christie's) £3,575

An early 18th century walnut hanging corner cupboard with re-entrant top corners enclosing three shaped shelves within reeded canted corners, 39¾in. high. (Tennants) £1,250

A Dutch painted corner cupboard, the top with two shelves above a bowed door depicting a Dutch admiral and a naval engagement, late 18th century, 14in. wide.
(Christie's) £546

One of a pair of Louis XV ormolu-mounted amaranth, kingwood and marquetry encoignures by Laurent Rochette, each with moulded grey and orange fossil marble top, 35in. wide.
(Christie's) (Two) £7,700

Louis XV kingwood parquetry hanging corner cupboard, circa 1760, the graduating scalloped sides enclosing three graduated tiers of serpentine outline, 34in. high.
(Butterfield & Butterfield) £630

A Federal painted pine corner cupboard, New England, 19th century, in two parts, on bracket feet, painted in an overall mustard ground with green detailing, 39^1/$_2$in. wide.
(Christie's) £44,330

A pair of green lacquer and chinoiserie decorated hanging bowfront corner cupboards each with tiered gallery, late 18th century, 24in. wide.
(Christie's S. Ken) £1,320

A Federal cherrywood corner cupboard, American, probably New England, first quarter 19th century, the shaped skirt continuing to bracket feet, 42^1/$_2$in. wide.
(Sotheby's) £3,970

A Federal walnut corner cupboard, Pennsylvania or Middle Atlantic States, circa 1810, the moulded and reeded cornice above a pair of glazed hinged doors, 51^3/$_4$in. wide.
(Sotheby's) £3,143

A George II red walnut corner cupboard, the hinged triangular top above a pair of panelled doors enclosing a serpentine-fronted shelf, on block feet, 25^1/$_2$in. wide.
(Christie's) £1,540

A rare yellow-painted pine 'turkey-breast' corner cupboard, Middle Atlantic States, circa 1780, on a moulded and dentil-carved base, 56in. wide.
(Sotheby's) £5,293

COURT CUPBOARDS

The term court cupboard first begins to appear in English inventories in late Elizabethan times and seems to have been derived from the French 'court' or short. Generally made of oak, those of this period usually consist of two or three shelves supported on square columns, and are seldom more than four feet high. They would be used for displaying silver or pewter vessels.

As the 17th century wore on, however, they tended to become much wider than their height, and by the last years of the century, a sideboard type was being introduced, the upper stage consisting of a pediment over a recessed back with doors, the lower with drawers and further cupboards under. Some walnut examples are found, and styles vary from the very plain to elaborately moulded and carved.

Court cupboards of the latter type continued to be made into the early 18th century for the country yeomanry, among whom they were often given as wedding presents.

A small oak court cupboard, basically early 17th century, 27½in. wide. **£8,000**

A 17th century carved oak court cupboard with moulded cornice, 5ft.2in. wide. **£1,000**

An early 17th century James I inlaid oak court cupboard, 49in. wide. **£4,450**

A walnut court cupboard, in the manner of A. W. Pugin, 147cm. wide. **£1,200**

An oak court cupboard inlaid with parquetry bands and applied with split mouldings, on block feet, parts 17th century, 50in. wide. (Christie's) **£880**

An oak court cupboard, with moulded cornice above frieze dated *1690 R.H.*, late 17th century, 54in. wide. (Christie's) **£1,870**

An oak court cupboard with strapwork panels, the canopy top with two doors above three fielded cupboard doors, 55½in. dated *1668 & 69.* Christie's S. Ken) **£1,100**

159

CRADLES

The earliest cradles were simply made from hollowed out sections of tree, the natural shape of the wood being ideally suited to rocking. Others were slightly grander, being made in the form of a box suspended between X supports. This method of construction allowed the cradle to be rocked while raising it clear of the damp floor.

At first they were panelled, box-like structures with turned finials at the corners and mounted on rockers. At the end of the 16th century, the end and sides at the head of the cradle were extended to offer protection against draughts.

The basic style of the 17th century cradle lasted throughout the following century, often with a curved hood, and even into the 19th century when it often bore Gothic decoration. By far the most important development, however, was the return of the swinging cot which made a brief appearance early in the 18th century before really coming into its own after Sheraton and Hepplewhite had honoured it with their attentions.

A Regency mahogany frame caned side baby's cot with hood, swinging on brass brackets, 3ft.5in.   £750

A 17th century Flemish oak fruitwood and marquetry cradle, 40in. wide.   £1,300

A Charles X period carved walnut cradle on foliate scroll dolphin supports. (Phillips)   £4,000

A Victorian mahogany cradle with swan neck head on turned supports. £1,000

A Regency brass-mounted mahogany cot, the arched canopy hung with orange silk, on four spreading turned supports each with vase-shaped finials, 57in. wide. (Christie's)   £2,750

A George III painted cradle with ogee-arched hood and cane-filled sides, 41in. long.   £1,000

A rare heart-decorated chestnut and cherrywood child's cradle on stand, Pennsylvania, 1780–1800, on an arched base joined by a double medial transverse, length 39in. (Sotheby's)   £3,783

A Queen Anne oak cradle with fielded panelled construction, 3ft.3in. long, circa 1705. £600

A late Federal mahogany child's crib with tester, American, first half 19th century, with a serpentine tester, width 48¹/₂in. (Sotheby's) £1,967

A 17th century-style oak cradle with arched canopy, panelled sides and ball finials, 33¹/₂in. high. (Bearne's) £520

A North Swedish carved cradle, the gadrooned sides painted with diamonds, the ends with polychrome fleur de lys and the date *1849*, 87cm. long. (Auktionsverket) £296

An Arts and Crafts oak crib, the cylindrical barrel type rocking body supported by tall triangular rounded plank ends, 1.27m. high x 1.10m. long. (Phillips) £280

An early 19th century North Italian walnut cradle, the rectangular body with folding ebonised hood bands, on gadrooned vase-shaped ends, 4ft. 1in. long. (Phillips) £800

A George III mahogany cot, with a fluted top domed hood, zinc liner for flowers, on rockers. (Woolley & Wallis) £320

A George III mahogany cradle of rectangular form, the scrolling side panels applied with roundels, 39in. wide.(Christie's) £495

An 18th century oak cradle with hinged canopy, baluster-turned finials and fielded panels to the sides, 33¹/₂in. long. (Bearne's) £1,100

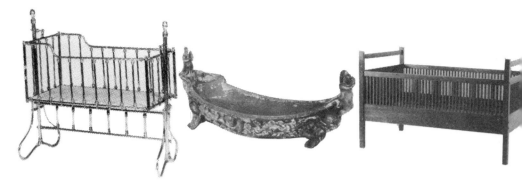

A tubular brass child's cot, circa 1910, 3ft. 8in. long.
£750

Early 18th century Spanish or Venetian parcel gilt and polychrome hanging cradle of navette form, 49½in. wide.
£2,500

A Gustav Stickley spindle-sided baby's crib, no. 919, circa 1907, 56½in. long.
£1,25

A Venetian giltwood cradle, the canopy hung with bells, the scrolled headboard carved with foliate trails and strapwork with dished base, first half 18th century, 24in. wide.
(Christie's)   £3,080

A French white painted wickerwork cradle, decorated with spandrels and scrolls, with a swing bed beneath a coronet cresting, 42in.
(Christie's)   £770

A rare Napoleon I ormolu-mounted mahogany cradle of slatted boat-shape suspended between two turned uprights, 52in. long.
(Tennants)   £7,00

A George II oak cradle, with fielded side panels and arched canopy with ball mounted rocker finials, 38in.(Christie's)
£605

Late 19th century French wickerwood bassinet with beechwood stand, 2ft. 8ins. long.   £125

An oak cradle with arched hood and panelled sides su mounted by turned finials. on rockers, 41in. wide.
(Christie's)   £605

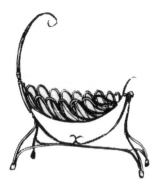

European bentwood hanging cradle, circa 1865, 56ins. wide. £700

Victorian Parisian style crib with cast iron side rails and net work sides, 4ft. 6ins. long. £250

A 17th century oak cradle with arched hood, 40in. wide. £1,300

Late Victorian iron swing cot, on iron stand, 3ft. long £150

An Italian baroque giltwood cradle in the form of a shell carved with flowerheads, each end with a putto, one leaning over the edge, the other seated and holding a garland of flowers, probably Roman, early 18th century, 61in. wide. (Christie's) £10,450

German gondola shaped cradle cross banded in black, slung between lyre shaped end pieces, on ogee feet, circa 1820. (Kunsthaus am Museum) £2,174

Child's metal cot by Theodore Lambert, 1910, 133cm. long. £600

Late 19th century ebonised bentwood cradle, Europe, 52in. long. £750

An oak cradle with turned finials, bearing the carved date 1739, 36in. long. £650

CREDENZAS

Although these items have been classed as anything from sideboards to chiffoniers, most dealers refer to them as credenzas. The word is Italian and applies to a long, low cabinet with up to four doors, a style which first made its appearance in this form during the last quarter of the 18th century.

They are quite large but have the virtue of combining the functions of various pieces of furniture, being suitable for displaying both china and silver while providing a covered storage area for less worthy pieces.

Many are veneered in burr walnut with ormolu mounts on the pilasters and have a small amount of inlay in the centre door. Another decorative style used on French credenzas made by various firms is that known as Boulle. This is the inlay of interlocking pieces of brass and tortoiseshell, introduced by Andre Charles Boulle back in the late 17th century.

During the later Victorian period many were subjected to the fashion for 'ebonising' wood, which was popular at that time.

A walnut credenza, the centre cupboard doors inset with Sevres panels flanked by two domed glass fronted cupboards. £2,000

A late 17th century credenza, the rectangular top with projecting corners, on toupie feet, Lombardy, 142cm. wide. (Finarte) £5,969

A Tuscan walnut and brass mounted credenza, enclosed by a pair of panel doors applied all over with cartouche moulded panels and brass boss and studded ornament, on bracket feet, 6ft. wide.
(Phillips) £4,000

One of a pair of 19th century French 'Boulle' credenzas in ebonised wood with copper banding and ormolu mounting, the top in white marble, 89cm. wide.
(Finarte) (Two) £2,388

An Italian baroque walnut credenza, mid 18th century, the serpentine crossbanded top over a pair of similar drawers, on bun feet, 52in. long.
(Skinner Inc.) £4,852

Italian Renaissance walnut credenza, rectangular moulded top over a panelled case fitted with a small frieze drawer, on bracket feet, 27½in. wide.
(Skinner Inc.) £1,669

A 19th century French ebonised and ormolu mounted credenza, the front inlaid with quatrefoil motifs in mother of pearl, with white marble top, 134cm. wide.
(Finarte) £2,388

Cupboards tended to become plainer as their development progressed, with hardly any ornamentation beyond the turned pediments below the frieze which, occasionally, had a wisp of foliated scroll carving.

The cupboard doors in the lower section are usually divided into an arrangement of one horizontal and two vertical panels, which is typical of 17th century furniture, and the doors on the upper section are fielded.

Totally genuine pieces should be open to the floor inside the bottom cupboard.

Early English furniture was usually made of oak, this being the tried and tested native hardwood but, by the end of the 17th century, the more refined tastes of the fashionable town dwellers demanded furniture of more exotic woods such as walnut.

The supply of walnut was met mainly from Europe but, in 1709 an extremely hard winter killed off most of the trees and the French, perturbed by the depleted state of their stocks, placed an embargo on the export of walnut in 1720.

About 1730, as a result of public pressure, the import duty on Spanish mahogany was lifted and designers were able seriously to turn their attention to exploiting the possibilities of this wood.

As trade was developing and the demand for finer detail, such as astragal glazed doors for example, importers turned their eyes towards Jamaica and the West Indies from where the fine grained Cuban mahogany was obtained and so great was the demand that in 1753 alone, over half a million cubic feet were imported.

19th century Chinese apothecaries cupboard, with numerous drawers, 81cm. wide. (Auktionshaus Arnold) **£1,146**

Late 18th century pine bacon cupboard with ornate pediment and bracket feet. (British Antique Exporters) **£500**

A Charles II walnut, elm and ash hanging-cupboard, the rectangular top with later moulded cornice and bolection-moulding frieze above a pierced door, 33in. wide. (Christie's) **£4,180**

Louis XIV carved walnut buffet à deux corps, each part enclosed by a geometrically moulded and grotesque mask-carved double-fronted door, 37³/₄in. wide. (Butterfield & Butterfield) **£2,730**

An oak and walnut food cupboard fitted with a pierced and carved rectangular panelled cupboard door, 17th century, 36in. wide. (Christie's) **£1,980**

Antique American Empire server in pine, one moulded drawer over two cupboard doors flanked by turned columns, 32in. wide. (Eldred's) **£280**

165

One of a pair of satinwood bed-side cupboards crossbanded with rosewood, on turned tapering legs, 17¼in. wide.
(Christie's)   (Two)   £1,650

An oak buffet, the rectangular top above **moulded frieze fitted** with two **panelled** doors applied with winged portrait masks, partly 18th century, 47in.
(Christie's)   £1,760

18th century oak two tier cupboard with baluster turned supports with turned finials, 21in. wide.
(G. A. Key)   £250

George III Provincial oak bacon cupboard, second half 18th century, the concave-fronted high fielded panelled backrest enclosed by two pairs of shallow doors over two pairs of double panelled doors, 5ft. 5in. wide.
(Butterfield & Butterfield) £1,092

An oak press cupboard of small size, carved overall with guilloche, conjoined scrolls, fluting and flowerhead designs, basically 17th century, 144cm. high.
(Lawrence Fine Arts) £1,320

A cupboard with drawer and doors, Cambridge, Massachusetts, 1680–1700, in two parts, the upper section with projecting cornice and dentil frieze mounted with corbels, 48⅞in. wide.
(Christie's)   £45,667

A Federal blue-painted cupboard, New England, late 18th/early 19th century, with deeply moulded rectangular cornice over a fielded panelled cupboard door, 40½in. wide.
(Christie's)   £3,643

A good late 17th century north of England oak press cupboard, the frieze carved with a band of stylised flower-heads, 75in. wide.
(Tennants)   £5,000

An antique oak court cupboard in the mid 18th century style, the recessed upper portion having three 'cupid's bow' panelled doors, 4ft. 8in. wide.
(Russell Baldwin & Bright) £3,100

A rare antique primitive cupboard, hewn from elm trunk with plank front and door, 4ft. x 2ft.
(Russell Baldwin & Bright) £1,700

Louis XV Provincial fruitwood buffet with shaped panelled doors with ebonised outline, raised on simple shaped feet, 4ft. 7in. wide.
(Butterfield & Butterfield) £1,639

A Continental oak cupboard, on sleigh supports, late 17th/early 18th century, probably North European, 41½in. wide.
(Christie's) £1,320

An oak press cupboard in three sections, with moulded rectangular cornice on column supports, above two panelled doors flanking a portico, on stile feet, the feet and back replaced, 17th century and later, 53in. wide. (Christie's) £2,420

A James I oak and parquetry press cupboard in two sections, the moulded rectangular cornice above a panelled central section flanked by two conforming doors, on carved baluster supports, 37½in. wide.
(Christie's) £3,960

A Chippendale walnut step-back cupboard, Pennsylvania, 1750–1800, the rectangular top with overhanging moulded cornice above five vertical beaded tongue-and-groove backboards, 61in. wide.
(Christie's) £10,010

A good painted and decorated pine hanging wall cupboard, Pennsylvania, circa 1780, the moulded cornice above a hinge glazed door opening to shelves, width 31in.
(Sotheby's) £3,783

An oak aumbry, the front with two doors pierced with roundels, flanked by pierced panels, 44¾in. wide, part 16th/17th century.
(Bearne's) £3,100

A green painted hanging cupboard with polychrome decoration, the arched pediment with a carved bird in relief, signed with initials and dated *1854*, 97cm. high.
(Auktionsverket) £837

A Charles II large chest in oak and walnut veneered with snakewood and ebony, in three sections, 50in. wide. £3,250

An oak and fruitwood food cupboard inlaid with geometric lozenge patterns, late 16th/early 17th century, 35¾in. wide. £5,600

An 18th century oak cupboard having a moulded cornice and double doors with shaped and fielded panels, 22in. wide. £1,150

An oak cupboard with moulded canted rectangular top and sides carved with Romayne panels flanked and divided by foliate capitals, basically mid-16th century, 34in. wide. (Christie's) £1,650

Pair of Italian neoclassical walnut and marquetry small cupboards, late 18th century, the single crossbanded frieze drawer over a horizontal tambour shutter, 13⅞in. wide. (Butterfield & Butterfield) £4,818

Louis XV Transitional stripped pine buffet à deux corps with a cavetto moulded cornice above a pair of fielded and shaped arched doors carved with sprays of cereal, 4ft. 5½in. wide. (Butterfield & Butterfield) £1,766

A George III inlaid mahogany portable croft, with a frieze drawer and panelled door enclosing twelve small drawers, 20in. wide. (Christie's S. Ken) £1,430

A Robert Thompson Mouseman oak cupboard, of rectangular two door construction with adze-finish, carved with a mouse, 108.5cm. wide. (Lawrence Fine Art) £1,320

An oak cupboard, three doors each carved with a saintly figure, on square uprights joined by an undertier, 17th century, 45in. wide. (Christie's S. Ken) £2,860

This is a very delightful little desk which originated during the final years of the 18th century.

Primarily a lady's desk, it is one of those rare pieces in which the virtues of practicality and elegance are beautifully combined to produce a comfortable yet compact piece of functional furniture.

Earlier davenports were usually made of rosewood or satinwood and were boxlike in structure apart from the sloping top, which would either pull forward or swivel to the side in order to make room for the writer's lower limbs.

While most examples are about two feet wide, it is well worth looking for the smaller ones, (about 15 inches to 18 inches wide), for these can fetch twice as much as larger models even though they usually have only a cupboard at the side instead of drawers.

It was during the William IV period that the davenport gained its name and its popularity.

The story goes that one Captain Davenport placed an order for one of these writing desks with Gillows of Lancaster, a well-known firm of cabinet makers at the time. Known during its manufacture as 'the Davenport order', the first desk was completed and the name stuck, being applied to all subsequent orders for a desk of this particular style.

Davenports were, at the middle of the 19th century, at the height of their popularity and at peak quality for, although they remained in vogue to a certain extent for the remainder of the century, the standard of workmanship employed in their construction declined steadily.

A late Victorian ebonised davenport banded in burr walnut, 22in. wide. (Dreweatt Neate) £780

A Victorian burr walnut and ebonised harlequin davenport, 1ft.11in. wide, circa 1870. £2,000

A Victorian walnut piano top davenport, the interior fitted with a lined sliding writing surface and pen trough, on bar feet and castors, 22in. wide. (Christie's S. Ken) £2,420

A Victorian figured walnut piano top harlequin davenport, the rising superstructure with rectangular hinged cover opening to reveal stationery slides, 1ft. 11in. wide. (Spencer's) £1,800

A late Victorian oak davenport, with three-quarter galleried hinged top enclosing a stationery cupboard, above four drawers to one side, 21in. wide. (Christie's) £550

Victorian walnut davenport with satinwood crossbandings, the rear has a stationery section, with four squat feet supporting, 1ft. 9in. wide. (G. A. Key) £1,100

A walnut davenport, Victorian, circa 1860, in well figured wood, the hinged top with pull-out writing drawer, 58.5cm. wide. (Sotheby's) **£2,185**

A rosewood-veneered davenport, early Victorian, circa 1850, with a pen drawer on the right, 61cm. wide. (Sotheby's) **£935**

An early Victorian figured walnut davenport, the surprise pop-up top with three-quarter gallery, 22½in. wide. **£2,000**

A mid-Victorian walnut piano top davenport, the rising superstructure with doors and pigeon-holes above a hinged fall enclosing an interior, 23¾in. wide. (Christie's S. Ken) **£2,200**

An Anglo-Japanese davenport, ebonised, the drawers at either side (one set dummy) and front columns decorated with floral inlay and supported by Japanese fretwork, 1.04m. high. (Phillips) **£720**

An Anglo-Indian Vizigatapam ivory, sandalwood and tortoiseshell davenport engraved overall with scrolling foliage, Indian figures, deities and beasts, 18in. wide. (Christie's) **£13,750**

A laburnum davenport with leather-lined slope and fitted interior above a pen drawer and four drawers, 19th century, 21in. wide. (Christie's S. Ken) **£550**

A William IV carved mahogany davenport of small size, the ratcheted top with inset tooled leather surface and gadrooned edge, 1ft. 8in. wide. (Phillips) **£2,200**

A mid-Victorian walnut piano top davenport, the rising superstructure with a concealed mechanism, drawers and pigeon-holes, 21in. wide. (Christie's S. Ken.) **£2,090**

A Victorian walnut davenport, surmounted by turned finials flanking a pierced gallery, 24in. wide.
(Bonhams) £1,500

An early Victorian calamander davenport with pierced scrolling three-quarter gallery and leather-lined sloping top, 21in. wide. (Christie's) £1,320

An early Victorian rosewood davenport, the slope revealing a bird's-eye maple interior of drawers, 22$\frac{1}{2}$in. wide. (Bonhams) £1,700

19th century walnut veneered davenport desk with walnut three-quarter gallery above slope front with fitted interior on 'piano' brackets. £1,000

A George IV rosewood davenport inlaid overall with boxwood lines, with rectangular top above a green leather-lined hinged slope, enclosing a mahogany-lined interior, 18in. wide. (Christie's) £1,540

A late Victorian walnut and ebonised davenport, the top with three quarter gallery above a hinged leather lined slope, supported by scrolling corbels, 28$\frac{1}{2}$in. wide. (Bonhams) £1,000

A George IV satinwood davenport, the three-quarter galleried top with sloping inset leather flap above two slides, 1ft. 8in. wide.
(Phillips) £2,900

A Victorian inlaid burr walnut davenport with a brass galleried superstructure, the top with a pull out writing slope, 22in. wide.
(Tennants) £1,700

A William IV rosewood davenport with spindle filled three-quarter gallery, tooled leather inset to the sloping flap, 23$\frac{1}{2}$in. wide.
(Bearne's) £720

A Victorian walnut davenport, the back with galleried hinged stationery compartment, on turned feet, 22in. wide. (Christie's S. Ken) £770

A William IV rosewood davenport, the sliding slope above ink tray slide and three drawers, 20in. wide. (Bonhams) £2,000

A Victorian walnut davenport, with fret gallery above a writing slide and two small drawers, four side drawers, 22in. wide. £1,950

A Victorian rosewood davenport with raised pen, ink and envelope compartments, the sloping top enclosing fitted interior. (Lawrence Fine Arts) £1,430

A Regency rosewood davenport with hinged sliding rectangular top with pierced three-quarter gallery and red leather-lined flap enclosing two mahogany-lined drawers, 15½in. wide. (Christie's) £3,960

A Regency rosewood davenport with a hinged pencil drawer and slide to the side above four drawers with dummy drawers to the reverse, 20in. wide. (Christie's S. Ken) £2,530

An attractive George IV rosewood davenport, with a pierced brass gallery, the writing slope inset with leather, circa 1825, 21in. wide. (Bonhams) £2,400

A Regency rosewood davenport, the sliding top with tooled leather inset to the sloping flap and a hinged pen and ink side drawer, 19in. wide. (Bearne's) £1,800

An Edwardian mahogany davenport with hinged three-quarter gallery compartment fitted with a pen trough above a lined-slope, 20in. wide. (Christie's S. Ken.) £49

A Regency rosewood davenport with three-quarter gilt metal gallery and leather lined flap, 20½in. wide.
£2,950

A mid Victorian amboyna and ebony davenport, the cupboard doors enclosing a fitted interior, 22in. wide. (Christie's)
£880

A Victorian burr walnut davenport with a rear hinged stationery compartment, 1ft.11in. wide, circa 1850.
£800

A Victorian burr-walnut davenport, with an open fretwork gallery above a serpentine writing slope, enclosing a satin-birch interior, 23in. wide. (Bonhams)
£1,300

A William IV rosewood davenport, the rectangular sliding box top with a leather-lined hinged sloping flap below a spindled three-quarter gallery, 20½in. wide. (Christie's S. Ken)
£3,850

Victorian walnut davenport, the rising lid serpentine formed having a green leather inset, the back superstructure with three quarter pierced gallery, 23in. wide. (G.A. Key)
£980

A George IV mahogany davenport by Gillows of Lancaster, with gilt metal three-quarter gallery and red leather-lined sloping flap, 20¼in. wide. (Christie's)
£4,400

A mid-Victorian burr-walnut davenport, with three-quarter gallery above hinged superstructure, on bun feet, 21in. wide. (Christie's)
£935

A Victorian walnut davenport with ledge back, rectangular top and hinged leather-lined writing slope inlaid with Classical and foliate motifs, 21in. wide. (Christie's S. Ken)
£550

A Victorian walnut davenport, the rectangular coffered top fitted with a sprung stationery compartment. £2,250

A Victorian burr walnut veneered piano top davenport with fitted interior, 22in. wide. £1,600

A Victorian burr walnut davenport with a sliding hinged writing slope, 33in. high. £1,000

A mid-Victorian walnut piano-davenport, with rising superstructure, fitted with drawers and pigeon holes, foliate scroll supports and turned feet, 28in. wide. (Christie's) £1,925

A late Victorian walnut and marquetry davenport, the panelled door to the side enclosing four drawers, on scroll feet, the marquetry panels probably German, late 18th century, 26¼in. wide. (Christie's S. Ken) £792

A mid Victorian walnut davenport with tulipwood radial inlay, the brass three-quarter galleried pen compartment above a hinged leather-lined slope, 21¼in. wide. (Christie's) £1,760

A late Victorian burr walnut inlaid davenport with hinged leather lined top above scrolled supports with drawers to the side.
(Bonhams) £1,100

A Victorian rosewood davenport, the rectangular top with a three-quarter gallery, 24in. wide. £1,000

A Victorian figured walnut piano top davenport with a hinged lid to the stationery compartment, the top 22½in. wide. (Tennants) £2,000

A Killarney arbutus wood
davenport inlaid with
architectural subject ovals,
31½in. wide.　　£5,350

Victorian carved and brass
inlaid mahogany davenport
desk, America, 19th century,
29¼in. wide.　　£900

A mid Victorian gilt and
mother-of-pearl, black japanned,
papier mâché davenport on bun
feet, 27in. wide.　　£2,600

A Victorian walnut davenport,
the superstructure with
rectangular top and small
drawers flanked by pigeon holes
enclosed by a pair of double
mirror panelled doors, 1ft. 9in.
wide.
(Spencer's)　　£690

An Irish Killarney arbutus
davenport inlaid with scenes of
ruins, Irish motifs and foliage,
on dark stained foliate carved
mahogany supports and
inverted plinth base, 32¼in.
wide.
(Christie's)　　£2,860

A George IV pollard oak davenport in the manner of Richard
Bridgens, the rectangular top
with undulating three quarter
gallery, on concave fronted
plinth base, 26in. wide.
(Christie's London)　　£1,650

A Victorian rosewood davenport
with shaped gallery, sloping flap
with tooled leather insert,
hinged pen and ink drawer,
21in. wide.
(Bearne's)　　£1,100

A rosewood and marquetry
inlaid davenport, in the manner
of T. Turner of Manchester.
　　£1,000

Victorian walnut and inlaid
davenport, fitted stationery box
top, four drawers and four
opposing dummy drawers, 21in.
wide.
(G.A. Key)　　£1,900

DAVENPORTS

A George IV rosewood veneered davenport, the sliding top with a pierced brass gallery, 19.5in. wide. £1,250

A Wheeler & Wilson type S. Davis & Co. walnut 'Davenport' treadle sewing machine, serial no. 21535, 96cm. high, 63cm. wide, circa 1870. (Phillips) £1,300

A late Victorian brass-mounted sycamore davenport with three quarter brass gallery and leather-lined fall, 21in. wide. (Christie's) £1,760

A Victorian walnut davenport, the baluster turned gallery above a hinged leather-lined writing slope, on turned baluster supports, 23½in. wide. (Christie's) £2,310

19th century mahogany davenport, the rising top, leather inset, reveals a drawer interior, with contemporary cabriole front supports, 22in. wide. (G. A. Key) £480

A Victorian ebonised and amboyna davenport inlaid with geometric boxwood lines, the leather-lined hinged sloping flap below a brass galleried lid, 22in. wide. (Christie's S. Ken.) £93

A late Victorian burr walnut davenport, with pierced gallery and leather lined sloping lid enclosing a fitted interior, 22in. wide. (Christie's) £1,100

A late Victorian bamboo and black-lacquer davenport decorated with birds amongst foliage, on splayed feet, 23½in. wide. (Christie's S. Ken.) £660

A mahogany davenport, Victorian, circa 1870, the wide sliding writing slope with an interior lined with marbled paper, 71cm. wide. (Sotheby's) £1,265

In the early 18th century, Oriental porcelain and Delftware became extremely popular and a need arose for suitably fine cabinets with glazed upper sections in which to display it to its full advantage.

Early styles had straight cornices and doors glazed in half round mouldings, the whole supported on turned legs with stretchers. As taste developed, however, heavy architectural styles in the manner of William Kent became popular, often displaying dentil cornices, and broken-arch pediments, with fielded panelled doors below the glazed section.

It was not long before the heavy, architecturally styled cabinets were recognised as being inappropriate for the display of delicate china and porcelain. They were quickly relegated to the libraries of the nation for the storage of books, their places being taken in fashionable drawing rooms by far more graceful display cabinets.

Never slow to turn an imported fashion to their advantage, designers such as Chippendale helped to perpetuate the taste for things Oriental by producing fine Chinese-influenced styles incorporating some incredibly delicate fretwork.

Dutch marquetry was another popular decorative style consisting of naturalistic birds and flowers executed in shaped reserves. Shading of the leaves and flowers was, during the first half of the 18th century, achieved by dipping the veneered shapes part way into hot sand but this later gave way to a method of engraving the shading on to the actual surface.

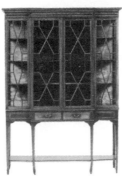

An Edwardian mahogany and satinwood banded breakfront display cabinet, with pair of central geometrically astragal glazed doors, 57in. wide.
(Christie's)   £1,430

A Glasgow style mahogany display cabinet, the rectangular top with mirror back above a pair of stained and leaded glass doors, 69in. high.
(Christie's)   £1,100

A pair of mahogany and brass-mounted display cabinets, each with glazed door and canted glazed sides, 21in. wide.
(Christie's)   £1,980

An Edwardian mahogany and marquetry display cabinet, with moulded cornice above swag-hung frieze, 45in. wide.
(Christie's)   £935

A good French gilt-bronze-mounted vitrine, Paris, circa 1900, of serpentine form, veneered in kingwood with shaped top, central door and six cabriole legs, 148cm. wide.
(Sotheby's)   £8,580

A fine English inlaid satinwood display cabinet, circa 1895, in George III manner, with pair of serpentine glazed doors and serpentine canted glazed sides, 5ft. wide.
(Sotheby's)   £6,600

An Edwardian satinwood
breakfront china cabinet
in Sheraton revival style,
4ft.9in. wide.   £3,200

A mahogany Art Nouveau
display cabinet, the mirrored
top with open canopy, 48in.
long.   £850

An Edwardian mahogany
display cabinet crossbanded
in satinwood, 57½in. wide.
                      £1,800

An Edwardian painted
satinwood display cabinet with
all-over ribbon-tied trailing
floral and bell-flower ornament,
on square tapering legs with
spade feet, 54½in. wide.
(Christie's S. Ken)   £5,500

A Regency amaranth, satinwood
and ebony display cabinet-on-
stand, with a glass-fronted door
enclosing a shelf, flanked by two
panelled doors, 50in. wide.
(Christie's)   £4,620

An ormolu-mounted kingwood
vitrine-cabinet, the stepped top
with three-quarter spindle
gallery above one long arched
glazed door, late 19th century,
50in. wide.
(Christie's)   £4,950

A Japanese hardwood dis-
play cabinet with asymmet-
rical arrangement of shelves,
cupboard and drawers, 4ft.
11½in. wide.   £1,000

Oak Art Nouveau design display
cabinet with two leaded glazed
doors with inlaid decoration on
shaped supports, 47½in. wide.
(Bigwood)   £700

An Edwardian Art Nouveau
mahogany side cabinet with
boxwood, satinwood and
harewood stylised floral inlay, 4ft. wide.   £750

One of a pair of mid Victorian ormolu mounted satinwood side cabinets, 36in. wide.
£4,100

An ormolu mounted king-wood vitrine cabinet with serpentine breccia marble top, 35in. wide.   £2,650

A Victorian ebonised and brass inlaid side cabinet with glazed bow-fronted doors, 4ft.6in. wide.   £650

A Dutch burr-walnut display-cabinet with arched moulded cornice centred by acanthus scrolls and two glazed doors above a bombé base, mid 18th century, 78in. wide.
(Christie's)   £9,900

A rosewood and gilt-metal mounted serpentine vitrine enclosed by a pair of glazed doors with arched Vernis Martin panels of cherubs below, 47in. wide.
(Christie's)   £1,540

An English painted satinwood display cabinet, Edwardian, circa 1910, of classical breakfront form, the whole painted with foliage and scènes galantes, 6ft. 4¹/₂in. wide.
(Sotheby's)   £4,620

A Colonial calamander display cabinet, the drawers with silver plated handles, early 19th century, 57in. wide.
£2,150

A Louis XVI ormolu-mounted tulipwood and mahogany parquetry vitrine, with a rectangular eared ochre marble top above a frieze, 41¹/₂in. wide.
(Christie's East)   £11,660

A brass mounted ebonised vitrine cabinet with simulated green marble top, 48in. wide. (Christie's)
£495

A Louis Philippe tortoiseshell display cabinet-on-stand with a pair of glazed doors enclosing shelves, on scroll supports joined by stretchers, 33in. wide. (Christie's) **£1,705**

Edwardian mahogany display table, with bevelled glazed side panels all round, moulded friezes, 21in. wide. (G. A. Key) **£430**

An attractive late Victorian mahogany salon cabinet, the arched canopied superstructure with foliate carved cresting, 4ft. 1in. wide. (Spencer's) **£750**

A Dutch mahogany display cabinet inlaid with marquetry foliate bands enclosed by two glazed doors and side panels, 19th century, 40in. wide. (Christie's S. Ken) **£1,980**

Pair of Edwardian satinwood vitrine tables, circa 1900, horseshoe shaped glass-inset top, raised on square tapered legs, 27^{1}/$_4$in. high. (Skinner Inc.) **£1,205**

A French giltmetal mounted mahogany vitrine with veined red marble top and pierced gallery above foliate scroll frieze, 27in. wide. (Christie's) **£825**

A good French rosewood and amboyna breakfront secrétaire display cabinet, Napoléon III, by Grohé of Paris, circa 1860, 120cm. wide. (Sotheby's) **£3,300**

An ormolu-mounted giltwood vitrine table, with a hinged serpentine top inset with a bevelled glazed panel and velvet-lined interior, late 19th/early 20th century, 31in. wide. (Christie's) **£990**

An unusual satinbirch display cabinet, attributed to Gillows of Lancaster, circa 1870, the glazed upper parts supporting Ionic columns, 3ft. 7^{3}/$_4$in. wide. (Sotheby's) **£2,420**

A Dutch walnut and mar-
quetry vitrine, inlaid
throughout with flowers
and foliage, on lion paw
feet, 60½in. wide.
(Bearne's)   £9,800

A Louis XV style mahogany
bombe display table with a
sloping and curved glazed
top, on cabriole legs, 31in.
high. (Bearne's)   £700

An attractive Edwardian
satinwood salon cabinet by
Edwards & Roberts, with
broken swan neck pediment, 3ft.
11in. wide.
(Spencer's)   £8,800

Louis XIV style gilt-bronze-
mounted boulle vitrine, late 19th
century, the glazed door with
boulle framework, enclosing a
mirrored interior with glass
shelves, 34¾in. wide.
(Butterfield & Butterfield) £1,891

A good French gilt-bronze-
mounted kingwood display
table, Napoléon III, by Raulin of
Paris, circa 1870, 61cm. wide.
(Sotheby's)   £5,280

An Edwardian mahogany
breakfront display cabinet, the
moulded cornice above a glazed
cupboard door with applied
astragals.
(Bonhams)   £1,100

German carved oak display
cabinet with carved cornice,
the upper doors glazed, the
lower with lozenge carvings,
161cm. wide. (Kunsthaus am
Museum)   £3,416

A circular vitrine in mahogany with ormolu mounts,
24in. diam.   £600

An Italian painted cabinet, the
scrolling pediment with a carved
rococo spray of foliage, 5ft. 3in.
wide.
(Woolley & Wallis)   £2,600

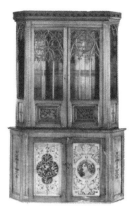

A mid Victorian oak and marquetry cabinet, 55in. wide, 85in. high. £3,500

A Dutch walnut and marquetry display cabinet with a pair of glazed doors, 59in. wide.
£3,750

Gustav Stickley one door china closet, circa 1907, no. 820, 36in. wide. £1,200

An attractive Edwardian mahogany bow front salon cabinet, the broken arch superstructure inlaid with laurel leaves, scrolling acanthus leaves and flowerheads in coloured woods and ivory, 3ft. 8in. wide.
(Spencer's)   £900

A good rosewood and kingwood-veneered side cabinet, circa 1850, the arched mirror back with a glazed door, flanked by open shelves with gilt-bronze mounts throughout, 4ft. 2³/₄in. wide.
(Sotheby's)   £2,970

An ormolu-mounted plum-pudding mahogany vitrine-cabinet, with stepped eared rectangular breakfront top, the frieze with blue glass panel painted with children, 46¹/₂in. wide.
(Christie's)   £2,750

A mid Victorian French Provincial oak cabinet of Louis XV design, with arched scroll crested cornice above two glazed double panelled doors, on cabriole legs, early 19th century, 56in. wide.
(Christie's)   £1,980

Biedermeier cherry display cabinet, circa 1810, with a tablet top above a chamfered frieze projecting above a pair of geometrically glazed doors, 5ft. 7³/₄in. wide.
(Butterfield & Butterfield)
£2,025

An 18th century Dutch oak china cabinet, the upper part with an arched moulded cornice centred with a 'C'-scroll flowerspray above a pair of arched geometrically glazed doors, 5ft. wide.
(Phillips)   £2,200

The name 'dresser' could possibly derive from the fact that its sole original function was to provide a surface on which the food could be dressed before serving, completion of this stage of culinary activity being signalled to ravenous diners by the beating of a drum.

In order to simplify their work and cut costs, cabinet makers of the late 17th century often neglected to produce elaborately turned legs for their products, making do with wavy shapes cut from flat boards instead.

It has been recorded that a few mediaeval cupboard-type dressers had a form of shelving above them but it was not until the beginning of the 18th century that the idea really caught on and became a fully developed, everyday reality.

Another popular innovation in the early 18th century was the inclusion of a row of small spice drawers set in front of the backboard along the top.

Most early dressers with shelves had no backboards to them, these often being added later in the century.

One of the reasons for shelves – apart from the obvious one that people were using more cooking utensils than hitherto – was to display the English Delftware which served most families as a substitute for the expensive Chinese porcelain displayed in the homes of people of wealth.

By the mid 18th century dressers had been ousted from fashionable dining rooms by large side tables or sideboards made of mahogany, the faithful old dressers being relegated to the kitchens.

A George I oak and elm dresser with later carving, circa 1720, 6ft.4in. wide. £1,300

A George III oak breakfront dresser with raised open shelf back, circa 1770, 6ft. wide. £2,550

**A mid-Georgian oak dresser, with moulded cornice above two shelves, the lower section with three drawers above two fielded arched panelled doors, 62³/₄in. wide.
(Christie's) £2,090**

**An oak dresser with associated rack, fitted with three geometrically carved drawers on turned legs joined by stretchers, late 17th century, restored, 73in. wide.
(Christie's S. Ken) £2,750**

**An 18th century oak Welsh dresser, the delft rack with shallow swept and stepped moulded cornice, over a deep scalloped frieze, 6ft. 8in. wide.
(Spencer's) £4,600**

**A fine George II oak dresser, the lower section with three frieze drawers above a pair of fielded panel cupboard doors flanking an arched door, 72¹/₂in. wide.
(Bonhams) £4,800**

Early 18th century oak
Welsh dresser on plank feet,
57½in. wide.   £6,200

A George II oak dresser with
moulded rectangular top above
three drawers and two panelled
doors, on stile feet, on foot
repaired, 53½in. wide.
(Christie's)   £4,620

An early Georgian oak high
dresser, the moulded cornice
with three shelves on shaped
trestle supports, 61in. wide.
£7,750

A mid-Georgian oak dresser, the
cavetto moulded cornice above a
pierced scroll frieze and three
shelf plate rack, on cabriole legs
and pad feet, 80½in. wide.
(Bonhams)   £1,900

An elaborate Art Nouveau
dresser, possibly designed by
Gustave Serurrier Bovy, in light
oak, the superstructure having a
central glass-fronted cupboard
flanked by recesses, 206cm. high.
(Phillips)   £1,300

An 18th century oak dresser, the
delft rack with ogee moulded
cornice over four open shelves
flanked by small shelves, 6ft.
4in. wide.
(Spencer's)   £2,500

An oak dresser, the top section
with a cavetto moulded cornice
and open shelves, on baluster
columns, 71½in. wide.
(Christie's S. Ken)   £4,400

A Georgian oak dresser with
open rack, the concave cornice
above a pierced frieze, 72in.
high.
(Lawrence Fine Art)   £2,200

A small oak dresser in the
Georgian style with a dentil
cornice above a pierced frieze,
on front cabriole supports,
201cm. high. (Lawrence Fine
Arts)   £1,375

An inlaid oak Welsh dresser outlined throughout with crossbanding on cabriole legs, 73in. wide. (Bearne's) £2,400

Victorian pine dresser with drawers and cupboards, 1855. £650

A late 18th century oak Welsh dresser, the front square legs partly reeded to a shaped front pot board, 5ft. 10in. wide. (Woolley & Wallis) £2,900

An oak dresser with shelved superstructure containing four small drawers, the base with two drawers and central panelled door, 57in. wide. (Christie's) £1,100

George III oak Welsh cupboard, late 18th century, with mahogany banding, plate racks and cubbyholes above, 72in. long.(Skinner Inc.) £3,185

An Arts and Crafts dresser, attributed to the Guild of Handicraft, circa 1900, stained oak, leaded glass, beaten copper, brass, 77in. high. (Sotheby's) £3,300

An early Georgian oak enclosed dresser with associated rack, the base fitted with three drawers flanked by cupboards, on block feet, 69in. wide. (Christie's) £1,540

An early 18th century oak dresser, the delft rack with moulded top and shelves, 65in. wide. (Andrew Hartley) £7,000

An early George III oak dresser and rack with moulded cornice above open shelves, on style feet, the rack possibly associated, 63$\frac{1}{2}$in. wide. (Christie's) £1,650

A reproduction oak and mahogany crossbanded Welsh dresser, the drawers with brass loop handles, 5ft.3in. wide.
£1,200

Louis XV Provincial walnut buffet, mid 18th century, the rectangular moulded top over two drawers, over a pair of panelled cabinet doors, 54in. wide.
(Skinner Inc.)   £1,096

Late 18th century oak Welsh dresser with three drawers in line and three smaller drawers beneath, 5ft. 3in. wide.
(G. A. Key)   £2,000

A Heal & Son black stained elm dresser, designed by Sir Ambrose Heal, the rectangular superstructure with two cupboard doors enclosing three shelves, circa 1914, 123.3cm. wide. (Christie's)   £1,650

An oak dresser designed by Sidney Barnsley, the shaped superstructure with open gridwork back, supporting two open shelves, on shaped bracket feet, 140.8cm. wide.
(Christie's)   £9,900

A J.P. White 'Daffodil' oak dresser, designed by M.H. Baillie-Scott, the superstructure with rectangular top above two open shelves flanked by single cupboard doors, 153.5cm. wide.
(Christie's)   £5,000

An oak dresser with associated stained pine rack, with moulded cornice and open shelves, parts early 18th century, 58½in. wide.
(Christie's)   £1,540

A Victorian oak kitchen dresser, the moulded fluted cornice centred by a stylised shell, on a moulded plinth, 114in. wide.
(Christie's)   £1,760

A George III oak and mahogany inlaid dresser with later platerack, the moulded cornice above three open shelves, 66½in. wide.
(Christie's)   £1,870

An Arts and Crafts oak dresser, attributed to Ambrose Heal, the plain sides extending to form the supports, 137cm. wide.
(Lawrence Fine Art)   £550

A pine dresser with shaped back and pot board with small drawers under, 5ft. wide.   £525

An Art Nouveau oak dresser, the mirrored superstructure having a crest with two supports, 1.68m. high.
(Phillips)   £750

An oak dresser, with three shelves and moulded cornice, the base with five drawers, on turned legs with undertier, early 19th century, 62in. wide.
(Christie's London)   £3,300

A George III oak dresser, crossbanded overall in mahogany, the superstructure with moulded rectangular cornice above a pierced foliate frieze, on square tapering legs with block feet, 76in. wide.
(Christie's)   £4,400

An oak dresser, the plate rack with moulded cornice and shaped frieze above three shelves, 18th century, restorations, 72in. wide.
(Christie's London)   £4,950

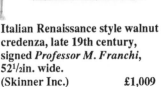

A mid Georgian oak dresser, with a later plate rack, the lower section with three drawers, on cabriole legs, 75in. wide.
(Bonhams)   £2,800

Italian Renaissance style walnut credenza, late 19th century, signed *Professor M. Franchi*, 52½in. wide.
(Skinner Inc.)   £1,009

A George III oak dresser and associated rack, with moulded cornice and open shelves, 65½in. wide.
(Christie's)   £1,650

Portfolio stands appeared towards the end of the 18th century. They resemble nothing so much as a manger set on a stretcher base. Both sides of the portfolio can be adjusted by bars dropping down between the sides of the stretcher base to operate a simple ratchet mechanism.

They were used to store prints, charts, pictures etc. so that these could easily be leafed through. They were rather esoteric pieces of furniture, not to be found in your average living room, and so are quite rare, hence fetching high prices.

Late 19th century Eastlake folio stand. £900

A Victorian rosewood folio stand, with two adjustable slatted panels resting on carved brackets, 112cm. wide. (Allen & Harris) £1,200

An early Victorian walnut folio stand with twin-flap with plain bars, on plain end supports and bun feet, 32in. wide x 44in. high, closed. (Christie's S. Ken) £2,750

An early Victorian mahogany folio stand with lacquered brass fitments, the two adjustable leaves with X-shaped splats on twin shaped supports joined by turned stretchers, 36in. wide. (Christie's) £15,950

A late Victorian mahogany folio stand with slatted adjustable sides on dual reeded scroll uprights joined by a flattened stretcher, 29in. wide. (Christie's) £1,210

A William IV rosewood and simulated rosewood folio stand adjustable by ratchet supports and raised on trestle end supports, 32in. wide. (Tennants) £2,200

A Gustav Stickley slat-sided folio stand, no. 551, 1902-03, 40½in. high, 29½in. wide. (Skinner Inc.) £1,785

An early Victorian mahogany folio stand, the two slatted sides hinged on to a central baluster and opening to form a table, 30in. wide. (Bearne's) £2,100

GUERIDONS

These date from 17th century France, and are small candlestands. The earliest usually consisted of a tall pedestal on a tripod base, the support baluster shaped, or in the form of a Negro. (The name guéridon is that of a famous Moorish galley slave.)

Guéridons are often made of ormolu, carved and gilded wood or sometimes silver or silver-gilt. The term subsequently came to be applied to any small table designed to support candles or a lamp.

A Restoration mahogany guéridon with circular fossilised grey marble top, on three spiral supports, 32in. diameter. (Christie's) £1,980

A gilt metal mounted mahogany gueridon in the style of Weisweiler, stamped Wright and Mansfield, 27¼in. diam. (Christie's) £4,180

A Louis XV ormolu-mounted tulipwood, kingwood and end-cut marquetry guéridon with a tambour shutter with later leather book-spines, on cabriole legs with foliate sabots, 19½in. wide. (Christie's) £8,800

A pair of giltmetal-mounted guéridon tables, the circular tops with pierced galleries, the friezes edged with berried foliage, 19½in. wide. (Christie's) £2,383

A Transitional ormolu-mounted tulipwood, harewood, amaranth and marquetry guéridon or table de chevet, the circular top with pierced entrelac gallery inlaid with flowerpots and an ink tray within a laurel wreath, 13in. diameter. (Christie's) £14,300

An ormolu mounted mahogany guéridon in the manner of Weisweiler, 30½in. high. £5,200

A fine pair of silver mounted and malachite gueridons in the style of Weisweiler, possibly Russian, 15¾ins. diam. £26,400

An ormolu mounted mahogany and parquetry gueridon in the manner of Weisweiler, 18in. diam. (Christie's) £1,320

HIGHBOYS

This is a uniquely American design, consisting of a tall chest of drawers mounted on a stand, or lowboy. The chest is often topped by a broken arch pediment with finials. They are often found in Cuban mahogany or walnut, or lacquered or veneered. The lowboy usually has cabriole legs. Tallboys were made in three styles, William & Mary, Queen Anne, and Chippendale. New England examples are usually fairly plain, in contrast with their Philadelphian counterparts which tend to be richly carved and decorated.

A Queen Anne maple highboy, New Jersey, circa 1730, 37in. wide. £7,100

Queen Anne maple bonnet top highboy, New England, circa 1760, 38in. wide. £3,750

A very good Queen Anne maple bonnet-top highboy, Rhode Island, circa 1765, the shaped skirt continuing to removable cabriole legs, 38¹/₂in. wide. (Sotheby's) £4,301

A good Queen Anne figured walnut flat-top highboy, Pennsylvania, circa 1760, in two parts, the upper section with moulded cornice above five short and three long moulded graduated drawers, 44¹/₂in. wide. (Sotheby's) £27,789

A very fine Queen Anne burl-walnut veneered and maple diminutive flat-top highboy, Boston, Massachusetts, circa 1740, 37¹/₂in. wide. (Sotheby's) £18,526

A William and Mary maple and burl walnut veneer highboy, Mass., circa 1730, 39½in. wide. £3,650

A Queen Anne cherrywood highboy, probably Wethersfield, Conn., circa 1740-65, 37½in. wide. £11,750

A Queen Anne style walnut veneered highboy on hipped cabriole legs with Spanish type feet, England, 62¼in. high. £1,300

JARDINIERES

The jardinière really typifies Victorian taste, when it was decreed that everything had to be covered, dressed up, and decorated. Few Victorian parlours would be without at least one of these, usually made either of earthenware or bronze.

New mass production techniques meant that decorated earthenware was now available to a wider public than ever before, and decoration could now be applied by the new transfer printing. Jardinières featured largely in the production of such firms as Copeland and Garrett, of Stoke on Trent.

One of a pair of oak jardinieres, each with open top, the sides carved with scrolling foliate angles, 7½in. high. (Christie's) Two £825

A rare Regency carved giltwood and gesso half round three-tier jardinière of undulating outline, with guilloche, lyre and husk ornament, 2ft. 2in. wide. (Phillips) £5,000

A Dutch fruitwood and parquetry jardiniere of serpentine bombe shape with detachable tin liner and cabriole legs, 20in. high. (Christie's) £935

A gilt metal mounted kingwood and tulipwood jardiniere, of large size, with detachable tin liner, on shaped feet, 49in. wide. (Christie's) £3,300

One of two Regency rosewood tripod jardinieres, one bearing the label of Richard Henry Masters, possibly Anglo-Indian, 34½in. high. £6,500

A French Empire giltwood jardinière, on square tapering moulded legs with swag headings and hairy paw feet joined by inverted platform stretcher, 15in. wide. (Christie's) £495

A George III mahogany jardiniere, the oval brass bound body with carrying handles on square chamfered legs with C-scroll brackets, 27in. wide. (Christie's London) £6,820

A 19th century Dutch mahogany and floral marquetry circular jardinière with brass carrying handle and slatted sides, with liner. (Phillips) £450

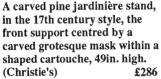

A carved pine jardinière stand, in the 17th century style, the front support centred by a carved grotesque mask within a shaped cartouche, 49in. high. (Christie's) **£286**

A George III green painted and gilded jardiniere after a design by Robert Adam, 36in. wide. **£40,000**

Victorian brass bound oak jardiniere, circa 1880. **£85**

An ormolu-mounted mahogany jardinière with hexagonal top and panelled frieze applied with alternating cornucopia and lyre-and-quiver motifs, 27in. wide. (Christie's) **£1,210**

A Regency rosewood double-sided jardinière with reeded rectangular top centred by a removable oval panel enclosing an associated green-painted removable metal tray, on turned tapering feet, 26¼in. wide. (Christie's) **£3,080**

A mahogany, ebonised and marquetry jardiniere in the style of Charles Bevan. 77.6cm. high. **£3,600**

A Victorian giltmetal mounted walnut and marquetry jardiniere the rectangular glazed top on cabriole legs, 31in. wide. (Christie's S. Ken) **£1,210**

A George III circular mahogany jardinière with a shallow everted rim and fluted frieze, 18in. diameter. (Lawrence) **£1,650**

A gilt metal mounted burr-walnut jardiniere on cabriole legs, 22½in. wide. (Christie's) **£550**

KAS

This heavy cupboard is, as the name suggests, Dutch in origin, coming from a misspelling of the Dutch word for wardrobe. The term is now used essentially to refer to the pieces made by Dutch settlers in America from the mid-seventeenth to late eighteenth century.

The kas changed little in style during this time, being large, with wide mouldings, a heavy cornice and usually on ball feet.

A Scandinavian painted kas, dated 1818, 67in. long.
£2,400

An 18th century Chippendale poplar kas, Hudson Valley, New York, 56in. wide. £1,750

A William and Mary carved cherrywood kas, Hudson River Valley, early 18th century, on turned feet, 6ft. 1in. wide. (Sotheby's) £3,970

A Flemish oak and ebonised kas with moulded cornice above acanthus scroll and putti frieze flanked by masks above four geometrically panelled doors, dated 1672, 19th century, 70in. wide. (Christie's) £4,620

A Dutch Colonial oak and rosewood kas applied with ebony fret mouldings, on turned onion feet, 18th century and later. (Christie's S. Ken)£3,080

A William and Mary gumwood kas in two sections, New York, 1725-55, 54in. wide.
£3,700

Late 18th century Dutch walnut kas on turned onion feet, 67in. wide. (Christie's) £935

An 18th century gumwood kas, in three sections, Long Island, N.Y., 74½in. wide. £5,800

Kneehole desks were originally designed for use as dressing tables and are, basically, chests of drawers with recesses cut to accommodate the knees of persons seated before the mirror which stood on top.

It soon became apparent, however, that they made ideal writing tables and they stayed as dual purpose pieces of furniture until the latter half of the 18th century.

A particularly fine example comes from the William and Mary period and is made of walnut with ebony arabesque marquetry panels. These are inlays of floral and geometric scrolls, usually found within a simple, rectangular frame. This desk rests upon small bun feet typical of the period and has a recessed cupboard with a small drawer in the apron above.

Although the kneehole desk with a centre cupboard was still popular in the mid 18th century, the style developed somewhat to incorporate two pedestals, each having three or four drawers, surmounted by a flat table top which itself contained two or three drawers.

At first these were made as single units, often double sided to stand in the centre of a room, and soon became extremely popular in libraries. They were, however, rather large and cumbersome in this form and later models were made in three sections to facilitate removal and installation.

Pedestal desks date from about 1750 until the end of the 19th century and the difficulty in pricing them stems from the fact that the style changed hardly at all during that time.

A mahogany kneehole desk, the arched kneehole flanked by four drawers, on short cabriole legs and paw feet carved with acanthus scrolls, 51½in. wide. (Christie's London) £4,400

A Flemish walnut and marquetry desk, the rectangular top depicting an episode from Classical mythology with an orator addressing a crowd, 67½in. wide. (Christie's London) £4,180

A Queen Anne walnut and featherbanded kneehole desk, fitted with a frieze drawer and six short drawers about an arched recess, on later bun feet, 3ft. wide. (Phillips) £2,400

A George III mahogany desk, with a leather lined and cross-banded rectangular top opening on hinges and supported on a ratchet, 44½in. wide. (Hy. Duke & Son) £3,200

A George III mahogany 'Harlequin' kneehole desk, the hinged top opening to reveal rising compartments with drawers and pigeonholes, on a plinth base, 3ft. 9in. wide. (Phillips) £5,500

An Edwardian mahogany and marquetry kidney-shaped writing desk, on short square tapered legs with socket feet, 4ft. wide. (Woolley & Wallis) £3,000

A mahogany partner's desk, the rectangular leather-lined top with gadrooned edge, on shell-headed cabriole legs and claw and ball feet, late 19th/20th century, 60¹/₂in. wide.
(Christie's) £1,650

An Italian walnut pedestal desk, the rectangular top with moulded edge, the frieze with brushing slide and three drawers, on bracket feet, 18th century, 54½in. wide.
(Christie's London) £4,400

A 19th century central European birchwood writing desk, the raised back section with galleried top, the lyre shaped pedestals on turned feet, 134cm. wide.
(Finarte) £4,132

A late George II mahogany kneehole desk, the rectangular moulded top above a frieze drawer and ogee arched apron drawer, on ogee bracket feet, 3ft. wide.
(Phillips) £3,000

An early Victorian burr walnut writing-desk, the moulded rounded rectangular top with leather-lined reading slope with ledge, the frieze with single drawer, 41¹/₂in. wide.
(Christie's) £9,900

A George II mahogany or 'red walnut' kneehole desk, having a central recessed cupboard enclosed by fielded panel door between six short drawers, on bracket feet, 2ft. 8¹/₂in. wide.
(Phillips) £2,600

A George III mahogany pedestal secrétaire library desk, in the manner of Gillows, the leather lined hinged double ratcheted slope with a hinged pen and ink tier, 4ft. 1in. x 2ft. 1in.
(Phillips) £4,700

A German oak and parcel ebonised piano front desk, the superstructure with three short drawers, above the fall front enclosing a rosewood interior, 55¹/₂in. wide, circa 1860.
(Bonhams) £2,200

A German walnut and burr walnut-veneered kneehole desk of inverted serpentine form and with cast brass mounts throughout, 40¹/₂in. wide, late 19th century.
(Bearne's) £720

A mahogany library pedestal desk, the moulded rectangular green leather-lined top with concave frieze with a drawer to each end, the pedestals with acanthus-carved volute-angles and a pair of panelled doors to each end, 89½in. wide.
(Christie's)   £7,150

A late Victorian mahogany roll top pedestal desk, with galleried top and panelled fall enclosing a fitted interior, 54in. wide.
(Christie's)   £1,540

A Regency mahogany partner's library table, with rectangular leather-lined top, above cupboards to each end and brass grille doors with upholstered panels, on plinth bases, 84in. wide.
(Christie's)   £17,600

A George II mahogany kneehole desk, the rounded rectangular top with moulded edge and re-entrant corners above a frieze drawer, 30¼in. wide.
(Christie's)   £4,180

A Chippendale mahogany block-front kneehole-bureau, Boston, 1760–1780, the rectangular top with blocked front and moulded edge over a conforming case fitted with a long drawer over a short scalloped valance drawer and recessed kneehole, 36½in. wide.
(Christie's)   £52,616

A George I walnut and feather-banded kneehole desk, with rectangular quarter-veneered top, above a frieze drawer and three drawers either side of the kneehole, on later bracket feet, 33½in. wide.
(Christie's)   £4,950

An early Georgian walnut knee-hole desk crossbanded in yew with moulded and quarter-venee-red rectangular top, 32in. wide.
(Christie's)   £6,600

A Louis XIV marquetry and ebony bureau mazarin, on later supports, the rectangular top inlaid with a basket of flowers on a dais flanked by birds and butterflies, 4ft. wide.
(Phillips)   £17,000

A Queen Anne pollard elm kneehole desk, the top crossbanded with oak her-ringbone bands, 33in. wide.
                    £5,000

A George II padouk and sabicu kneehole desk possibly by John Channon, with breakfront rectangular top above a central frieze drawer, on bulbous acanthus-scrolled feet, 55in. wide.
(Christie's) £77,000

A Makers of Simple Furniture laminated beechwood kneehole desk designed by Gerald Summers, the overhanging rectangular top with D-end, 72.5cm. high.
(Christie's) £495

An English walnut corner twin-pedestal writing table designed by Sir Edwin Lutyens, the triangular top with faded red leather writing surface, 96cm. wide.
(Christie's) £15,400

An attractive Edwardian mahogany cylinder bureau, with a panelled fall enclosing drawers and pigeonholes and a leather inset writing surface.
(Bonhams) £1,500

A Chippendale block-front kneehole-desk, Massachusetts, 1760–1780, the rectangular top with moulded edge and blocked front over a conforming case fitted with a long drawer over a short scalloped valance drawer and recessed kneehole backed by a fan-carved door, 35in. wide.
(Christie's) £19,731

Chinese carved teak desk, 19th century, raised on bracket feet, carved throughout with dragons, 46in. wide.
(Skinner) £375

A George I walnut veneered kneehole desk/writing chest with herringbone line inlay, 35in. wide. £2,800

A George III mahogany knee-hole desk with seven various sized drawers, 33in. wide. £2,300

A George III mahogany military dressing table, the hinged top enclosing a fitted interior, 36in. wide. £2,200

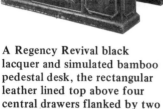

A Regency Revival black lacquer and simulated bamboo pedestal desk, the rectangular leather lined top above four central drawers flanked by two false drawers, 53½in. wide.
(Christie's S. Ken)   £15,950

An early Victorian mahogany and brass-bound military pedestal desk with a rectangular leather-lined top above three frieze drawers about the kneehole, 51in. wide.
(Christie's S. Ken)   £3,080

A Regency mahogany library desk, on four panelled pedestals, two enclosing three drawers, one enclosing six pigeon-holes, and one a removable double-divide folio section, 73in. wide.
(Christie's)   £15,400

A late George II mahogany kneehole dressing- and writing-table, the rectangular moulded top with serpentine front and canted angles edged with ribbon-and-rosette ornament, 41in. wide.
(Christie's)   £37,400

A fine Louis XV style kingwood parquetry and ormolu bombé bureau rognon, on outswept legs terminating in cast scrolling sabots, 50in. wide, late 19th century.
(Bonhams)   £7,000

A George II mahogany kneehole desk, having a moulded edge, containing a long frieze and an arched apron drawer, fitted with six short drawers about a central enclosed recessed cupboard, 3ft. 1in. wide.
(Phillips)   £2,600

A Restauration mahogany bureau à cylindre with rounded rectangular black fossil marble top with three frieze drawers above the solid cylinder enclosing a bird's-eye maple interior, 58¾in. wide.
(Christie's)   £4,620

An early Georgian walnut kneehole desk with moulded rectangular top above one drawer and six short drawers around a recessed fielded panelled cupboard door, 30¾in. wide.
(Christie's)   £6,600

A golden roll top desk with cherrywood inlay, the ends embellished with carved leaf decoration, by Schrenk & Co., Connecticut, bearing patent date 1888, 60in. wide.
(Schrager Auction Galleries)   £3,563

An Edwardian mahogany kidney-shaped kneehole desk inlaid with boxwood lines and satinwood banded borders, on square tapering legs, labelled *Hamptons, Pall Mall, London*, 55in. wide.
(Christie's) £2,970

A Louis XIV premier partie boulle bureau Mazarin, the rectangular top inlaid with dancing figures amid strapwork and foliage after Bérain, on kingwood cabriole legs and foliate sabots, 48in. wide.
(Christie's) £15,400

A mahogany, boxwood lined and satinwood crossbanded twin pedestal partner's desk of George III design, with nine variously sized drawers, on bracket feet, 58in. wide.
(Christie's) £1,760

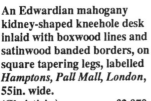

A mid-Victorian burr-walnut kidney-shaped desk with inset gilt-tooled brown leather writing-surface above one long and two short mahogany-lined frieze drawers, the concave kneehole flanked by two convex-fronted pedestals, 52in. wide.
(Christie's) £25,300

A Louis XIV contre partie boulle bureau Mazarin, inlaid in pewter, brass, ebony and tortoiseshell, in the manner of André-Charles Boulle, the rectangular overhanging top inset with a panel of tooled leather, 2ft. 7in. high.
(Phillips) £21,000

A William and Mary stained burr kneehole desk with moulded rectangular part-hinged top crossbanded with geometric walnut borders, enclosing a green baize-lined fitted interior of three short and two long drawers, 43in. wide.
(Christie's) £2,750

A Queen Anne walnut knee-hole desk inlaid overall with featherbanding with moulded rectangular quarter-veneered top, with one long and six short drawers, 34in. wide.
(Christie's) £4,950

An early Georgian mahogany architect's kneehole desk, the waisted lower part with ovolo mouldings and brass carrying handles to the sides, 1.27m. wide. (Phillips London) £3,000

An Italian tulipwood, parcel-gilt, ebonised and ivory-inlaid bureau Mazarin in the style of Luigi Prinotto, banded overall with kingwood, inlaid overall with geometric strapwork and foliage, circa 1730, 52in. wide.
(Christie's) £33,000

A mahogany small pedestal desk with rectangular red leather-lined top above three mahogany-lined frieze drawers, 39in. wide. (Christie's) £770

A walnut kneehole desk with moulded rectangular top, the frieze with a fitted secretaire drawer on bracket feet, 31in. wide. (Christie's) £935

An 18th century Italian walnut kneehole desk with moulded rectangular quartered top, 42½in. wide. (Christie's) £7,150

A walnut and feather kneehole desk, the banded cross rectangular top above eight drawers, on bracket feet, modern, 36in. wide. (Christie's S. Ken) £1,045

A George I kneehole desk with crossbanded quarter veneered fold out top above a frieze drawer, on bracket feet, adapted, 30in. wide. (Christie's London) £4,950

A walnut kneehole desk with crossbanded rectangular top and central recessed cupboard door flanked by eight drawers, Queen Anne and later, 30½in. wide. (Christie's) £4,620

A late George II mahogany kneehole desk, the rectangular moulded top above a long frieze drawer, apron drawer and recessed cupboard, bracket feet, 3ft. 1in. wide. (Phillips) £1,400

A Victorian mahogany kneehole desk, the three-quarter galleried top above one long and two short frieze drawers, on pedestals of three graduated drawers with plinth bases. (Bonhams) £900

A George II mahogany or possibly 'red walnut' kneehole desk, the moulded edge with re-entrant rounded corners containing a long frieze, on ogee bracket feet, 2ft. 6in. wide. (Phillips) £4,500

LINEN PRESSES

These are similar in form to clothes presses, except that the doors conceal a further arrangement of drawers, rather than hanging space. These drawers are always low-fronted, so that the contents can readily be seen before they are pulled out.

Its changes in style at various times were largely to accommodate the changing fashions in the clothes it was designed to contain.

A late Georgian mahogany linen press, the wide cornice above a pair of crossbanded doors enclosing slides, 216cm. wide. (Allen & Harris) £780

George III mahogany linen press, the panelled doors enclosing sliding trays, 4ft. x 7ft.6in. high. £1,150

Late 18th century George III inlaid mahogany linen press on bracket feet, 47½in. wide. £4,300

A George III mahogany and rosewood banded linen press, the dentil moulded cornice above a pair of panelled doors and two short and two graduated long drawers, 49in. wide. (Christie's S. Ken) £2,090

A mid 18th century mahogany press cupboard with dentil cornice, 3ft.8in. wide. £1,100

An oak press, carved with strapwork panels and bands, the finialled crenellated canopy top above five cupboard doors, 65in., 1687. (Christie's) £2,860

A William IV mahogany linen press, the moulded cornice above a pair of panelled doors enclosing drawers, on turned feet. (Bonhams) £600

A George III mahogany linen-press in two sections, with moulded rectangular top above two long panelled doors, on bracket feet, 50in. wide. (Christie's) £4,180

201

An oak linen press by Edward
Barnsley, of plain form and
construction, the chest having
two long drawers with two short
above, 168cm. high.
(Phillips)   £1,200

A 19th century Dutch
marquetry press or cupboard on
chest, decorated with scrolling
foliage and oval panels centred
with birds, urns and floral
bouquets, on bracket feet, 4ft.
wide.(Phillips)   £3,400

George III mahogany linen
press, circa 1800, rectangular
cornice over a pair of panelled
doors, on bracket feet, 79½in.
high.
(Skinner Inc.)   £6

A George III mahogany linen
press, the oval panel doors with
rosewood banding, the lower
section with two short and two
long drawers, on splayed legs,
48¾in. wide.
(Bonhams)   £1,100

An early George III mahogany
linen press with architectural
pediment above two panelled
doors, 48in. wide. (Lawrence
Fine Arts)   £1,870

A George III mahogany linen
press, the lower section with t
false drawers and a long draw
below, on bracket feet, 39¾in.
wide.
(Bonhams)   £3

A Federal mahogany linen
press, New York, circa 1820, the
removable projecting cornice
above a pair of hinged panelled
doors, 54in. wide.
(Sotheby's)   £2,647

A late George II mahogany linen
press with a dentil cornice and
bracket feet, 47¼in. x 73in.
high. (Lawrence Fine Arts)
                             £1,760

A late George III mahogany
linen press with moulded and
crossbanded cornice above a
pair of crossbanded oval
panelled doors, 50in. wide.
(Christie's)   £1,87

A well coloured early George III mahogany linen press, the upper section with dentil cornice, 49½in. wide.
(Bonhams)   £1,500

A George III mahogany linen press with moulded cornice and pair of panelled doors above two short and two long drawers, on bracket feet, 50¼in. wide.
(Christie's)   £1,100

A Federal inlaid mahogany linen press, in two sections, probably New York, circa 1785-1805, 45in. wide.
£5,600

An early 19th century mahogany linen press with moulded cavetto cornice, two crossbanded panelled doors, four graduated long drawers below and on splayed bracket feet, 55in. wide.
(Bearne's)   £880

A late George II mahogany linen press, the base with a long drawer and slide (possibly of late date) above six various drawers on ogee bracket feet, 4ft. 3in. wide.
(Phillips)   £2,600

A William IV mahogany linen press with crossbanded doors set with moulded panels, four graduated long drawers below with lotus-carved knob handles, 58½in. wide.
(Bearne's)   £800

A George IV mahogany linen press, the arched scroll carved cornice above a pair of figured arched panel cupboard doors, on spirally lobed feet, 47in. wide.
(Bonhams)   £950

Early 19th century mahogany linen press, the unusual raised cornice above a pair of ebony banded panel doors, 43in. wide.
(Phillips)   £1,940

A Regency mahogany linen press, inlaid overall in boxwood stringing, the lower section with two short and two long drawers, on splayed feet, 49½in. wide.
(Bonhams)   £1,000

A Chippendale mahogany
and mahogany veneer linen
press, circa 1780, 48in. wide.
£12,250

A Queen Anne burr walnut
press cupboard, 5ft. wide,
circa 1710.   £10,000

A Federal mahogany linen
press, signed by I. Bailey,
New Jersey, 1807, 48in.
wide.   £6,750

A Marsh & Jones inlaid linen
press, the design attributed to
Charles Bevan, scalloped and
moulded cornice above a pair of
cupboard doors with various
wood inlay, 123.5cm. wide.
(Christie's)   £2,420

A handsome George III
mahogany linen press, with a
pair of oval panelled cupboard
doors, crossbanded in satinwood,
the lower section with two short
and two long drawers, 49³/₄in.
wide. (Bonhams)   £1,400

A late 18th century Dutch
kingwood side cupboard inlaid
with boxwood and ebonised
lines, with a cavetto moulded
cornice above a pair of panelled
doors, with splayed legs, 5ft. 5in.
wide. (Phillips)   £2,600

A mid-George III oak press
cupboard with moulded cornice
above a pair of arched panelled
doors, 47in. wide.
(Christie's S. Ken)   £1,045

A George III mahogany linen
press with two panel doors
crossbanded and inlaid with
oval bands, 48in. wide.
(Lawrence Fine Arts) £2,090

A fine George III mahogany
linen press by Gillows,
Lancaster, the upper section
with moulded and dentil cornice,
50¹/₂in. wide.
(Bonhams)   £2,200

LOWBOYS

Although many more sophisticated dressing tables were constructed during the 18th century, the lowboy remain extremely popular – probably a sign of its great versatility as a piece of furniture.

The normal construction was an arrangement of three drawers disposed around a kneehole, though some examples have an additional pair of drawers, or one long, single drawer, set immediately below the top.

The most expensive examples are those made of mahogany or walnut, with bold cabriole legs, often enhanced with shells on the knees, but their country cousins of elm or oak are much more reasonably priced. The latter usually have straight, square legs chamfered on their inside edges or rounded legs with pad feet.

The lowboy was often set against the wall below one of the new Vauxhall plate glass mirrors, which were about eighteen inches high and set in plain moulded frames.

Early 18th century walnut lowboy, 29½in. wide.
£2,000

A 19th century Dutch walnut and foliate marquetry lowboy, 27in. wide. £1,300

A fine Chippendale mahogany lowboy, Pennsylvania or New Jersey, circa 1765, the shaped skirt continuing to cabriole legs, 34¼in. wide.
(Sotheby's) £16,541

A Chippendale carved walnut lowboy, Pennsylvania, circa 1770, having shell-carved cabriole legs ending in claw-and-ball feet.
(Sotheby's) £7,279

A mid Georgian oak lowboy, the moulded rectangular top above three drawers around the shaped apron, 33in. wide.
(Bonhams) **£900**

A Dutch walnut and marquetry serpentine lowboy, decorated with birds amongst scrolling foliage, on husk carved cabriole legs and claw-and-ball feet, mid 18th century, 33in. wide.
(Christie's) **£3,080**

A fine Queen Anne walnut lowboy, New York, 1730–60, the incised cyma-shaped skirt continuing to faceted cabriole legs, width 36¼in.
(Sotheby's) **£12,105**

A walnut lowboy with moulded rectangular top above three drawers and shaped apron on cabriole legs, 29in. wide. (Christie's) £1,100

An oak lowboy, the rectangular top with re-entrant corners, on cabriole legs and pad feet, mid 18th century, 29in. wide. (Christie's) £550

A George II padouk lowboy with moulded rectangular top above a drawer and shaped apron on cabriole legs, 28½in. wide. (Christie's) £1,980

A George II mahogany side table with moulded rounded rectangular top above three drawers and waved apron, on cabriole legs headed by acanthus, 29in. wide. (Christie's) £5,720

An 18th century Dutch walnut, mahogany and marquetry lowboy, the shaped top with projecting corners inlaid with a bird perched upon an urn of flowers, 2ft. 8in. wide. (Phillips) £3,000

An early 18th century oak lowboy, the rectangular top with deep crossbanding, re-entrant corners, with short drawer flanked by two deep short drawers, 2ft. 8in. wide. (Spencer's) £1,100

A George III mahogany lowboy, the rectangular top with deep crossbanding, thumb moulded edge, a long drawer to the frieze, 2ft. 8in. wide. (Spencer's) £750

An early Georgian oak low boy with mahogany crossbandings, with one frieze drawer above two short drawers, 33in. high. (Lawrence Fine Art) £1,540

A walnut lowboy inlaid with feather banding, the rounded rectangular top above three drawers, on club legs and pad feet, mid-18th century. (Christie's) £1,430

A George II oak lowboy, the bevelled rectangular top above three short drawers and a shaped apron, 32¼in. wide. (Bonhams) £2,800

A burr walnut lowboy, featherbanded in ash with quarter veneered moulded top, 33½in. wide, basically late 17th century. £2,000

18th century oak three drawer lowboy, each drawer with crossbanded detail, standing on four tapering legs, 2ft. 6in. wide. (G. A. Key) £280

A George II mahogany lowboy, the rectangular top with thumb moulded edge, a long drawer to the frieze over a shaped scroll apron set with two further small drawers, 2ft. 6in. wide. (Spencer's) £2,000

A walnut lowboy with quarter veneered moulded rectangular top and three drawers on cabriole legs with pad feet, 30in. wide. (Christie's London) £1,100

A Chippendale walnut lowboy, Pennsylvania, circa 1765, the rectangular moulded top with notched front corners above four moulded drawers, width 36¾in. (Sotheby's) £8,322

A George II 'red walnut' and mahogany lowboy, containing three drawers in the arched apron, on cabriole legs with pad feet, 2ft. 6in. wide. (Phillips) £4,400

A walnut lowboy, the quarter-veneered crossbanded rect-angular top above a frieze drawer, on square-section cabriole legs, 29½in. wide. (Christie's) £2,420

An early Georgian walnut and oak side table, with two drawers flanking a kneehole drawer, on cabriole legs and pad feet, 32in. wide. (Christie's) £5,500

A Queen Anne maple dress-
ing table on four cabriole
legs ending in pad feet, circa
1760, 33in. wide.   £7,750

An early Georgian walnut
side table with arched and
waved frieze, 29in. wide.
£5,750

A mid Georgian mahogany
side table on cabriole legs
and pad feet, 29¼in. wide.
(Christie's)   £825

An attractive early George III
mahogany low boy, the top with
moulded edge and re-entrant
corners above an arrangement
of three drawers with brass
handles, 31½in. wide.
(Tennants)   £900

A very fine Chippendale carved
mahogany lowboy, Philadelphia,
circa 1770, the shaped skirt
continuing to shell-carved
cabriole legs ending in claw-and-
ball feet, 36⅞in. wide.
(Sotheby's)   £62,857

An early 18th century green
japanned and chinoiserie
decorated lowboy, the top with
a moulded edge painted with
pagoda landscapes, 2ft. 5in.
wide.
(Phillips)   £4,400

A Queen Anne japanned, carved
walnut and pine lowboy,
Massachusetts, circa 1765, the
japanning first quarter 19th
century, 34in. wide.
(Sotheby's)   £3,639

A good lacquered lowboy, the
bevelled rectangular top
decorated with figures and
pavilions in a watery landscape,
47in. wide.
(Bonhams)   £1,100

A Chippendale carved
mahogany lowboy, signed
Wallace Nutting, early 20th
century, in the Philadelphia
manner, width 36½in.
(Sotheby's)   £2,081

A Queen Anne walnut dressing table on tapering cylindrical legs with disc feet,
33in. wide, 1735-50. £7,350

A George II mahogany
rectangular lowboy, the
drawers with wooden handles,
32in. wide.   £3,350

An 18th century Scottish
red walnut lowboy with
carved and scrolled kneehole,
33½in. wide.   £2,600

An 18th century oak low-
boy, the rectangular top
with moulded edge and re-
entrant corners, on cabriole
supports with pad feet, 2ft.
6½in. wide.
(Greenslades)   £2,640

A Queen Anne burr walnut and
fruitwood lowboy, the
rectangular quarter veneered
top with cusped corners above a
long drawer and two short
drawers flanking a false drawer
in the shaped apron, 2ft. 6in.
wide.
(Phillips)   £3,200

A George I walnut lowboy,
the quartered top crossbanded in ash, with three drawers,
brass handles, shaped apron
on cabriole legs, 29in x 18in.
(Dreweatt Neate)   £3,800

A late George I oak lowboy, the
crossbanded top above one
shallow and two deeper drawers,
on square section cabriole legs,
25½in. wide.
(Bonhams)   £480

A George I walnut lowboy, the
moulded rectangular top above
three drawers around the shaped
apron, on cabriole legs and pad
feet, 29½in. wide.
(Bonhams)   £1,400

A Georgian oak lowboy, with
moulded rectangular top above
two deep drawers flanking a
kneehole drawer, on cabriole
legs and pad feet, 30in. wide.
(Christie's)   £1,430

A George I style burr walnut lowboy, with featherbanded inlay, on cabriole legs with pad feet, 31in.
(Christie's) £550

A good George II 'red walnut' lowboy, the rectangular moulded top with re-entrant corners, on cabriole legs with pad feet, 2ft. 6in. wide.
(Phillips) £6,200

A walnut lowboy with tw short and one long drawe on cabriole legs and pad feet, 28½in. wide.
(Christie's) £1,8

A walnut and feather-banded lowboy with rounded rectangular moulded top above two graduated drawers on cabriole legs with pointed pad feet, early 18th century, 30½in. wide. (Christie's S. Ken) £1,320

An 18th century oak lowboy fitted with three drawers with shaped apron, on four square chamfered legs with reeded edges, 2ft. 7in. wide.
(Russell Baldwin & Bright) £880

A late 18th century Dutch walnut, crossbanded featherstrung and marquetry lowboy in the William and Ma style, on polygonal tapered leg united by fret scroll stretchers 2ft. 11in. top.
(Phillips) £3,5

A walnut lowboy, the canted rectangular top above four frieze drawers, part 18th century, 31in. wide. (Christie's S. Ken) £1,430

A mahogany lowboy, on cabriole legs with claw and ball feet, 32in. wide, basically 18th century. (Christie's) £1,595

An early Georgian oak side table, the frieze with three drawers on lappeted club l and pad feet, 34in. wide.
£1,60

Pedestals, in the Greek and Roman manner, returned to favour with the Classical Revival of the early 18th century, when they were placed in many of the Palladian mansions of the day to support busts, bronzes, candelabra and the large oriental or delft vases which were all the rage at the time.

Designs varied throughout the 18th century but were usually of tapered form with much elaborate decoration. Ormolu and marble were commonly used materials, and they are very expensive today.

The Victorians, too, produced pedestals but these are mainly squat and unattractive, the possible exceptions being those in the eastern style, whether of bamboo, intricately carved hardwood, or in the Moorish taste.

The Edwardians once again favoured a more elongated style, the examples being somewhat spindly in appearance, and these can still be obtained quite reasonably.

Pair of Napoleon III gilt-metal-mounted kingwood and satinwood pedestals, third quarter 19th century, 47½in. (Butterfield & Butterfield) £2,521

A rectangular black marble and boulle work pedestal, the marble top supported by a tapering shaft, 19th century, 48³/8in. high. (Christie's) £990

One of a pair of massive William IV figured and pollard oak dining room pedestals, each of waisted square form, with boldly carved borders and scroll feet, 31in. wide.
(Tennants) (Two) £4,800

A pair of gilt-metal and pink-onyx-mounted Sèvres-pattern pedestals in the form of Corinthian columns, the dark-blue grounds painted by B. Guérin in a pale palette with lovers in pastoral landscapes, late 19th century, 43¼in. high. (Christie's) £10,450

A gothic painted wood pedestal, probably designed by the office of William Burges, the square overhanging moulded entablature supported on a column with cushion capital, 79cm. high.
(Christie's) £2,200

A pair of ormolu mounted satinwood and marquetry pedestals of Louis XV style with serpentine mottled pink marble tops, 42½in. high. (Christie's) £3,960

A Gramophone & Typewriter Ltd 'Melba' gramophone pedestal, ebonised with gilt incised Art Nouveau floriate decoration, 39in. high, circa 1905.
(Christie's S. Ken) £1,540

An Aesthetic Movement brass pedestal, the square top with shallow well, supported on triangular brackets and four tubular columns, 82cm. high. (Christie's) £660

A pair of early 20th century cutlery urns on pedestals, in the manner of Robert Adam, the urns carved in high relief with ram masks and husk pendants, 65in. high. (Tennants) £2,700

A Louis-Philippe red and green-painted and gilt-gesso pedestal table of Gothic style with later leather-lined quatrefoil top, 23in. diameter. (Christie's) £7,150

One of a pair of classical Revival carved and gilt pedestals with marble tops, circa 1835, 36½in. high. £4,250

A pair of George III mahogany pedestals, the moulded tops above fluted friezes, some repairs, each 25¼in. wide. (Lawrence Fine Arts) £3,630

A late Victorian ormolu mounted rosewood and mahogany pedestal with a square brown and grey marble top, 45¾in. high. (Christie's) £1,100

A mid-Victorian giltmetal-mounted ebonised pedestal with circular moulded top above a frieze of acanthus scrolls and paterae, 15¼in. diameter. (Christie's) £660

A pair of 19th century French ebony and pietra dura pedestals, inset with black marble panel tops, 4ft. high. (Phillips) £3,000

An Italian walnut pedestal with shaped rectangular top on a bombe support, 50¼in. high. (Christie's) £1,210

POT CUPBOARDS

Pot cupboards are exactly what they say they are, bedside cupboards for holding a chamber pot. It was thus that they were known in the 18th century, before the prissier Victorians coined the more decorous term, 'night table'. There is usually a solid or tambour door to the front and sometimes a sliding cabinet below with a close stool. The top is sometimes of marble with a galleried top. By and large, however, they are smaller and plainer than their relative, the commode.

Pair of George III mahogany bedside tables, late 18th century, with ebonised stringing, serpentine apron, tapering legs, 20in. high.
(Skinner Inc.) £2,160

An early 19th century flame mahogany pot cupboard with a figured marble top. £200

A Renaissance Revival walnut demi-commode, 20in. wide. £650

A pair of Italian walnut and parquetry bedside commodes, the doors, back and sides with rectangular panels of parquetry squares, 2ft. 3in. high.
(Phillips) £4,200

Victorian walnut pot cupboard, circa 1860. £100

One of a pair of English painted satinwood bedside tables, 20th century, in the Georgian manner, 41cm. wide.
(Sotheby's) (Two) £2,990

A pair of Holland and Sons oak bedside cabinets, the chamfered rectangular top above cupboard doors, on chamfered and turned legs with gothic arch aprons, 93.6cm. high.
(Christie's) £880

A mahogany bowfronted bedside cupboard with three-quarter galleried top, stamped Gillows, Lancaster, 15¾in. wide. (Christie's) £880

One of a pair of painted bedside tables with con-cave-fronted rectangular tops, 22¼in. wide. (Christie's) £4,400

A pair of late Regency mahogany bedside tables, each with a folded rectangular twin flap top, stamped *Gillows Lancaster*, 32in. wide open. (Christie's) £4,180

An early George III mahogan bedside cupboard with pierce galleried top, and chamfered square legs. 16in. wide. (Christie's London) £99

An Empire mahogany table de chevet, the square grey marble top above a drawer, a hinged fall front door and a further cupboard under, 1ft. 1in. square. (Phillips) £650

A matched pair of mahogany bedside cabinets inlaid with ebonised and fruitwood lines, each with square top on square tapering legs joined by an X-framed stretcher, 14in. square. (Christie's) £1,760

One of a pair of tulipwood, walnut and marquetry brass-mounted tables de nuit of Transitional style, crossband overall with green-stained beechwood, each with key-pattern gallery, 19th centur 22in. wide (Christie's) £30,8

A Louis XVI mahogany and brass mounted oval pot cup-board with marble top and dummy drawer door, 1ft6½in. high. (Phillips) £1,500

Pair of Venetian rococo painted bedside cabinets, mid 18th century, 18½in. wide. (Skinner) £5,657

A Biedermeier mahogany pedestal cabinet, the swivell door enclosing three shelves 25½in. wide. £9

A George III mahogany bedside cupboard attributed to Thomas Chippendale, on tapering legs headed by roundel bosses, 29in. high.
(Christie's) £33,000

A pair of 19th century walnut veneered Lombard bedside tables, with coloured fruitwood inlay of female heads within ornate palm leaf borders, 88cm. wide.
(Finarte) £2,525

A late George III mahogany bedside cupboard, the rect-angular tray-top with carrying handles, on square tapering legs. (Christie's) £715

One of a pair of Continental bedside cupboards, probably French, third quarter 20th century, in Louis XV manner, 38cm. deep.
(Sotheby's) (Two) £2,990

A pair of George III mahogany pot cupboards, the tray tops with pierced handles fitted with sliding cupboard doors, on moulded square legs, 2ft. 2in. wide.
(Phillips) £6,800

A North Italian walnut and marquetry bedside cupboard, on associated square channelled legs with block feet, parts late 18th century, 16in. wide.
(Christie's) £2,090

Table de nuit, Continental, brass inlaid with a drawer, cupboard and marble top, 1ft.8in. wide. £550

A pair of mid Victorian mahogany bedside cupboards with slightly raised backs, moulded tops and with opposed panel doors, 15½in. wide.
(Tennants) £750

A Biedermeier mahogany pedestal cupboard with D-shaped top and frieze drawer above a cupboard door and base drawer, 23½in. wide. £900

Screens have been in widespread use since at least the fifteenth century, for warding off draughts, for protecting sensitive complexions from the fire's heat or for privacy.

Not surprisingly, perhaps, the quality of screens manufacture has varied but little from those early days, and the materials used are still very much the same too; from simple buckram, wickerwork, wood and needlework to extravagant finishes for royalty, including gold lace and silk. During the reign of Charles II, some fine examples, having up to twelve folds, and decorated with superb lacquer work, were imported from the East. Today, of course, one of these would cost many thousands of pounds.

By the William and Mary period, small screens fitted with sliding panels of polished wood or embroidery had become popular and these developed into the cheval screens of the 18th century. Small pole screens also put in an appearance at this time, though these became more numerous as the eighteenth century gave way to the nineteenth.

Chinese four panel screen, 19th century, with scenes in relief carved in small pieces of multi-coloured soapstone, agate and quartz, 69in. high. (Skinner Inc.) £1,783

A four-fold transfer printed screen, designed by Piero Fornasetti, one side polychrome decorated with birds in an ornate aviary, 136.6cm. high. (Christie's) £6,600

Charles X three panel paper screen, c. 1830, grisaille decorated with arched crests painted with a laurel leaf frame surrounding an Italian landscape scene, 67in. high. (Skinner Inc) £1,363

A four-fold screen, designed by Piero Fornasetti, one side depicting a collector's bookshelves, the other showing guitars, each panel 130cm. high x 35cm. wide. (Christie's) £3,30

A six leaf coromandel lacquer screen, the top with a wide border of Buddhist emblems, Chinese, circa 1700, 7ft. high. (Schrager Auction Galleries) £2,500

'The Four Seasons', a four panel screen, circa 1900, incised and polychrome stained wood, the reverse decorated with stylised flowers, 5ft. 11in. high. (Sotheby's) £1,760

An Art Nouveau carved three leaf screen, the rectangular panels with bud finials, fluted borders and tapering legs, 135cm. wide. (Christie's London) £46

A four fold screen representing the Four Seasons, carved and pierced with birds among flowering plants, 63in. high. (Lawrence Fine Arts)   £418

An 18th century style mahogany framed firescreen, the arched rectangular panel set with a gros point chair seat cover, 40½in. high. (Bearne's)   £240

A Dutch painted leather four-leaf screen decorated overall with exotic birds perched amidst branches, in a nailed border, 19th century, each leaf 84 x 24in. (Christie's)   £2,530

A Dutch leather four-leaf screen painted with exotic birds, shrubs and vases of flowers and fruit on a gilt ground, the leather 18th century, each leaf 20 x 74¾in. (Christie's)   £1,650

A pair of early Victorian black lacquered papier mache pole screens, with decoratively pierced borders and finely painted with differing designs of exotic birds, flowers and scrolls. (Geering & Colyer)   £1,050

A Chinese coromandel lacquer six-leaf screen, decorated overall with cranes, mandarins, ducks and other birds, late 18th/early 19th century, each leaf 67¼ x 16in. (Christie's)   £1,840

A Dutch gilt-leather decorated six-leaf screen, each leaf painted in the manner of Nicolas Lancret with courting couples, late 18th/early 19th century, each leaf 96½ x 21¾in. (Christie's)   £4,620

A French giltwood cheval firescreen inset with a cartouche-shaped Aubusson tapestry panel of a girl with a dog in a farmyard, the frame 19th century, 29in. wide. (Christie's)   £1,430

A Dutch embossed leather four leaf screen, decorated in gilt with strapwork scrolls, on a green, red and grey ground, the leather 17th century, each leaf 85 x 23½in. (Christie's)   £1,320

217

A Dutch six-leaf painted leather screen decorated with a musician seated before a pagoda, 18th century, each leaf:
22in. x 96¹/₂in.
(Christie's)   £3,520

A painted leather six-leaf screen, painted by a follower of Pierre Mignard with the Muses of Music, Geometry, Painting, Astronomy, Horology and Poetry, late 17th century, each leaf 21¹/₄in. x 77¹/₂in.
(Christie's)   £10,450

An Italian pale-green painted and parcel-gilt three-leaf screen, the arched panelled side leaves carved on one side with putto heads headed by a coronet and on the other painted with kneeling angels, assembled in the 19th century, 82in. x 37in.
(Christie's)   £2,420

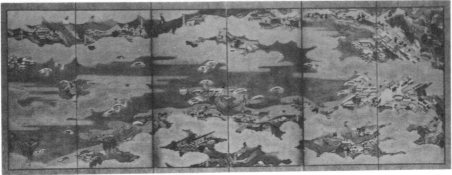

A well painted six-leaf screen, depicting a panoramic view of shrines, castles, temples and village houses around Lake Biwa, in sumi, gofun and colour on a gold paper background, early 18th century, each leaf approx. 107 x 46cm.
(Christie's)   £11,000

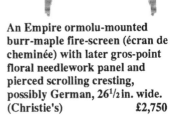

'The Salutation of the Dawn', a painted and gilded screen, by Jessie Bayes, designed in the manner of a medieval manuscript, 54cm. x 68cm.
(Phillips)   £1,200

A Louis XVI giltwood fire-screen (écran de cheminée) by Jean-Baptiste-Claude Sené with adjustable screen with a Beauvais tapestry panel, and another en suite of later date with a Louis XVI Beauvais tapestry panel en suite, 30³/₄in. wide.
(Christie's)   £14,850

An Empire ormolu-mounted burr-maple fire-screen (écran de cheminée) with later gros-point floral needlework panel and pierced scrolling cresting, possibly German, 26¹/₂in. wide.
(Christie's)   £2,750

218

SCREENS

A Chinese polychrome-painted four-leaf screen painted with a woman holding swords and posing for an artist at a table, 19th century, each leaf: 25in. wide; 74in. high.
(Christie's) £4,180

A Louis XV style giltwood firescreen, late 19th century, with cartouche-shaped tapestry panel with silver thread ground depicting a peacock, 41³/₄in. high.
(Christie's East) £816

A Chinese black, silver and gilt-lacquer eight-leaf screen decorated on both sides with butterflies amidst bamboo plants, 19th century, each leaf: 83in. x 21³/₄in.
(Christie's) £5,280

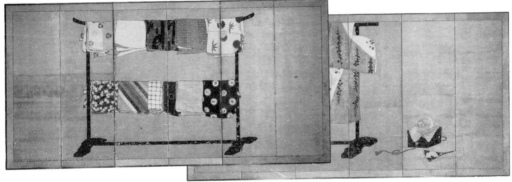

A superb pair of six-leaf screens, painted in sumi, colour and gofun on gold painted silk, with Ta ga sode 'Whose sleeves?' motif, one with folded robes on a rack and the other with three robes hung on a rack, unsigned, each leaf 174.3 x approx. 60cm.
(Christie's) £50,600

A Chinese polychrome painted six-leaf coromandel screen painted with figures and buildings by the sea and boats in a mountain landscape on a hardwood ground, 19th century, each leaf: 14¹/₄in. x 68¹/₂in.
(Christie's) £2,200

'Song, Drama, Poetry and Music', an English four-leaf embroidered screen, each panel in mahogany frame, embroidered in greens, reds, blues, pinks and yellows against a green ground, 192.9cm. high.
(Christie's) £1,540

A Dutch painted leather six-leaf screen painted in imitation of coromandel lacquer with a palace courtyard with courtiers and other figures, distressed, 18th century, each leaf: 21¹/₄in. x 90in.
(Christie's) £3,520

An eight-fold gold-ground coromandel screen decorated in polychrome, each fold 7ft. high, 1ft.4in. wide. £1,450

An Arts & Crafts oak fire-screen, the framework enclosing a panel of Morris & Co. fabric woven with 'The Tulip and Rose', 55.5cm. high.
£275

English six-panel paper floor screen, 19th century, decorated with maps, each panel 81½in. high.
(Skinner)   £1,199

A four-leaf screen covered in Brussels verdure tapestry, the tapestry 17th century, each leaf 84½ x 25½in.
(Christie's)   £6,600

A walnut firescreen of Régence style, with rectangular gros-point needlework panel, in a moulded frame carved with scrolls and foliage on scroll feet, 29in. wide.
(Christie's)   £550

Late 19th century ivory mounted two-leaf lacquer table screen decorated in Shibayama style, signed Masayuki, each panel 30 x 16.5cm.   £2,000

An 18th century Dutch painted and gilded leather six-leaf screen, each leaf 108in. high, 21in. wide.   £5,200

A George II mahogany and needlework cheval fire-screen with a petit point needlework scene depicting The Rape of Proserpine in a chariot, 32in. wide.
(Christie's)   £60,500

An Indian hardwood three-leaf screen, each leaf 76 x 32in.
£700

A six-leaf Japanese screen, sumi and colour on gold paper, signed, 26 x 80in. each leaf. £3,000

An early George III walnut polescreen, the adjustable panel with gros and petit-point needlework, 51in. high. (Christie's) £2,090

A decorative chinoiserie four-fold screen, painted with oriental landscape, figures amongst pavilions, 75$^{1}/_{2}$in. x 24$^{1}/_{2}$in. (Bonhams) £750

A Chinese amboyna wood screen, each panel mounted with porcelain plaques depicting figures, animals, foliage, flowers and insects, 74$^{1}/_{4}$in. high. (Bearne's) £1,600

An early Victorian walnut firescreen, the central glazed section with a display of exotic stuffed birds, 46in. high. (Bearne's) £550

Louis XVI style giltwood four-panel floor screen, panels painted with neoclassical motifs, 68$^{1}/_{2}$in. high. (Skinner Inc.) £927

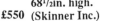

A four-leaf screen decorated with 18th century Chinese wallpaper, each leaf 86 x 21$^{1}/_{2}$in. £5,000

Early 19th century rosewood fire screen with rising centre panel of a woolwork floral tapestry, 21in. wide. (G. A. Key) £210

A painted Japanese two-part folding screen, gouache and silver leaf, circa 1860, 55 x 49$^{1}/_{2}$in. £3,150

Charles X paper four-panel floorscreen, second quarter 19th century, grisaille decoration, 84in. high.
(Skinner Inc.) £713

An 18th century tapestry panel, depicting a vase with flowers and fruit, with two parakeets, within a mahogany stand, 3ft. 9in. tall. (Phillips) £500

An early 18th century japanned five fold screen decorated with chinoiserie figures, each panel 9ft. x 1ft.10in. (Phillips) £4,000

An ebonised and marquetry four-leaf screen inlaid in satinwood, beechwood, walnut and stained fruitwood, 190cm. high, 141cm. wide. £2,000

A Napoleon III gilt three fold screen, the crests carved with cornucopiae and a basket of flowers, 145cm. wide. (Bonhams) £520

Two screens by Sue Golden, undulating moulded plywood, the larger black lacquered, the other gilded and patinated, 180cm. high. (Christie's) £2,200

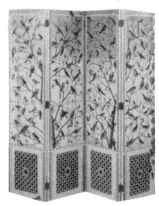

A four-fold screen, designed by Piero Fornasetti, one side depicting brightly coloured birds, the other showing guitars, each panel 200cm. high x 50cm. wide. (Christie's) £3,960

A giltwood three-leaf screen with arched panels applied with silk and painted with paeonies and foliage, each leaf 59 x 22½in. £3,800

A Japanese Export lacquer and Shibayama inlaid two-fold screen, decorated in bone, mother-of-pearl, ivory and hardwood, each fold 2ft.5½in. wide, 5ft.7in. high. £800

SECRETAIRE BOOKCASES

Not unnaturally, secrétaire bookcases were developed at about the same time as bureau bookcases and were dictated by the same fashionable taste.

A useful, though not absolutely reliable guide to dating a piece is to look closely at the interior fitting of the secretaire drawer; generally speaking, the better the quality the earlier the date. It is often disappointing to find that, among the late 19th century reproductions of earlier furniture, the rule was, 'what the eye doesn't see, the heart doesn't grieve over' – finely finished exterior surfaces concealing a considerable amount of scrimping on the small drawers and pigeon holes in the fitted compartments of secrétaires and bureaus.

Attention should also be centred on the oak lined drawers as a guide to date of manufacture, for it was in about 1770 that a constructional change occurred.

Until this time, the drawer bottoms were made with the grain of the wood running front to back but, from this time onward, the grain will be found to run from side to side, the bottom often being made of two separate pieces of wood supported by a central bearer.

It still has the basic shape of an 18th century piece but the classical pediment with its scroll ends is typical of the Regency period as is the delicate carving on the curved pilasters.

Pieces of this kind are made of mahogany or rosewood, the latter being the most expensive, and they always present an attractive and well finished appearance.

A George III 'plum pudding' mahogany secrétaire breakfront library bookcase, the key-pattern cornice with fret-carved swan-neck pediment, 81in. wide. (Bearne's) £6,800

A George III mahogany secrétaire bookcase, the base with a secrétaire drawer enclosing an interior of nine drawers and pigeonholes around a central cupboard, on later splayed bracket feet, 4ft. 2in. wide. (Phillips) £2,700

A Federal inlaid mahogany and eglomise gentleman's desk-and-bookcase, Salem, Massachusetts, 1790–1810, in two sections, on cylindrical tapering legs, 61¼in. wide. (Christie's) £3,415

Late George III satinwood bureau bookcase, first quarter 19th century, upper case with a pair of glazed doors, on bracket feet, (restorations), 66in. high. (Skinner Inc) £2,922

A fine Louis XVI style ormolu-mounted amboyna and mahogany secretaire, twice stamped *Henri Dasson*, with an eared rectangular ochre and violet marble top, bearing the date 1881, 34in. wide. (Christie's East) £4,664

A satinwood secretaire bookcase with a moulded cornice above a pair of astragal glazed doors, the hinged fall-flap enclosing a fitted interior, part 18th century, 34in. wide. (Christie's S. Ken) £1,650

SECRETAIRE BOOKCASES

A Regency mahogany secretaire bookcase, the base with fall-front fitted writing drawer, 47½in. wide. £5,850

A mahogany secretaire bookcase with four glazed doors enclosing adjustable shelves, 55in. wide. £2,150

A George III mahogany secretaire cabinet, the secretaire drawer with fruit-wood and maple veneers, 43½in. wide. £3,900

A Georgian mahogany secretaire bookcase with a dentil frieze above two thirteen pane glazed doors, on bracket feet, 112cm. wide. (Lawrence Fine Arts) £3,520

A William IV mahogany breakfront secretaire bookcase, the later moulded cornice applied with foliate motif above open shelves, 112in. wide. (Christie's S. Ken) £4,620

George III mahogany bureau/bookcase, the base with serpentine top over fret and floral carved fold-down writing surface, 46in. wide. (Skinner Inc.) £5,480

A George III mahogany breakfront secretaire bookcase, the central fitted writing drawer above a pair of panelled doors flanked by two other doors, 68in. wide. (Christie's S. Ken) £6,050

A mid Victorian mahogany bowfront secretaire bookcase, the breakfront lower section with fall front secretaire drawer enclosing a fitted leather-lined interior, 57¼in. wide. (Christie's) £4,400

A Queen Anne walnut secretaire cabinet, with moulded rectangular top above two mirrored doors each with later bevelled plate, on later bun feet, 44in. wide. (Christie's) £14,300

A late 18th century mahogany secretaire bookcase on swept bracket feet, 118cm. wide. (Wellington Salerooms)
£3,600

A George III satinwood and rosewood secretaire cabinet, the baize-lined fall-flap enclosing a fitted interior, 36in. wide. £11,750

A George III satinwood secretaire bookcase with circular enamelled ring handles, 30¾in. wide. £50,000

A Regency mahogany and crossbanded secrétaire bookcase, the secrétaire drawer fitted with a satinwood interior, on splayed feet, 40½in. wide. (Bonhams) £4,500

A George I cream lacquer secretaire cabinet with bow-shaped moulded cornice, 43¾in. wide, 86½in. high. (Christie's) £264,000

An early 19th century mahogany secrétaire bookcase inlaid with ebony and parquetry lines, on reduced slender bracket feet, 46¼in. wide. (Bearne's) £2,800

A Regency mahogany secretaire bookcase, with secretaire drawer enclosing a part satinwood-lined interior with eight mahogany-lined drawers and pigeon-holes, 36½in. wide. (Christie's) £5,500

A George III mahogany secretaire-cabinet attributed to Thomas Chippendale, the breakfront upper part with arched centre and moulded cornice, 45½in. wide. (Christie's) £53,900

A Regency Egyptian-Revival mahogany secretaire-bookcase, the upper part with a pair of glazed doors below a pediment with ebony-inlaid acroteria, 42in. wide. (Tennants) £1,600

Federal tiger maple desk/
bookcase, New England, circa
1820, 39¹/₂in. wide.
(Skinner)   £2,444

An English 19th century
Chippendale style maho-
gany secretaire cabinet,
86in. long.   £16,750

A Federal mahogany inlaid
desk/bookcase, probably
Mass., circa 1800, 37½in.
wide.   £3,100

A George III mahogany
secrétaire bookcase, the moulded
dentil cornice with broken
pediment centred by a patera,
the lower section with fitted
secrétaire drawer, on ogee
bracket feet, 49½in. wide.
(Christie's)   £2,970

**A Regency mahogany secretaire
bookcase with moulded cornice
above open shelves flanked by
spiral-reeded uprights, 69in.
wide. (Christie's S. Ken)   £1,650**

**A Biedermeier cherrywood and
ebonised bureau bookcase, the
moulded rectangular cornice
with two obelisk-shaped finials,
above two trellis-filled doors, on
square tapering legs, first half,
19th century, 47¹/₂in. wide.
(Christie's)   £10,450**

**A George III satinwood
secrétaire bookcase banded
overall with rosewood and inlaid
with boxwood, 37in. wide.
(Christie's)   £12,100**

A Georgian carved mahogany
secretaire breakfront library
bookcase in the Chippendale
taste, 2.20m. wide.   £9,600

A Federal mahogany secre-
tary with glazed panel doors
above a fold-down writing
surface, circa 1795, 40in.
wide.   £6,350

The name escritoire (or, scritoire as it was originally) was applied to the piece of furniture produced towards the end of the 17th century in answer to the demand for a cabinet with a falling front; prior to this time, all larger pieces had been equipped with double doors.

Although this design has been used ever since with only minor variations, it has never achieved the overwhelming popularity attained by some of the other writing cabinets and desks. The upper level, revealed by dropping the front, contains a multitude of drawers with pigeon holes above.

A secrétaire chest is, basically, a chest of drawers whose deep fitted top drawer has a fall front which pulls forward to allow a sizeable writing area with room below for the knees.

Having been made from the last quarter of the 18th century until the present day, they are to be found in an extremely wide range of styles, qualities and prices.

When buying such a chest it is wise to bear in mind the similarity between it and a chest of drawers – you might well be buying an old chest of drawers which has undergone a modern conversion.

Look carefully at the sides of the secrétaire and the depth of the top drawer; the sides need to be thicker and stronger for a secrétaire than an ordinary drawer, therefore a conversion will show if the sides appear to be of newer wood than those of the other drawers. The depth of the top drawer should be the largest in the chest and marks will show on the side of the carcass if the supports have been altered to achieve this.

A Beidermeier walnut secrétaire chest, with rectangular moulded top and fall front drawer below with galleried sides, central European, 52in. wide.
(Christie's) £990

An early 18th century walnut-veneered secrétaire by John Coxed, with feather banding throughout, on bracket feet, 43$\frac{1}{2}$in. wide.
(Bearne's) £10,000

A George III mahogany secrétaire chest with rectangular moulded top above hinged fall faced as two drawers enclosing fitted interior, 41$\frac{1}{2}$in. wide.
(Christie's) £935

Spanish walnut vargueno, mid 17th century, with gilt metal mounts and elaborately fitted compartment fitted with various drawers, 41$\frac{1}{2}$in. wide.
(Skinner Inc.) £4,384

A late 18th century Dutch marquetry and satinwood secretaire **à abattant**, the fall-front enclosing plain interior, 106 x 157cm.
(Phillips) £2,100

A Dutch mahogany and marquetry secrétaire à abattant, with overall floral, urn and ribbon-tied drapery decoration, 38in. wide.
(Christie's) £1,320

A 16th century Spanish vargueno, the interior has seventeen ivory and gilt moulded drawers, 38in. long. £2,250

A 19th century faded teak secretaire military chest, the top drawer fitted inside with tooled leather to the fall front, 3ft. wide. (Wooley & Wallis) £1,900

Late 18th/early 19th century gilt metal mounted mahogany secretaire à abattant, 37½in. wide. £2,150

A George III satinwood and marquetry secrétaire crossbanded in tulipwood and amaranth, the rectangular top above a fall-front inlaid with swagged drapery and a medallion of a musician, 35¼in. wide. (Christie's) £4,950

A Marsh & Jones satinwood and marquetry bureau cabinet, the design attributed to Charles Bevan, the superstructure with galleried shelves above elaborated brackets, 174cm. wide. (Christie's London) £13,200

A French Empire mahogany secrétaire à abattant with later moulded top above an overhanging frieze drawer, the baize-lined fall-flap enclosing an architectural mirror back interior, 35½in. wide. (Christie's) £993

An early Georgian walnut secretaire, the convex frieze drawer and fall-flap inlaid with chevron lines, 43½in. wide. £2,900

A George III mahogany secretaire chest, the writing drawer enclosing a fitted interior, circa 1770, 2ft. 10in. wide. £1,200

A Louis XVI tulipwood and chequer inlaid secretaire à abattant with later gilt metal ornament, 97cm. wide. £1,750

A Queen Anne walnut secretaire with a moulded cornice
above a cushion frieze drawer,
40½in. wide. £4,400

A French Empire mahogany
secrétaire à abattant, applied
with gilt bronze foliate motifs
and figures, 31½in. wide.
(Bearne's) £1,850

A George III mahogany
secretaire press with Gothic
cornice and fitted trays to
upper section, 48in. wide.
£3,200

A Queen Anne walnut escritoire
of small size, inlaid with
boxwood and ebony lines, the
fall front enclosing twelve
various small drawers and
pigeonholes around a central
cabinet, 3ft. wide.
(Phillips) £3,000

A Regency mahogany secrétaire
in the manner of Gillows of
Lancaster, with three-quarter
galleried inverted-breakfront
superstructure supported by
twin foliate-scrolled and
anthemion-carved volutes,
44¼in. wide.
(Christie's) £3,960

A George III satinwood
secrétaire-chest, inlaid overall
with ebonised lines, with
moulded rounded rectangular
top above a fitted secrétaire
drawer with marquetry paterae
to the corners, 28½in. wide.
(Christie's) £1,870

A George III satinwood
secretaire, with fitted secretaire drawer above two long
and one deep drawer, 32½in.
wide. £7,150

An ormolu mounted, par-
quetry and marquetry
secretaire à abattant, of
Louis XVI style, on toupie
feet, 30in. wide. £2,200

A George III satinwood, mahogany, marquetry and painted
secretaire cabinet, on turned
tapering legs, 28½in. wide.
(Christie's) £12,100

A late George III mahogany and partridgewood secretaire, 30½in. wide. £1,850

A pale mahogany campaign chest with central secretaire drawer. £1,350

A Regency rosewood secretaire cabinet, the baize-lined drawer with fitted interior, 23in. wide. £12,500

Empire mahogany and ormolu secrétaire à abattant, first-quarter 19th century, mottled grey rectangular marble top, (with later mounts, damaged), 54½in. high.
(Skinner Inc) £974

Biedermeier mahogany and part ebonised fall-front secretary, probably German, second quarter 19th century, on shallow block feet, 46in. wide.
(Butterfield & Butterfield) £1,766

A Louis XVI walnut secrétaire à abattant, the fall front concealing six small drawers and pigeonholes, with black veined marble top.
(Galerie Moderne) £2,863

A German mahogany secretaire with eared rectangular top above frieze drawer and hinged fall enclosing fitted interior with baize-lined slide, mid 19th century, 39½in. wide.
(Christie's) £1,595

A George III mahogany secrétaire chest, the moulded rectangular top above a secrétaire drawer enclosing boxwood strung drawers and pigeonholes.
(Bonhams) £680

A Dutch kingwood and marquetry inlaid pedestal secretaire chest, the pierced three quarter galleried top above a writing drawer, 20in. wide. (Christie's S. Ken) £1,375

A Biedermeier satin-birch secrétaire, with stepped moulded cornice above frieze drawer and hinged fall enclosing fitted interior, mid 19th century, 39¹/₂in. wide.
(Christie's) £2,640

A Victorian mahogany secretaire campaign chest, the central drawer fitted with four bird's-eye maple-veneered drawers and pull-out writing slide, 39in. wide.
(Bearne's) £1,300

A Queen Anne walnut burr veneered, crossbanded and featherstrung secrétaire cabinet, the upper part with fitted interior, on bracket feet, 3ft. 8in. wide.
(Phillips) £4,800

An early 19th century Austrian flame mahogany secrétaire à abattant, the upper part with arched moulded pediment above a central drawer, on block feet, 111cm. wide.
(Finarte) £5,050

A late George III mahogany secretaire chest, the upper fall front drawer with applied moulding and concealing an arrangement of drawers and pigeon holes, 45in. wide.
(Tennants) £1,100

A cream lacquered and painted secrétaire à abattant, painted with ornate floral borders and scenes galantes, on cabriole legs, Piedmont, second half 18th century, 123.5cm. wide.
(Finarte) £18,365

A Queen Anne walnut-veneered secretaire with moulded cornice, the fall front enclosing pigeon holes and small drawers around a central cupboard, 45¹/₄in. wide.
(Bearne's) £2,600

An early 19th century Austrian walnut secrétaire, the fall front concealing pigeon hole and five drawers, with three long drawers under, on gilt claw front feet, 133cm. wide.
(Finarte) £1,837

A Louis XVI tulipwood, crossbanded and inlaid secrétaire à abattant, the fall front veneered 'à quatre faces' and enclosing a fitted interior, on later tapered feet, 3ft. 1¹/₂in. wide. (Phillips) £2,400

A Louis Philippe mahogany secrétaire à abattant, with rounded rectangular black marble top, frieze drawer and fall front, 37½in. wide.
(Christie's) £1,760

A Regency rosewood secrétaire breakfront cabinet, the top crossbanded with tulipwood and kingwood, the frieze with a fall front secrétaire drawer, 4ft. 6in. wide.
(Phillips) £2,600

Antique American Sheraton blind-front secretary in mahogany, bonnet top, two panelled doors in upper section, rope-turned legs, 37½in. wide.
(Eldred's) £841

A German Empire style mahogany and gilt-metal mounted secrétaire à abattant, the long frieze drawer with central anthemion motif, 19th century, 37in. wide.
(Lawrence Fine Art) £2,640

A late 18th century German walnut, fruitwood and marquetry secrétaire, the fall with a cartouche panel of flowers and foliage within interlaced strapwork, on bracket feet, 3ft. 11in. wide.
(Phillips) £3,000

A Biedermeier birchwood and ebonised secrétaire, the stepped pediment with a drawer above a long frieze drawer and fall flap inlaid with lozenge panels, on square tapering legs, 3ft. 3in. wide.
(Phillips) £2,000

A Charles X ormolu-mounted secrétaire à abattant with frieze drawer and hinged fall, enclosing fitted interior, 42in. wide.
(Christie's) £1,760

A 17th century Lombard walnut veneered secrétaire, the fall front revealing six small drawers with six fielded drawers under, on bracket feet, 140cm. wide.
(Finarte) £11,916

A small French kingwood veneered secrétaire writing desk, Paris, circa 1890, in Louis XV/XVI Transitional manner, 52cm. wide.
(Sotheby's) £3,410

Settle, settee, sofa, chaise longue or daybed – they are all basically alike yet each has its exclusive character and shape and its exclusive place in the scheme of things. A settle is a wooden bench having both back and arms; a settee is a settle with an upholstered seat, arms and back. A sofa is a more luxuriously upholstered settee; a couch, a luxurious sofa, although more suitable for reclining than sitting on. A chaise longue is a daybed with the addition of an armrest.

There are a number of Regency couches, all of which are influenced by the styles of Egypt, Rome or early Greece.

It was Sheraton in his *Cabinet Dictionary* who first introduced a couch of this style to England and its scroll ends and lion's paw feet made it one of the most elegant fashions to have been seen at that time.

Until the decline of the Regency period, the upholsterer played a very minor role in the production of home furnishings and was really not in the same league as the cabinet maker, his work consisting mainly of hanging curtains and tapestries and lining walls with material.

Around the 1840's, however, there was a small, bloodless revolution within the furniture factories, the upholsterer rising to hitherto unheard of heights in his craft, virtually dictating the shape and style of chairs and settees and leaving the cabinet maker only the responsibility for making relatively simple frames of birch or ash.

An Anglo-Dutch mahogany metamorphic wing open armchair, the back with hinged support, opening to become a daybed, on cabriole legs with pad feet, mid-18th century, 88in. long. (Christie's) £5,500

A French calamander and ebonised daybed with dual scroll ends and splayed bracket feet, complete with mattress, 86in. wide. (Christie's) £660

A walnut and ebonised Egyptian style daybed in the style of J. Moyr Smith, the rectangular headboard with Egyptian gods and goddesses, the bed with gently curving profile, 170cm. long. (Christie's) £4,730

A red painted ebonised and parcel-gilt boat shaped daybed of antique Egyptian style, the dished seat covered in black horsehair, 76in. wide. (Christie's S. Ken) £1,650

An Art Deco walnut day bed made in Austria, circa 1930, fitted with a compartment 'at one end', 92in. long, 37in. wide. £1,250

Piedmontese giltwood centre-bed, second half 18th century, 180cm. long. (Finarte) £3,736

A French Provincial fruitwood daybed with outscrolled ends and moulded rail, 19th century, 78in. wide. (Christie's S. Ken) £770

Italian Empire carved and painted pine daybed, first quarter 19th century, with panelled scrolled ends, the sides of the headboard each carved in relief with a recumbent leopard-headed sphinx, 5ft, 7¹/₂in. long. (Butterfield & Butterfield) £1,606

CANAPES

Late 18th century Louis XVI painted canape, repainted white and gilt, probably Sweden, 86in. long. £600

A Louis XV parcel gilt and grey-painted canape, with waved upholstered back and seat, 77in. wide. (Christie's) £2,640

An Italian stained beechwood canape, the undulating back with channelled surround, mid-18th century, stencilled indistinctly *Coleman...?*, 75in. wide. (Christie's) £1,540

An Italian giltwood canapé, the moulded frame carved with flowerheads, rockwork and foliate scrolls, mid-18th century, the seat-frame partly reinforced, 77in. wide. (Christie's) £7,150

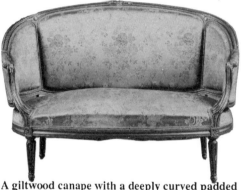

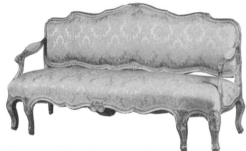

A giltwood canape with a deeply curved padded back, sides, arm-rests and bowed seat covered in golden floral material, the back headed by a foliate clasp, on turned tapering fluted legs headed by flowerheads, 54¹/₂in. wide. (Christie's) £880

A Genoese giltwood canape, the waved serpentine moulded top-rail centred by a floral cartouche within a stylised C-scroll flanked by eared C-scrolls to the frame, mid-19th century, repairs to both arms, 84in. wide. (Christie's) £990

An Italian Neo-classical grey-painted and parcel-gilt canapé, the arms with scrolled terminals and downswept supports, the square tapering fluted legs headed by roundels, circa 1800. (Christie's) £3,080

Louis XV style tapestry-upholstered carved walnut canape à orielles, the tapestry 18th century, the frame circa 1900, raised on cabriole legs, 6ft. 2in. (Butterfield & Butterfield) £2,364

CHAISES LONGUES

'Djinn series', an upholstered chaise longue designed by Olivier Mourgue, in green nylon stretch jersey, circa 1965, 170cm. long. (Christie's) £756

A George IV brass inlaid mahogany and rosewood chaise longue with scrolling padded back, sides and foot rest, 82in. wide. £1,600

A late Regency rosewood chaise longue, the scrolled carved top rail above an upholstered seat with scrolled back rest, on sabre legs. (Bonhams) £950

A pair of chaises longues by De Sede fashioned as a pair of giant boxing gloves. (Christie's) £6,500

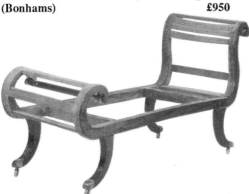

A Regency mahogany chaise longue frame, with scroll ends, channelled seat rail and reeded sabre legs, 73in. wide. (Christie's) £1,650

An Italian walnut chaise longue, with cream floral upholstery, on outswept legs with scroll feet, mid 19th century, attributed to Luigi Bruscelli, 67in. high. (Christie's) £1,210

An early Victorian rosewood chaise longue with foliate scroll carved end and button upholstered back on turned lappeted legs, 71in. wide. (Christie's) £825

A tubular chromium-plated chaise longue designed by Le Corbusier and Charlotte Perriand, the adjustable seat upholstered in brown and white pony skin, on black painted steel base. (Christie's) £880

CHAISES LONGUES

William IV rosewood chaise with scroll carved arm and back rail, lotus carved foot, 86in. long. £775

A laminated birchwood chaise longue designed by Bruno Mathsson, Made in Sweden, 151cm. long. (Christie's) £486

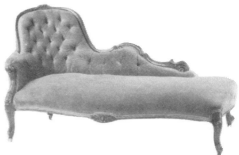

A Victorian chaise longue with carved mahogany show wood frame and cabriole legs and gold damask cover. £800

A Victorian walnut chaise longue carved with flowerheads, foliage and C-scrolls, on cabriole legs with knob feet, 64in. wide. (Christie's S. Ken) £770

One of a pair of mid-Victorian stained-beech chaises-longues of scrolled form, the padded backs, arms and seats upholstered in pale russet cloth, on ring-turned tapering front legs, 66in. wide.
(Christie's) (Two) £1,291

A Regency carved rosewood chaise longue with single scroll end and downswept back carved with acanthus leaves, the seat rail and turned tapering legs with lotus carved decoration, 79in. wide. (Christie's) £1,980

A Victorian walnut chaise longue with buttoned graduated back panel, 83in. long. £1,750

A William IV giltwood chaise longue with scrolled upholstered back, seat and footrest, 92in. wide. £1,350

DAYBEDS

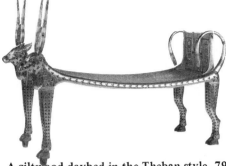

A mahogany and parcel gilt daybed of George II style, on shell-headed cabriole legs with hairy paw feet, 99in. wide.
(Christie's)   £23,100

A giltwood daybed in the Theban style, 79½in. wide.   £14,500

A Victorian mahogany patent adjustable daybed, the double-hinged rectangular seat adjusting by means of a winding handle, 80in. wide.
(Christie's S. Ken)   £660

An Art Deco ebony, macassar and vellum covered day bed, the rectangular gondola-shaped form with vellum covered moulding on plinth base, with band of bone inlay, 81cm. wide. (Christie's)   £5,500

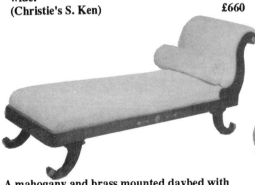

A mahogany and brass mounted daybed with single scroll end and padded seat on reeded scroll legs, 19th century, 74in. wide.
(Christie's)   £1,430

A giltwood day bed, the arched back, down-swept arms and bowed seat upholstered in blue silk damask, on cabriole legs and scroll feet, 19th century, 80in. long. (Christie's S. Ken)   £1,485

A fine classical diminutive carved mahogany recamier, probably by Charles White, Philadelphia, circa 1825, on acanthus-carved legs ending in animal paw feet, 65½in. long.
(Sotheby's)   £2,150

Regency ormolu-mounted grain-painted recamier, circa 1815, the supports mounted with ormolu plumes and foliate scrolls, raised on lobe-carved out-scrolled legs ending in foliate brass feet on casters, 6ft. 4in. wide.
(Butterfield & Butterfield)   £2,364

An Adam period carved mahogany settee with arched stuffover back and seat, on ringed fluted tapered legs, 5ft.9in. wide. (Phillips)   £4,830

A turned Windsor settee, American, 1785–1810, the U-shaped back above twenty-nine bulbous spindles, length 6ft. 4¹/₂in. (Sotheby's)   £3,594

A fine quality bergère settee, in the Hepplewhite style, the highly decorative back with three ovals centred by paterae and surrounded with continuous harebell and ribbon outline, 76in. wide. (Boardman)   £2,900

A late Victorian grained knole settee, the rectangular padded back and ratchet-sides with turned finials, with squab cushion and on turned legs, 85in. wide. (Christie's)   £3,850

Italian Neoclassical fruitwood settee, late 18th century, pierced interlaced gothic back, bowed seat rail, 64in. long. (Skinner Inc.)   £899

An attractive Victorian mahogany cameo back settee, scroll arm terminals extending down to cabriole front supports. (Henry Spencer)   £1,000

Italian neoclassical grey painted settee, circa 1790, the channel-moulded frame with dark grey line borders, the straight back with shallow downswept sides ending in scroll finials, 6ft. 1in. long. (Butterfield & Butterfield)   £1,445

A George III mahogany settee with arched padded back and seat upholstered in yellow floral damask, with channelled scrolling padded arms above channelled tapering cabriole legs headed by stylised shells and foliage, 75in. wide. (Christie's)   £7,700

SETTEES

Regency style mahogany quadruple chair-back settee, 19th century, raised on turned legs (fretwork sections showing breaks), 80in. long. (Skinner Inc.) £1,975

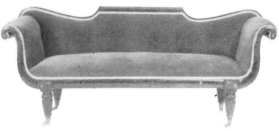

A late Regency mahogany framed couch, the shaped and gadrooned top rail over upholstered back and seat with scroll-over arms, 137cm. (Phillips) £550

A Federal inlaid mahogany settee, circa 1800, the back with four rectangular crests above an upholstered back rest and arms, 5ft. 11½in. wide. (Sotheby's) £2,316

George III mahogany camel back settee, arched upholstered back with scrolled arms over rectangular seat raised on blind fret carved H-form stretcher, 63in. wide. (Skinner Inc.) £932

An attractive Victorian rosewood framed settee, the rectangular padded back with foliate carved cushion moulded cresting rail. (Spencer's) £650

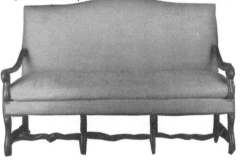

Louis XIV style walnut settee, 19th century, with a camelback and straight seat raised on eight S-scroll supports, 5ft. 8in. wide. (Butterfield & Butterfield) £1,215

A French beech settee, the outscrolled buttoned end and bowed cushioned seat upholstered in calico, the waved seat rail and cabriole legs carved with flowers and foliage, late 19th century, 70in. wide. (Christie's) £880

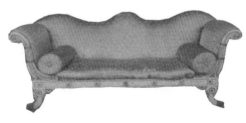

A Regency cream and gilt painted dual scroll end sofa, the seat rail carved with roundels on splayed legs headed by scrolls, later decorated, 86in. wide. (Christie's) £825

SETTEES & COUCHES

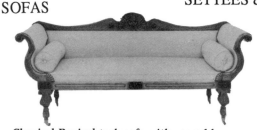

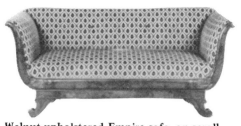

Classical Revival teak sofa with carved lyre legs terminating in turned feet with brass cap castors, China, circa 1840, 86in. long. £1,850

Walnut upholstered Empire sofa, on scroll feet. 197cm. wide.
(Auktionshaus Arnold)   £1,004

A George III parcel gilt and cream painted sofa, the waved back and serpentine seat lacking upholstery, 84in. wide. (Christie's) £2,530

A George III mahogany sofa upholstered in apricot silk, 66in. wide.   £2,900

A William and Mary walnut sofa, covered in nailed later turkey work, on faceted baluster legs joined by conforming stretchers, possibly Flemish, 68in. wide. (Christie's)   £6,050

A George III giltwood small sofa in the manner of Thos. Chippendale, the back and seat covered in blue and white floral printed cotton, 58in. wide.   £2,900

A Regency mahogany and green moire upholstered sofa with a padded back and dual scroll ends above a padded seat, on reeded splayed legs, 86in. wide.
(Christie's S. Ken)   £2,420

A George IV cream-painted and parcel-gilt sofa, the out-scrolled back, arms and bowed seat upholstered in pink floral repp, on ring-turned fluted tapering feet, 79in. wide.
(Christie's)   £496

SOFAS

A Federal upholstered mahogany sofa on ring turned and reeded legs, circa 1800-15, 75½in. long. £4,600

A Federal mahogany sofa, the padded back with arched crest, 1790-1810, 80¼in. wide. £4,000

A neo rococo walnut sofa with scrolling sides and cabriole legs on castors, upholstered in green floral damask.
(Herholdt Jensen) £620

A George IV white-painted and parcel-gilt sofa, the scrolled padded back, outward-scrolling arms and seat with squab cushion and two bolsters covered in pink and white striped silk, 91in. wide.
(Christie's) £6,600

A French walnut sofa, the channelled backrail and seat-rail centred by flowerheads, on cabriole legs, restorations and some replacements, basically mid-18th century and adapted, 42½in. wide.(Christie's) £2,640

One of a pair of Irish mahogany sofas, on cabriole legs carved with scallop shells and claw-and-ball feet, 56in. wide.
(Christie's) (Two) £6,453

A mahogany sofa with shaped arched back, padded arms and triple serpentine seat upholstered in yellow silk, on cabriole legs with acanthus, 78in. wide. (Christie's London) £2,200

A very fine Federal carved mahogany sabre-leg sofa, attributed to Duncan Phyfe, New York, circa 1810, the reeded seat rail on volute-carved and reeded sabre legs, 7ft. 6in. long.
(Sotheby's) £14,556

SOFAS

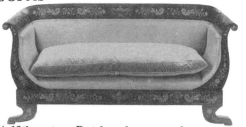

A 19th century Dutch mahogany and marquetry scroll-end sofa, decorated with foliate scrolls, and floral tendrils, on outswept legs, 6ft. 5in. wide. (Phillips) £2,000

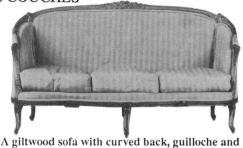

A giltwood sofa with curved back, guilloche and floral-carved frame, serpentine seat and cabriole legs, 81in. wide. (Christie's) £880

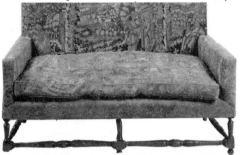

A walnut sofa, covered in close-nailed 17th century and later Flemish tapestry, on turned legs joined by turned stretchers, on bun feet, 63in. wide. (Christie's) £3,300

A late Victorian painted satinwood sofa, the rectangular top with central tablet of putti above scroll arms, 75in. wide. (Christie's) £1,045

A Biedermeier satinbirch sofa with pedimented back and side finials, the arms with applied half columns with scroll capitals, mid 19th century. (Christie's S. Ken) £1,595

A fine Federal mahogany sofa, attributed to Slover and Taylor, New York, circa 1815, on reeded square tapering legs ending in spade feet, 6ft. 6½in. long. (Sotheby's) £5,293

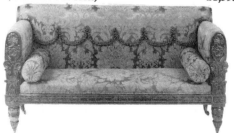

A William IV rosewood sofa, the scrolled rectangular padded back, arms and seat with two bolsters upholstered in close-nailed red silk damask, on turned tapering legs. (Christie's) £1,980

A classical carved mahogany sofa, Boston, Massachusetts, circa 1820, the scrolled crest above swan's head-carved arm supports, length 7ft. 1in. (Sotheby's) £1,891

SOFAS

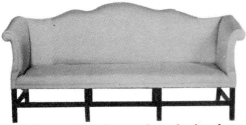

A George III mahogany humpback sofa with plum-coloured floral damask loose cover, squab and four cushions, 85in. wide. £6,500

A carved fruitwood Biedermeier sofa with serpentine back and outward scrolled end supports, 203cm. wide
(Arnold) £1,035

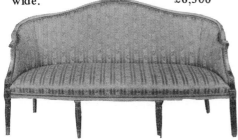

A George III white-painted and parcel-gilt sofa, on turned tapering fluted legs headed by lotus-leaf and flowerheads, on turned feet, 72in. wide.
(Christie's) £2,200

A Dutch mahogany and floral marquetry scroll end sofa with undulated back and padded seat on splay legs, mid 19th century, 79in. wide.
(Christie's) £1,210

A mid Victorian carved walnut button-back sofa with bowed back and serpentine fronted seat between open padded scroll arms on cabriole legs, 65in. wide.
(Christie's S. Ken) £605

A George III hump-back sofa with scroll arms, on a mahogany frame with four grooved square legs joined by stretchers and on brass barrel casters, 72¹/₂in. wide.
(Christie's) £5,956

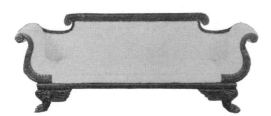

A classical carved mahogany sofa, New York, circa 1825, the columnar crest with scrolled leaf-carved terminals above scrolled arms, 7ft. 9in. long.
(Sotheby's) £1,323

A Chippendale carved mahogany camel-back sofa, late 18th century, on moulded square tapering legs joined by a recessed stretcher, 7ft. 6in. wide.
(Sotheby's) £1,985

SOFAS

A George III mahogany sofa with rectangular back, on square tapering legs headed by paterae, 72½in. wide.
(Christie's) £2,090

A George III Irish hump-back sofa, on four blind-fretwork square legs with pierced brackets, 73in. wide.
(Christie's) £10,920

A George III mahogany sofa with arched padded back, on square chamfered legs joined by square stretchers, later blocks, restorations to back legs, 94in. wide.(Christie's) £5,544

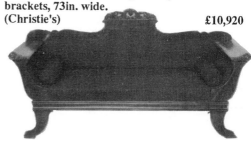

An Empire mahogany sofa with out scrolled, flat topped mahogany arms and on splayed legs, 19th century.
(Herholdt Jensen) £344

A Biedermeier satin-ash sofa, with undulating back, scroll ends and padded seat on outswept legs with scroll feet, second quarter 19th century, possibly Scandinavian, 92in. wide.
(Christie's) £1,540

A William IV mahogany sofa, the crested back, scroll arms and buttoned seat upholstered in green striped moire above a rope-twist apron on splayed legs, 81½in. wide.
(Christie's) £1,760

A good Federal carved mahogany sofa, Philadelphia, circa 1815, the crest carved with drapery swags, tassels and flowerheads on a punchwork ground, 6ft. 4in. long.
(Sotheby's) £3,143

George III mahogany sofa with a high square back sloping down to downswept upholstered arms, on four square tapering front supports joined by H-form stretchers, 6ft. 10in. wide.
(Butterfield & Butterfield) £1,927

SOFAS

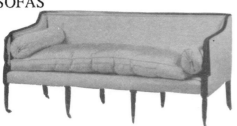

A Regency mahogany sofa, the arms with reeded vase-turned supports on reeded tapering legs headed by paterae, 78in. wide.
(Christie's) £2,200

A mid Victorian walnut sofa with arched deep buttoned back, curved sides and serpentine seat covered in bottle green velvet, 79½in. wide. (Christie's) £1,320

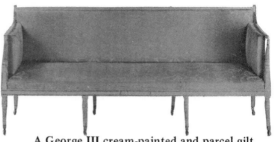

An Art Deco two seater sofa, upholstered in coloured velvet fabric depicting tigers walking through foliage, 166cm. long. (Phillips London) £280

A George III cream-painted and parcel gilt sofa, the padded back, arms and seat with spirally-turned spreading arm supports, 77in. wide. (Christie's) £1,320

A Regency mahogany sofa, the rectangular padded back, outscrolled arms and squab cushion covered in pale cream and green floral silk, 64in. wide.
(Christie's) £1,980

An American mahogany scroll end sofa, the back with ribbon-tied laurel-leaf toprail, the scroll end with eagle's head terminals, mid 19th century, possibly Philadelphia, 81in. wide.
(Christie's) £1,320

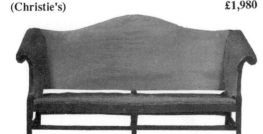

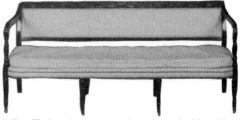

A Chippendale mahogany sofa, Philadelphia, 1770–1790, the canted back with serpentine crest flanked by down-sloping outward scrolling arms above a serpentine seatrail, 85¹/₂in. wide.
(Christie's) £23,019

A fine Federal carved mahogany sofa, New York or Philadelphia, circa 1810, the panelled crest carved with drapery swags and tassels centring a reserve carved with a bow with arrows, 6ft. 6in. wide. (Sotheby's) £5,624

A George III mahogany sofa with serpentine back, Irish, late 18th century, 86in. wide.

£3,000

A mahogany Empire-style sofa with curved scrolling arms, 19th century
(Herholdt Jensen)

£538

A fine and rare classical brass-inlaid mahogany sofa, attributed to Joseph Barry, Philadelphia, circa 1820, on brass-inlaid sabre-legs ending in sleeping lion's head-cast brass caps, length 7ft. 2in.
(Sotheby's)

£12,105

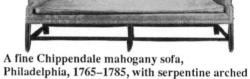

A fine Chippendale mahogany sofa, Philadelphia, 1765–1785, with serpentine arched and canted back flanked by downward sloping and outward flaring scrolled arms above a straight seatrail, 98in. wide.
(Christie's)

£11,839

A small, George III, mahogany humpback sofa with upholstered back, scrolled arms and waved seat on square tapering legs, 63in. wide.

£7,500

A walnut sofa with padded back and seat, with outscrolled arm supports, on shell and husk cabriole legs and pad feet, 62in. wide.

£4,600

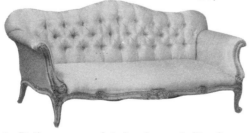

An Italian cream painted and parcel-gilt sofa, the shaped button back, serpentine seat and outswept scroll arms with pale blue upholstery, mid 19th century, 86in. wide.
(Christie's)

£1,210

A Danish ormolu-mounted mahogany sofa, with curved arms and front rail with mythological mounts, on splayed legs, 19th century, 74in. wide.
(Christie's)

£1,320

A Kelim upholstered three seater sofa.
(Bonhams)   £450

A classical upholstered mahogany cylinder
arm sofa, circa 1810-30, 72in. long.
                                             £900

An early 19th century carved giltwood sofa in
the Louis XV manner, the buttoned back
serpentine seat and squab cushion upholstered
and piped in pale green silk with scrolled arm
terminals, on cabriole legs, 6ft. 6in. wide.
(Phillips)   £1,400

A Federal mahogany sofa, possibly Baltimore,
1790–1810, on square tapering legs with green-
painted flower and trailing vine decoration,
joined by medial and rear stretchers, 92³/₄in.
wide.
(Christie's)   £12,870

A mid Victorian satinwood sofa, with vase-
turned arm supports and square tapering legs
headed by paterae, 66in. wide.
(Christie's)   £1,320

A walnut sofa of William and Mary style with
padded back, outscrolled arms and seat upholstered with fragments of 17th century tapestry,
82in. wide. (Christie's)   £6,050

A Regency brass-inlaid rosewood sofa, the
waved padded back centred by a scrolled
tablet inlaid with paterae, the seat-rail carved
with anthemia on turned reeded legs, the back
legs plain, 75in. wide.(Christie's)   £3,520

A good Federal carved mahogany sofa, New
York, circa 1810, the crest carved with three
rectangular reeded panels flanked by reeded
downcurving arms, 6ft. 6in. long.
(Sotheby's)   £2,647

Shelves, from medieval times, were used mainly for the storage of books, until in the late 17th century they came into their own as a place for standing the oriental porcelain and delft which were then being avidly collected. These valuable items soon retreated to the safer reaches of the china cabinet or vitrine, but open shelves continued in fashion, receiving mentions in both Hepplewhite and Sheraton's key works. At this time, they were made strictly in the neo-classical taste, with Sheraton giving alternative designs for fretwork and solid ends.

A George III hanging shelf with chinoiserie and Gothic fretwork back and sides, 26¼in. wide. £2,150

A hanging Dutch curio shelf with cupboard doors in the base, circa 1800, 22½in. wide. £30

A Victorian mahogany display stand, the four graduated open shelves with scroll supports, 3ft.6in. (Greenslades) £726

A set of Dutch oak egg shelves, the arched back carved with *K I H ANNO 1723*, the front and sides decorated with chip carving with two arched pierced doors, first quarter 18th century, Friesian, 13in. wide. (Christie's) £880

A grain painted wall shelf with scalloped sides, New England, circa 1840, 25½in. wide. £95

A Regency simulated rosewood hanging open bookshelf, 57cm. wide, 75cm. high. £2,500

A pair of late George III mahogany hanging shelves with fretwork sides and drawers in the base. £10,000

A set of George III pierced fret side mahogany wall shelves, 19in. wide. £72

Most pieces of furniture have clearly traceable roots planted firmly in the distant past. Not so the sideboard. In the form we know it today, this particular item first appeared on the scene in or around 1770.

Prior to that, certainly, there were sideboards, (Chaucer – and who would argue with his evidence? – mentions a 'sytte bord') but these were no more than side tables, sometimes marble topped, which contained neither drawers nor cupboards.

The introduction of a sideboard as a piece of furniture designed for storage came about for one main reason; the hard-drinking habits of 18th century Englishmen established a need for a convenient hidey-hole in which to keep large quantities of drink close by the dining table.

It is Adam, who, along with Shearer, Gillows, Sheraton, Chippendale and Hepplewhite, contends for the title of 'Father of the Modern Sideboard' i.e. of being the first to couple the drawerless side table with a pair of pedestals, one to either end, often placing knife boxes on top. One of the pedestals houses a wine drawer, and the other, a tin-lined cupboard with racks for stacking plates. Some also contained a pot cupboard in one of the pedestals, the door to which is usually quite inconspicuous and opens by means of a catch at the back. The explanation for this quaint variation seems to be that gentlemen, left by the ladies to put the world to rights over port and cigars, would often prefer not to permit calls of nature to interrupt the conversation!

An Art Nouveau sideboard by Johnson & Appleyard, the upper section with railed gallery and repoussé copper panels depicting stylised trees and fruit, 6ft. wide.
(Spencer's) £950

A Morris & Co. ebonised sideboard designed by Philip Webb, the carved and moulded canopied superstructure mounted with a single moulded shelf supported on turned columns, 1863, 157cm. wide.
(Christie's) £2,200

Classical revival mahogany and mahogany and wavy birch veneer inlaid carved sideboard, Massachusetts, circa 1825, 46½in. wide.
(Skinner) £883

Edward Wormley designed 'Janus' sideboard and superstructure, 1957, for Dunbar Furniture Corp., black faux marble drop-in top over four cabinet doors, 66in. wide.
(Skinner) £1,551

An inlaid oak sideboard designed by J. P. Seddon, the castellated rectangular mirrored superstructure ornately carved, moulded and inlaid, with two tiled friezes, on moulded plinth base, circa 1870, 197cm. wide.
(Christie's) £6,050

Lifetime Furniture buffet, no. 5272, circa 1910, three short drawers over single long drawer with cabinet doors below, brass hardware.
(Skinner) £423

A late Georgian mahogany break-front sideboard, the top edge inlaid with a brass band, on six turned reeded supports, 73in. (Lawrence Fine Arts) £2,090

A William IV mahogany sideboard, the scroll-capped shaped panel back above a shaped front base, 198cm. wide. (Allen & Harris) £1,500

A late George III mahogany bowfront sideboard, the central frieze drawer flanked by two deep drawers divided by reeded panels, on canted tapering legs, 60¼in. wide. (Christie's London) £5,280

A good Federal bird's eye maple and mahogany inlaid cherrywood small sideboard, New England, probably Connecticut, circa 1815, 46in. wide.
(Sotheby's) £3,143

An early Victorian D-shaped side cabinet, covered overall with paper scrap design, on plinth base. (Lawrence Fine Arts) £1,980

An ebony, purplewood and holly-inlaid pollard oak sideboard, by Marsh and Jones, to a design by Charles Bevan, circa 1870, the upper section with mirror.
(Sotheby's) £3,960

A George III mahogany bowfront sideboard with five drawers around a waved kneehole, on square section legs terminating with spade feet.
(Bonhams) £1,400

A Heal & Son oak sideboard with quarter-galleried rectangular top above two short and one long drawers and original curtain rail, 122.3cm. wide.
(Christie's) £462

A George III elliptical mahogany sideboard, the top with feather stringing to the edge, on shell inlaid square tapering legs, 5ft. wide.
(Woolley & Wallis) £3,000

A George III mahogany breakfront sideboard inlaid with ebonised lines, the frieze with a drawer above an arched apron flanked by a cupboard and a deep drawer, 5ft. wide. (Phillips) £1,600

A French Provincial oak buffet, the two drawers flanked by two panelled doors carved with scrolls and foliage, on incurved feet, 18th century, 66½in. wide. (Christie's London) £4,180

A George III mahogany sideboard with D-shaped breakfront top, on square tapering legs and spade feet, 67in. wide. (Christie's London) £1,485

An inlaid mahogany demi-lune dwarf sideboard, with boxwood and ebony lines, on square tapering legs with spade feet, early 19th century, 48in. wide. (Christie's) £5,720

A large oak sideboard by Romney Green, the top with four open shelves flanked by two stepped compartments, on four bracket feet, 298cm. wide, (Christie's London) £8,250

A Regency mahogany sideboard, the bowfronted top with three quarter gallery above a drawer and kneehole drawer flanked by deep drawers on ring turned legs, 48in. wide. (Christie's London) £3,080

A George II mahogany bowfront sideboard with tulipwood crossbanding and inlaid with boxwood lines, on square tapering legs and spade feet, 3ft. 5in. wide. (Phillips) £2,800

A Shapland and Petter oak sideboard, the rectangular cornice overhanging a central reserve decorated with a copper relief panel of stylised flowers above shelf, 228cm. wide. (Christie's) £4,950

A small George III mahogany veneered serpentine front sideboard with shell marquetry inlay, the square tapering legs on socket feet, 4ft. 6in. wide. (Woolley & Wallis) £3,400

A large Regency mahogany pedestal sideboard with curved back and two centre drawers, on six brass hairy paw supports.
(Greenslades) £3,300

A classical mahogany sideboard with marble top, New York, 1815-25, 75in. long. £3,000

A George III Scottish mahogany sideboard, the eared rectangular superstructure formerly with a gallery and with bowed tambour doors, 71¾in. wide. (Christie's) £2,420

George III style inlaid mahogany pedestal sideboard, third quarter 19th century, the rectangular top with outset ends and concaved splashboard, the frieze fitted with two drawers, 7ft. 6in. wide.
(Butterfield & Butterfield) £1,891

A Hille sideboard, the rectangular superstructure with three sliding glass doors each enclosing single glass shelf, on four bowed carved legs, 167.5cm. wide.
(Christie's) £605

Fine Louis XVI style gilt-bronze-mounted mahogany console desserte, the rectangular mirror plate with downswept sides and gilt-bronze framework, the green marble top above three frieze drawers, 7ft. 9½in. wide.
(Butterfield & Butterfield) £3,152

William IV brass-mounted mahogany pedestal sideboard, second quarter 19th century, the bowed cross-banded rectangular top with arched splashboard, 8ft. 1½in. wide.
(Butterfield & Butterfield) £1,576

A mahogany sideboard of George III style, on channelled legs carved with satyr masks and acanthus and headed by paterae on block feet, 80¼in. wide.
(Christie's) £4,950

A Regency mahogany sideboard, inlaid with bands of brass ovals on an ebonised ground, 88½in. wide.   £14,250

A George III mahogany and satinwood sideboard with gilt metal and enamel handles, Scottish, 103in. wide.   £11,000

A Liberty & Co. break-front cabinet, shaped central glazed cupboard doors above rectangular top, flanked on each side with arched and columned open recesses and adjustable shelves, 122.5cm. wide.
(Christie's)   £550

A Regency mahogany pedestal sideboard, supported by two pedestals, each with one top drawer above a convex panelled door with two twisted side columns.
(Bonhams)   £550

A George III mahogany bowfronted sideboard with a mahogany-lined drawer in the arched centre flanked by oval-inlaid cupboard door on the left and a cellaret drawer on the right, 60¼in. wide.
(Christie's)   £14,300

A Regency parcel-gilt rosewood side cabinet inlaid overall with boxwood lines, on hairy paw feet, bearing a label *Hugh Cecil Earl of Lonsdale* with coat-of-arms; and a Chinese Kangxi blue and white covered porcelain vase, 66½in. wide.
(Christie's)   £99,000

George III inlaid mahogany sideboard of large size, circa 1800, the top crossbanded in rosewood within boxwood strung borders, 7ft. 11¼in. wide.
(Butterfield & Butterfield)   £1,518

Edwardian inlaid and penwork decorated mahogany sideboard in the neoclassical taste, circa 1900, the whole on a plinth base, 6ft. 9½in. wide.
(Butterfield & Butterfield)   £2,868

A George III mahogany sideboard inlaid overall with boxwood and ebonised stringing, on square tapering legs and block feet, 51in. wide. (Christie's) £3,850

A Regency mahogany sideboard in the manner of Gillows, with double brass rail back, with later feet, 184cm. wide. (Lawrence Fine Arts) £3,300

A George III mahogany sideboard, inlaid with boxwood lines and crossbanded with rosewood, on square tapering legs with spade feet, 71in. wide. (Christie's) £6,600

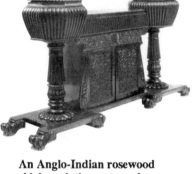

One of a pair of George III mahogany bow-fronted sideboards, each with two lead-lined doors flanking a kneehole drawer on square tapering legs, 42in. wide. (Christie's) (Two) £3,850

An Anglo-Indian rosewood sideboard, the rectangular centre section with pierced backboard centred by an anthemion, flanked by a pair of cellarets of octagonal shape with ribbed lids, circa 1830, 94in. wide. (Christie's) £1,160

A George IV mahogany breakfront pedestal sideboard outlined with boxwood stringing, to the tapering pedestals, 39¾in. wide. (Bearne's) £1,050

A late Georgian small mahogany sweep front sideboard fitted with a drawer above a tambour cupboard, on six turned supports, 48in. wide. (Lawrence Fine Art) £2,200

A Victorian carved mahogany sideboard, the crested back above a rectangular re-entrant top with three frieze drawers and three panel doors below, 65in. wide. (Christie's S. Ken) £1,210

A late Georgian mahogany sideboard with bow-front, inlaid with ebony stringing and fitted with two central drawers, on six turned supports, 60½in. wide. (Lawrence Fine Arts) £2,640

Such was the ingenuity of past craftsmen and designers that there is a purpose built stand for just about everything from whips to cricket bats.

The 17th century ancestor of the anglepoise lamp was the candlestand. Its purpose was to supplement the general lighting, and the ordinary style was made of walnut or elm and consisted of a plain or spiral turned shaft supported on three or four plain scrolled feet.

At the turn of the 18th century a vase shape was introduced at the top of the pillar. This was often as much as a foot across and decorated with acanthus.

There were a number of delicate little stands made during the second half of the 18th century for the purpose of supporting books or music. The earliest of these resemble the mahogany tables which were popular at the time, having vase-shaped stems and tripod bases but with the addition of ratchets beneath their tops which permitted adjustment of the surface angle.

Ince and Mayhew improved the design by adding candle branches either side of the top and Sheraton (anything you can do ...) made his stands adjustable for height by means of a rod through the centre column which was clamped or released by the turn of a thumb screw.

The Victorian walnut duet music stand is particularly good with its turned central column and carved cabriole legs. These stands often have intricate fretwork tops, and the lyre design may give way elsewhere to a series of scrolls or leaf patterns.

A late 17th century Flemish giltwood stand, the foliate carved frieze above a pierced fascia carved with strapwork, flowerheads and an urn, 2ft. 2in. wide.
(Phillips) £1,050

A maple stand, on a shaped joined trestle base, painted green, 24in. high.
(Christie's) £787

A George III mahogany tripod caddy-stand, the circular top with baize-lined well, fitted with an associated contemporary circular silver caddy, by William & Aaron Lestourgeon, 1777, 23¼in. high.
(Christie's) £39,600

Japanese roironuri lacquer Chinese style stand, 18th/early 19th century, with cabriole legs and rectangular base, inlaid with flowers and figural landscape, 22in. high.
(Skinner Inc.) £750

An Irish mid-Georgian mahogany bottle-stand, the tray-top with inverted lambrequin border and arched carrying-handle flanked by eight divisions, 28½in. wide.
(Christie's) £9,350

A late 18th century Dutch mahogany tea comfort, the cylindrical body with a brass liner, the sides carved with trailing flower stems, 10in. diameter.
(Phillips) £900

Victorian parcel-gilt and turned walnut birdcage, 19th century, suspended within a ring-turned and moulded-arch frame, 6ft. high.
(Butterfield & Butterfield) £946

A pair of Venetian painted and gilded blackamoor stands, each in the form of a negro boy doing a handstand, 31in. high. (Christie's) £14,300

A Biedermeier style mahogany stand, on double S-scroll supports with finial on serpentine platform base with gilt feet, 38in. high. (Christie's S. Ken) £550

One of a pair of ormolu-mounted ebonized stands, each of square tapering form, with a moulded rectangular top, centred by a female mask within an inset pierced scroll panel, late 19th century, 25½in. wide. (Christie's) (Two) £3,850

A George III mahogany cellaret, the top with one rectangular well and D-shaped section with spindle gallery, the central divide with carrying handle, 25in. wide. (Christie's) £1,980

A George III mahogany tripod stand, the circular top edged with ribbon-and-rosette and pendant lozenges, on triple scrolled supports of double C outline, 31in. high. (Christie's) £31,900

A pair of Italian red-painted and parcel-gilt columns each with acanthus-carved pilasters decorated with vine leaves and grapes, on a turned base, 56in. high. (Christie's) £1,210

An early 18th century Italian carved giltwood stand with a simulated green marble top, 1.10m. high. £1,000

A pair of fruitwood and ebonised fluted columns with square capitals and plinths, 40¼in. high. (Christie's S. Ken) £880

BOOKSTANDS

A mahogany book trough on moulded square legs and cross stretchers, 31in. wide.
(Christie's London)   £550

A late George III mahogany booktray with carrying handle and galleried sides, 17in. wide.
(Christie's London)   £385

A George IV mahogany library bookstand with a panelled fall-flap, 45½in. wide.   £1,000

An early 20th century banded mahogany circular revolving bookstand, the radially-veneered top centred by a small inlaid florette motif, 34½in. high.
(Tennants)   £650

A pair of Louis XV ormolu-mounted kingwood and end-cut floral marquetry bibliothèques basses inlaid overall with ebonised and fruitwood lines and inlaid with leaves and flowerheads, English 19th century.
(Christie's)   £90,200

A mahogany drum bookstand, the circular top with later brass gallery above four piers in the form of simulated bookspines and four shelves, the Regency base with a gadrooned turned baluster shaft, 23½in. diameter.
(Christie's)   £3,520

A Gustav Stickley V-top bookrack, signed with red decal in a box, 1902-04, 31in. wide, 31in. high.
(Skinner Inc.)   £833

A Georgian style walnut wine table with two tiers of revolving book racks, 30in. high.   £650

Roycroft 'Little Journeys' bookrack, circa 1910, rectangular overhanging top, two lower shelves with keyed tenons through vertical side slats, 26¼in. wide.
(Skinner)   £240

257

BUTLERS STANDS

A plain mahogany early 19th century rectangular butler's tray, on baluster turned folding stand. (David Lay) £500

A mid-Georgian brass-inlaid padoukwood tray in the style of John Channon with rectangular top, the gallery pierced with ovals, 18¾in. wide. (Christie's) £4,950

A George III mahogany and satinwood oval tray, inlaid with a fanned oval and leafy bands, on a later stand, 27in. wide. (Christie's) £1,650

A mid 19th century tole oval tray, painted flowers and clouds, gilt foliage sprays to the serpentine border, 25in. (Woolley & Wallis) £480

Victorian papier mâché tray on later stand, with scalloped rim, painted with a central flower-filled urn, a peacock perched on a branch to one side, 32in. wide. (Butterfield & Butterfield) £1,009

A George III inlaid mahogany serving-tray, probably English, 1780-1800, centring an oval reserve engraved and shaded with a shell on a green ground, 28¼in. wide. (Christie's) £850

A Gallé marquetry tray on stand, inlaid in various fruitwoods with five sailing boats, on carved trestle ends, 78cm. high. (Christie's) £880

A three-tiered muffin stand, by Charles Rohlfs, Buffalo, N.Y., 1907, 34in. high. £702

A George III mahogany butler's tray, the rectangular galleried top pierced with carrying handles on a turned beech folding stand, 26in. wide. (Christie's S. Ken) £1,100

CANDLESTANDS

A Federal inlaid cherrywood candlestand, Connecticut River Valley, 1790-1810, 26¾in. high. £11,500

A pair of George II walnut and parcel-gilt candle-stands, on tripod cabriole base carved with acanthus and C-scrolls ending in scrolled feet, 42½in. high. (Christie's) £99,000

A Federal inlaid mahogany candlestand on a vase-turned pedestal, 1790-1810, 29½in. high. £1,600

A painted pine candlestand, New England, circa 1780, 27in. high, 20in. diam. £825

A very fine and rare Chippendale cherrywood scalloped-top candlestand with drawer, attributed to the Chapin family, East Windsor or Hartford, Connecticut, circa 1785. (Sotheby's) £40,740

A tripod cherry candlestand with candle drawer, Mass., circa 1760, 25½in. high. £4,700

A classical mahogany tilt-top candlestand, N.Y., circa 1820/40, 30¾in. high. £900

A pair of Georgian carved mahogany candle stands, with moulded edge circular tops on baluster turned columns with flowerhead ribbon and gadrooned ornament, 2ft. 4in. high. (Phillips) £3,800

A Chippendale mahogany bird cage candlestand, Phila., circa 1760, 27½in. high. £4,150

HAT STANDS

A polished chromium hat stand made for Bazzi in Milan, 51.6cm. high. (Christie's) £453

A late Victorian mahogany hat rack with central mirror and brass fittings. £100

An early Victorian mahogany hat-stand with arched toprail above seven rails, between octagonal column supports, 60in. wide. (Christie's) £1,870

KETTLE STANDS

A mahogany kettle stand, with hexagonal solid galleried top, on ring-turned vase-shaped shaft, $20^{1}/_{2}$in. high. (Christie's) £990

A carved mahogany galleried kettle stand, the top with open baluster gallery, 30cm. diam., 75cm. high. £2,150

A George II mahogany kettle-stand with plain circular tray-top on stop-fluted shaft and tripod cabriole base, $21^{1}/_{2}$in. high. (Christie's) £19,800

MAGAZINE STANDS

An L. & J. G. Stickley magazine rack, no. 45, circa 1912, $44^{1}/_{2}$in. high. (Skinner Inc.) £812

Early 20th century Mission oak magazine stand with cut out arched sides, 49in. high. (Skinner Inc.) £312

An L. & J. G. Stickley slat-sided magazine rack, no. 46, circa 1910, signed with decal, 42in. high. (Skinner Inc.) £1,312

MUSIC STANDS

A mid Victorian black, gilt and mother-of-pearl japanned papier mache music stand, 50¼in. high.   £700

A mid Victorian walnut music stand, the slope on an adjustable brass shaft, 23in. wide.   £935

A Regency rosewood double-sided music stand, the sides with candle sconces, 48in. high.   £2,750

An Emile Gallé walnut and marquetry music stand, 90.4cm. high when not extended.   £1,300

An early Victorian mahogany duet music stand, the hinged lyre shaped easel on a ratchet with adjustable brass twist stem candle brackets.
(Woolley & Wallis)   £1,200

Gustav Stickley inlaid tiger maple open music stand, circa 1904, no. 670, signed with Eastwood label, 39in. high.   £6,100

Unusual Victorian music stand with papier mâché top inlaid with mother-of-pearl, circa 1850.   £900

A Louis XVI fruitwood, mahogany and marquetry music stand, stamped *Canabas and Jme*, 2ft. 4in. high.
(Phillips)   £1,400

Double sided walnut music stand, last third 19th century, each ratcheted side of pierced scrolling foliage, 67½in. high.
(Skinner Inc.)   £581

READING STANDS

A Regency mahogany reading stand with adjustable top, 30½in. wide. £1,150

An early 19th century mahogany adjustable map reading/ buffet stand, 3ft. £550

George III mahogany pedestal reading table with adjustable slope, 24in. wide. (Prudential Fine Art) £1,500

A George II mahogany reading stand, the rectangular ratchet adjustable hinged top with a rising bookcase and two drawers to each side of the frieze, 2ft. 4in. wide.
(Phillips) £1,800

A Regency mahogany reading table, on a square column and stepped platform base with 'X'-shaped legs, ring turned feet, casters, 2ft. 4in. wide.
(Phillips) £900

A George III mahogany reading table crossbanded in kingwood with a rising rectangular screen filled with an embroidered panel, 23½in. wide.
(Christie's) £3,520

A George III mahogany reading table with crossbanded rectangular easel top and square tapering legs, 25in. wide.
(Christie's) £2,750

William IV rosewood reading/ duet table, with two adjustable flaps and single drawer, carved column on tripartite base, 31in. wide. (G.A. Key) £680

A Regency mahogany reading stand, the sloping writing surface lined with tooled green leather, 23½in. wide. £16,500

TEA TROLLEYS

A Finmar tea trolley, designed by Alvar Aalto, raised on bentwood supports with two large circular disc shaped wheels, 90cm. long.
(Phillips London) £977

Barley twist oak trolley with tray, 1900. £50

American Colonial inlaid mahogany tea cart with glass top and tray, 30in. high. £600

A George IV mahogany serving whatnot, the three-quarter galleried tiers joined by baluster supports, 40½in. wide. £1,200

An Arthur Simpson of Kendal oak tea trolley, the swivel hinged rectangular top above carved frieze of stylised flower-heads, on square section legs, 75cm. high. (Christie's London) £770

A late Victorian ebonised and ivory two-tier trolley by Howard & Sons, the rectangular top with balustrade gallery and ring-turned finials, 30½in. wide. (Christie's) £4,620

A Makers of Simple Furniture laminated birch tea-trolley by Gerald Summers, consisting of three keyhole-shaped shelves, 43.9cm.
(Christie's) £2,860

A Victorian mahogany trolley with canterbury beneath, approx. 2ft. x 1ft.6in. (G. A. Key) £100

Bent plywood tea cart, mid 20th century, top fitted with beverage holder, centering tray, bent wood legs joined by lower median shelf, 20in. wide. (Skinner Inc.) £122

TORCHERES   STANDS

One of a pair of walnut torchères with lobed tray-tops and hexagonal shaped shafts, 10in. wide, 30½in. high.   £1,000

A Regency burr walnut and giltwood torchère with concave-sided triangular top, 17in. wide.   £4,600

A William and Mary walnu torchère with moulded cir cular top, spirally-turned shaft and scrolled tripartit base, 12in. diam.   £80

A pair of walnut torchères, each with hexagonal galleried mahogany top, on spirally-twisted central support and tripod base, part late 17th century, 40in. high. (Christie's)   £825

A mid-Victorian giltwood torchère with stiff-leaf moulding on tapering leafy support with three storks among bulrushes, on claw feet, 63in. high. (Christie's)   £1,870

A pair of Regency parcel-gilt and simulated rosewood torchères, on baluster shaft with triple scroll monopodia and concave-sided panelled triangular base, on bun feet, 88in. high. (Christie's)   £6,05

A Regency satinwood and parcel gilt torchère stand, on reeded shaft with foliate ornament and tripod splayed supports, 2ft. 11in. high. (Phillips)   £1,500

An early George III mahogany torchère with hexagonal galleried top on a stop-fluted stem carved with acanthus, 49in. high. (Christie's)   £1,760

A Regency mahogany, ebonis and parcel gilt torchère with i set circular white bordered Portor marble top, 36½in. hig (Christie's)   £8,25

1930's oak framed corner umbrella stand with metal liner. £35

Victorian mahogany hall stand, 1860. £200

Victorian oak stickstand with brass plaque, circa 1900. £150

An ebonised and parcel-gilt umbrella-stand, the rectangular top above a vertical-railed slightly-tapering body, on a moulded stepped plinth base, 32in. high.
(Christie's) £1,430

A fine pair of mid Victorian oak and ebonised umbrella stands in the Gothic taste, 66in. wide. £900

A metal transfer printed umbrella stand, designed by Piero Fornasetti, the beige ground decorated with polychrome walking sticks, crops, umbrellas and golf clubs, 57cm. wide.
(Christie's) £396

Roycroft oak umbrella stand, East Aurora, New York, circa 1910, signed with logo, 29¾in. high.
(Skinner Inc.) £307

Arts & Crafts umbrella stand, probably Europe, early 20th century, shaped flat sides with spade trailing to circle cut-out, 22in. wide.
(Skinner Inc.) £161

A black and gold-painted umbrella stand with scrolling foliate sides, 32in. wide.
(Christie's) £550

A mahogany urn table, the top with pierced fretwork gallery, 13in. square.
£2,150

A Chippendale style mahogany urn table, 25in. high.
£725

A George III mahogany urn stand, on tapered legs, 12¼in. wide.
(Dreweatt Neate)   £1,500

A George III mahogany urn-stand with serpentine tray-top edged with beading, fitted with a slide on tapering moulded cabriole legs.
(Christie's)   £24,200

A Japanese carved padouk-wood urn stand with circular inset marble top, 10in. diam.
£250

A George III mahogany urn-table with square galleried top above a plain frieze with candle-slide, on canted square legs headed by pierced fretwork angles, on block feet, 11¾in. square. (Christie's)   £1,485

A George III mahogany urn stand with undulating gallery fitted with a candle slide, 1ft. square.
(Phillips)   £1,600

A George III figured mahogany urn table, on moulded cabriole legs with shell headings and pendant flowerheads, 27½in. high. (Christie's)   £22,000

A mahogany urn-stand of George III style, the square top with waved solid gallery, the panelled frieze with candle-stand, 19th/20th century, 11½in. square.
(Christie's)   £1,650

STEPS

Steps are very often associated with libraries (of the domestic sort) where it was necessary to have some means of reaching books on the top shelves. Many were ingenious in their design, not simply folding when not in use, but often metamorphosing also into a chair, footstool or table. Though some were produced earlier, it was not until midway through the 18th century that they came into general use.

An 18th century mahogany library steps chair, the seat on square legs with a pull out step and bracketed stretchers. (Woolley & Wallis) £1,050

A set of late George III mahogany bedside steps, circa 1800, 1ft.11in. high. £2,950

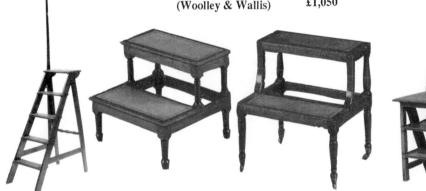

A set of Regency mahogany library steps, surmounted by a tapering upright hand support with five treads.
(Phillips) £2,600

A set of Regency bedsteps, both treads with inset green leather surface, on columnar supports and turned tapering legs, 12¼in. and 18in. high. (Christie's) £935

A walnut folding step chair, circa 1860, in gothic revival manner, the pierced lancet arched back tipping forward to reveal a six-tread step ladder. (Sotheby's) £2,035

A Regency mahogany bowfront three-step commode, each step with leather lining, on ring-turned legs, 17½in. wide.
(Christie's S. Ken) £1,045

A set of George III mahogany metamorphic library steps folding into a stool with padded rectangular green leather seat and hinged top opening to reveal a step with square legs, 18½in. wide. (Christie's) £3,300

A set of Regency mahogany and ebony strung library steps, fitted with a commode, and cupboard door, with brass handle, 16½in. wide. (Christie's) £3,300

Set of Italian baroque walnut library steps, late 18th century, 41in. high.
(Skinner) £2,200

A set of late George III mahogany bedside steps, circa 1820, 2ft.6in. high.
£2,350

One of a set of George III mahogany library steps, with carrying handles, 30in. wide. £3,75

A set of George III mahogany library steps with moulded rail and baluster banisters divided by stop-fluted columns above pierced risers, 67in. wide.
(Christie's) £55,000

A set of George IV metamorphic mahogany library steps, with four rectangular red leather-lined treads on turned and baluster supports, 36in. wide.
(Christie's) £4,180

A set of Regency rosewood library steps with six fluted treads, brass hand-supports (partly deficient) and turned supports, 51in. wide.
(Christie's) £25,30

A George III set of mahogany metamorphic library steps, the rectangular green baize-lined top with three-quarter spindle gallery, 18³/₄in. wide.
(Christie's) £2,640

One of a pair of Regency mahogany metamorphic library armchairs, the seat opening to reveal four treads, 23in. wide. £14,250

George III mahogany library steps, late 18th century, rectangular moulded hinged top opening to eight steps, 49¹/₂in. high.
(Skinner Inc.) £1,138

Stools have not always occupied the humble position they are accorded today, and in the Middle Ages they were an essential part of the social equipment of every household. At court, the sovereign alone sat on a chair, raised on a dais to ensure that no head was higher than his, while stools were provided for the wives of princes, dukes and other important court officials.

A similar hierarchy was observed in most households, which would boast at best only one or two chairs. It was not till Elizabethan times that chairs became more plentiful, by which time too, as a further concession to comfort, stool seats were often padded and upholstered. By the Restoration period stools were being made to match the new chairs which were being imported from the Low Countries.

For the next century and more, stool styles tended to follow those of chairs, though they retained their status, and in the great saloons of houses designed by Robert Adam, an elegant and stately effect was achieved by long stools ranged against the walls, or before windows. Both Hepplewhite and Chippendale feature stools in their Directories, and though Sheraton omits them from his Drawing Book, he does mention them later in his Dictionary. Style thereafter changed little until the anglicised version of the Empire style became popular, but by late Victorian times, the stool had become as often used for resting one's feet upon as any other part of the anatomy.

A walnut stool, the padded seat covered in floral needle-work on turned baluster legs, with scrolled feet, 17¾in. wide. (Christie's)   £2,090

A Biedermeier mahogany tabouret with padded seat, stamped G. Jacob with a fleur-de-lys, 24in. wide.   £1,900

One of a pair of Regency oak and ebonised stools attributed to George Bullock, 24½in. wide. (Christie's)   £20,900

An ebonised and gilt oak circular piano stool, by Lamb of Manchester, circa 1880, the upholstered screw top, above a waisted tripod base. (Sotheby's)   £418

A Regency mahogany adjustable foot-stool with beaded horizontal plain frieze and close-nailed tan-leather hinged seat with tablet splat, on sabre legs, 16¼in. wide. (Christie's)   £660

A Regency beechwood tabouret, the waved seat-rail centred with scallop-shells and carved with acanthus, on cabriole legs headed by scrolls and husks, 21in. wide. (Christie's)   £5,280

A Queen Anne walnut stool, the rectangular seat covered in floral tapestry woven with a fable, 18¾in. wide. £5,500

An unusual painted pine patriotic footstool, Henry G. Perry, New York, circa 1875, painted with a waving American flag with gilt finial, length 18½in.
(Sotheby's) £3,026

A George I red walnut stool with a slip-in seat and shaped apron, on cabriole legs.
£4,500

A Chinese hualiwood stool with pierced frieze and bowed supports joined by a shaped stretcher, 16½in. wide.
(Christie's S. Ken) £330

Pair of Italian neoclassical carved giltwood stools, late 18th century, each with a square brocaded and cut velvet upholstered seat above a panelled frieze, 16in. wide.
(Butterfield & Butterfield) £2,569

Late 19th century mahogany framed revolving piano stool, supported by four fluted turned legs.
(G. A. Key) £260

A Queen Anne walnut stool with a slip-in gros point needlework seat, on cabriole legs. (Phillips) £1,700

Victorian rosewood stool of tapering step and waisted form with green velvet top and cabriole formed front legs.
(G. A. Key) £200

A Dutch 18th century style mahogany marquetry stool on claw and ball feet, 21in. wide. £600

A Georgian rosewood stool with a floral tapestry covered seat, 22½in. wide.
£1,000

A Victorian giltwood stool, on cabriole legs with scroll feet and cabochon headings, 25in. wide. (Christie's S. Ken.) £308

One of a pair of George I needlework covered walnut stools, 1ft.7½in. wide, circa 1715. £23,000

A Charles II silvered wood stool, the padded circular seat with an applique crest surmounted by a coronet, 17in. diam. (Christie's) £1,265

A pair of Willam IV mahogany stools with rectangular needlework tops on baluster turned legs, 11in. wide x 9in. high. (Christie's S. Ken) £385

Late 19th century pottery garden seat, probably France, whimsically depicting a cushion resting on a basket, 20in. high. (Skinner Inc.) £528

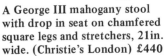

A George III mahogany stool with drop in seat on chamfered square legs and stretchers, 21in. wide. (Christie's London) £440

A Middle Eastern hardwood stool with saddle seat, inlaid with ivory stylised flower-heads, 17in. wide. £600

A William IV mahogany rectangular stool in the manner of Bullock, 15in. wide. (Dreweatt Neate) £300

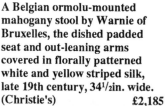

A George I walnut stool, on cabriole legs headed by scrolled brackets, with pad feet, 19½ in. wide. (Christie's) £4,620

A Belgian ormolu-mounted mahogany stool by Warnie of Bruxelles, the dished padded seat and out-leaning arms covered in florally patterned white and yellow striped silk, late 19th century, 34½ in. wide. (Christie's) £2,185

A Queen Anne carved walnut stool, having an arched seat rail on cabriole legs with C-scroll carved spandrels to the knees. (Phillips) £2,70...

A George III Gothic cream-painted stool, the waved arcaded seat-rail carved with pigs and pierced with trefoils, on square tapering legs headed by satyr masks, 16in. wide. (Christie's) £1,485

One of a pair of mahogany stools, the seats with petit point needlework sprays on a camel-coloured ground, the cabriole legs carved with clasps and claw-and-ball feet. £5,150

A Chippendale period carved mahogany stool with a stuffover needlework seat, on pierced angular chamfered legs with Gothic ogee and pierced fretwork. (Phillips) £3,300...

A walnut stool of Queen Anne style, the rectangular seat with squab cushion, on cabriole legs and pad feet, late 19th century, 21in. wide. (Christie's) £715

An ormolu mounted satinwood stool, the padded rectangular seat upholstered in green velvet and decorated with laurel wreaths, 22½ in. wide. (Christie's London) £825

A James II walnut stool, the cabriole legs headed by cabochons with scroll feet joined by moulded waved stretchers, 20in. square. (Christie's London) £2,640

A walnut and parcel gilt stool of George I style, the drop-in seat painted in gilt and scarlet with a coat-of-arms, 26in. wide. £3,900

A walnut stool, with turned baluster legs and stretchers, late 17th century, with restorations, 19in. wide. (Christie's London) £1,100

A George I walnut stool with rectangular needlework drop-in seat, on shell and foliate cabriole legs, 22in. wide. £2,900

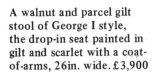

One of a pair of walnut stools each with padded rectangular seat on cabriole legs headed by acanthus on claw-and-ball feet, later blocks, 24in. wide. (Christie's) (Two) £4,620

One of a pair of early George III mahogany stools, on cabriole legs headed by scallop-shells, scrolls and acanthus ending in scrolled feet, 26¼in. wide. (Christie's) (Two) £93,500

A mahogany stool of George I design, the inset rectangular upholstered seat on cabriole legs with pad feet joined by stretchers, 21in. wide. (Christie's S. Ken) £1,430

A George I walnut stool, the ring turned cabriole legs and pad feet headed by unusual pierced and scrolling angle brackets 22¼in. wide. (Christie's) £24,200

A mahogany stool with solid panelled dished rectangular seat with moulded edge, the frieze carved with pendant rockwork, 22¾in. wide. (Christie's) £12,100

A mahogany stool of Empire design, on winged lion's head supports with cabriole legs and gilt metal paw feet, 22in. wide. (Christie's S. Ken) £2,090

A mahogany stool with rounded rectangular padded seat on cabriole legs carved with acanthus, 19th century, 23in. wide.
(Christie's)   **£2,860**

An oak stool of William and Mary style with machined tapestry circular seat and turned scrolled legs, 19in. wide.
(Christie's)   **£600**

A George III mahogany meta-morphic stool, on square cham-fered legs joined by slanting stretchers incorporating three treads.
(Christie's London)   **£1,210**

One of a pair of North Italian giltwood rococo stools, the serpentine seats upholstered with maroon velvet with silver thread borders, 23in. wide.
(Christie's)   **£17,050**

A pair of Victorian stools, with rectangular stuffed over seats, the serpentine frames on cabriole legs, 19in. wide.
(Woolley & Wallis)   **£1,200**

A gilded walnut stool, the rounded rectangular padded seat covered in rose and laurel needlework, on acanthus-enriched carved cabriole legs and claw-and-ball feet, 18½in. wide.
(Christie's)   **£1,540**

A George III cream-painted and parcel-gilt stool, the waved channelled seat-rail centred by flowerheads, on cabriole legs headed by flowerheads, 19½in. wide.
(Christie's)   **£1,210**

A mahogany stool, the rectangular padded seat covered in close-nailed floral patterned needlework on eared cabriole legs headed by lion-masks, on paw feet, 26½in. wide.
(Christie's)   **£3,520**

A late 18th century Continental giltwood and gesso stool, with a tapestry cover depicting an angelic lady pointing to a peacock, possibly Scandinavian, 1ft. 11in. wide.
(Phillips)   **£500**

A walnut stool with rectangular seat, the waved frieze carved with acanthus on cabriole legs headed by lion-masks and paw feet, 28in. wide.
(Christie's) £1,870

An antique carved dressing stool in the Louis XV style having floral petit point upholstered seat on six scroll carved supports, 3ft. 6in. wide.
(Russell Baldwin & Bright) £720

An Irish mahogany stool, the seat rail carved with leaves and scrolls on a pounced ground, on cabriole legs and paw feet, 18th century, 28½in. wide.
(Christie's London) £1,430

A French giltwood stool after a design by A. C. M. Fournier, the four legs and X-shaped stretcher carved in the form of knotted rope, 19in. diam.
(Christie's) £2,860

A pair of Queen Anne carved walnut oval stools, on cabriole legs with foliate and flowerhead carved knees terminating in claw and ball feet.
(Phillips) £12,500

An oak and walnut stool, in the Carolean style, with a stuffover seat, on cabriole legs joined by pierced stretchers with cherubs supporting a crown.
(Phillips) £500

An early Georgian walnut stool, the rectangular seat upholstered in needlework depicting a bird among flowering branches, 18in. wide.
(Christie's London) £2,310

A Napoleon III giltwood stool attributed to A.M.E. Fournier, with waved rope-twist apron and conforming legs and stretchers, 21in. diameter.
(Christie's) £3,300

George III mahogany stool, the upholstered top supported on four cabriole legs with 'C' scrolled shoulders and club feet, mid 18th century.
(G. A. Key) £1,000

FOOTSTOOLS

STOOLS

An unusual upholstered hooked rug footstool, New England, circa 1850, on turned maple 'turnip' feet, length 28½in. (Sotheby's) £719

A Classical carved mahogany footstool, English, 1820-1830, on reeded baluster feet, 6¾in. high. (Christie's New York) £345

Louis XVI giltwood footsto signed *P. Forget*, late 18th century, rectangular needle-point upholstered seat, 13in. long. (Skinner Inc.) £1

A Regency mahogany footstool after a design by George Smith, of lotus-carved S-scroll form with reeded rails and on bun feet. (Bearne's) £290

Gustav Stickley spindle-sided footstool, circa 1907, no. 395, 15in. high. £200

An Italian walnut stool, a fol scroll bar to each end on bearded satyr supports with later turned feet, late 19th century, 40in. wide. (Christie's) £1,

A fancy-painted and decorated footstool, New England, first quarter 19th century, the bowed rectangular top centring a rush seat, on turned cylindrical legs joined by ring and block stretchers, 15¼in. long. (Christie's) £2,105

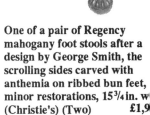

An early Victorian oak gout stool, the hinged and ratcheted close-studded green leather rest on baluster-turned front legs, 22¼in. wide. (Christie's S. Ken) £220

One of a pair of Regency mahogany foot stools after a design by George Smith, the scrolling sides carved with anthemia on ribbed bun feet, minor restorations, 15¾in. w (Christie's) (Two) £1,9

A Gordon Russell oak stool, the rectangular top woven with hide straps, on square section notched legs, 72cm. wide. (Christie's London) £418

A Regency oak footstool, attributed to George Bullock, with padded seat covered in white-striped blue silk, 13½in. square. (Christie's) £13,750

Pair of Italian Neoclassical cream painted parcel gilt footstools, early 19th centur (one foot repaired), 19¾in. lo (Skinner Inc) £1,2

STOOLS

One of a set of six 17th century oak joint stools, 18in. wide. £28,500

Late 17th/early 18th century oak and elm joint stool, 18½in. wide. £2,300

An Elizabethan joint stool, circa 1580, made of inlaid padoukwood. £5,350

**A Charles I oak joint stool with moulded rectangular top on slightly splayed turned spreading legs joined by square stretchers and block feet, 18½in. wide.
(Christie's) £1,430**

An oak joint stool, the seat rail with chiselled edge on turned and squared legs with stretchers, 17th century, one foot restored, 18½in. wide.
(Christie's) £1,210

**A Tudor oak stool with later canted rectangular plank seat and waved arcaded apron, on faceted legs joined by arcaded stretchers, legs shortened, mid-16th century, 17½in. wide.
(Christie's) £4,950**

An oak joint stool, the seat with a moulded edge, on ring-turned supports joined by stretchers, part 17th century.
(Phillips) £380

A 17th century oak joint stool with moulded rectangular seat and shaped seat rail on turned legs, 19in. wide.
(Christie's) £1,100

A 17th century oak joint stool with ring-turned legs joined by plain stretchers, 17¼in. wide. £1,350

STOOLS

A Federal carved mahogany window seat, attributed to the shop of Duncan Phyfe, N.Y., 1810-20, 40in. wide. £19,250

A Regency mahogany window seat, the scrolling X-frame applied with paterae and joined by spirally reeded arms and stretchers, 64½in. wide. (Christie's London) £8,800

A George III-style window seat of Chippendale design, upholstered in hide with brass studding. £550

A late 18th century Italian carved giltwood neo-classical window seat, having a stuffover seat, on square tapered legs, with trailing husks, 4ft. 8in. (Phillips) £1,300

A Regency ebonised and parcel-gilt window seat, the padded seat and scrolled arms covered in buttoned pale yellow silk, the channelled frame with flowerhead terminals and on sabre legs with shell spandrels, 46in. wide. (Christie's) £3,300

A George III carved mahogany window seat frame, the scroll ends with serpentine front fluted seat rail with oval paterae, on fluted tapered legs. (Phillips) £2,700

A Derby & Co. oak window seat, the cut-out armrests with spindle supports, circa 1910, 28in. high. (Skinner Inc.) £260

Italian rococo carved walnut window seat, the scroll ends each with a fluted crestrail above two arched pierced rungs, 7ft. 3½in. long. (Butterfield & Butterfield) £1,156

A George III mahogany window seat, the seat and arms upholstered in pale pink floral damask, 30in. wide. £900

WINDOW SEATS

One of a pair of George III pine window seats with differently upholstered bowed seats and double-scrolled ends, 48½in. wide. £7,150

One of a pair of Victorian oak window seats, each with raised sides on C-scroll supports, 60in. wide.(Bearne's)
Two £2,500

A George IV mahogany window-seat, the demi-patera carved frieze mounted with ball finials, 42in. wide.
(Christie's) £4,370

A George III mahogany window seat with serpentine seat covered in gold damask, 37in. wide. £11,250

A Regency gilded-mahogany stool, the rectangular seat with padded squab cushion between scrolled horizontally-fluted padded end supports, 50in. wide.
(Christie's) £38,900

A Dutch walnut and marquetry window seat, 29½in. wide.
(Dreweatt Neate) £480

A George III carved and decorated window seat, the seat with a cushion and a fluted frieze on turned fluted tapering legs.
(Phillips) £2,600

A William IV rosewood window seat with carved scrolling ends, on turned tapered reeded legs headed by rosettes, 54½in. wide.
(Christie's) £4,620

A George III mahogany-framed window seat with raised over-scrolled sides, on moulded square tapering legs with spade feet, 50in. wide.
(Bearne's) £1,300

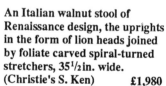

An Italian walnut X-framed stool by V. Aimoni, with foliate-carved baluster-turned arms supported by grotesque figures, 33in. wide.
(Christie's) £5,175

One of a pair of Liberty oak folding stools, each consisting of ten slats forming X-shaped frames. (Christie's) £242

A George IV gilt stool, on fluted 'X'-shaped supports with acanthus capitals, tied by a fluted stretcher, 36½in. wide.
(Bonhams) £650

A Regency white-painted and parcel-gilt stool, on X-framed legs carved with flowerheads and cleft feet joined by a baluster stretcher, 19¾in. wide.
(Christie's) £2,200

A pair of George IV walnut X frame stools, with brass escutcheons, 23in. x 16½in.
(Dreweatt Neate) £1,900

An Italian walnut stool of Renaissance design, the uprights in the form of lion heads joined by foliate carved spiral-turned stretchers, 35½in. wide.
(Christie's S. Ken) £1,980

An Empire giltwood tabouret pliant with padded rectangular seat covered in close-nailed blue watered silk, on channelled x-shaped supports carved with paterae, 25½in. wide.
(Christie's) £8,250

A Regency parcel gilt and simulated rosewood X-framed stool, the seat with a squab cushion covered in striped silk, 35in. wide. £3,000

An oak stool by A.W.N. Pugin, the upholstered square seat on rounded carved 'X'-shaped trestle ends with stylised paw feet.
(Christie's) £880

Sets of furniture which have stayed together over the years, be they from the bedroom or the parlour, will always command a premium well in excess of the sum of the individual articles.

Matching beds, dressing table, wardrobe and chests are always keenly sought after but by far the most popular are the parlour suites. A set of four dining chairs together with two easy chairs and a chaise longue from any period will fetch good money but deep buttoned examples from about 1850 with rosewood or walnut frames will always achieve sums in excess of four figures.

Of particular interest are those suites which include a set of six or more dining chairs, especially if their frames sport carving on the top rail and knees or if they are enhanced with ormolu embellishments.

Two of a set of six 18th century German walnut fauteuils and canape, upholstered in gros and petit point needlework, the canape 51in. wide.
£6,500

Two of a set of eight open armchairs, one of three window seats and a sofa all with caned seats with squab cushions, the sofa 72½in. wide.   £47,500

A Victorian carved giltwood salon suite in the Louis XV style, having leafage scroll decoration, floral tapestry upholstered back panels and seats, on slender cabriole front supports.
(Russell Baldwin & Bright)   £3,300

An Art Deco maple dining room suite, comprising: a dining table, a similar side table, a set of six dining chairs with arched rounded back, a three tiered trolley and a glazed display cabinet.
(Christie's S. Ken)   £1,980

An Art Deco dining suite, probably Hille, veneered in light walnut, consisting of: a table, a sideboard of geometric form, a small buffet and eight chairs en suite.
(Phillips)   £4,200

Assembled suite of Edwardian satinwood seat furniture, circa 1900, comprising a settee and two tub chairs, each back and seat caned, raised on square tapered legs, 37in. high.
(Skinner Inc.)   £2,082

An Art Deco three-piece suite, consisting of a three-seater settee with two matching armchairs, the solid wooden rounded geometric frame veneered with walnut, upholstered, with matching cushions, 175cm. long.
(Phillips)   £1,900

An Art Deco macassar ebony bedroom suite, comprising: a double bed, two similarly decorated bedside cabinets, and a large wardrobe with central mirrored door flanked by two other doors, concealing adjustable shelving.
(Christie's)   £1,430

An English Art Deco leather upholstered three-piece suite, the sofa with cloud-shaped arms and back upholstered in grey leather with walnut stringing to arms, 162.5cm. length of sofa.
(Christie's)   £3,960

A suite of George III mahogany seat furniture, now parcel gilt and cream painted, comprising five open armchairs and a sofa, the sofa 60½in. wide. (Christie's)
£49,500

Early 20th century group of carved bear furniture of Swiss origin.
£3,500

Part of a suite of George II ebonised and parcel gilt seat furniture with velvet upholstered rectangular padded backs and seats on foliate cabriole legs and claw feet, comprising six side chairs, an armchair and two sofas, the sofas 69in. long. (Christie's)   £41,800

A Regency suite of seat furniture previously black and gilt by John Gee, comprising: a pair of
open armchairs and a settee, the overscrolled backs with caned top panels, lower crossbars and
cane filled seats on ring turned legs.
(Phillips)   £1,800

A suite of rootwood furniture formed of links, comprising: a pair of chairs with planked seats
and a pedestal table with planked top, late 19th century.
(Christie's)   £3,850

An Art Nouveau pearwood salon suite, comprising a three seater settee, 175cm. long, two
elbow chairs and four upright chairs. (Phillips)   £2,600

A Victorian parcel-gilt and polychrome-painted gothic suite comprising: a sofa and a pair of open armchairs each with square back, pointed finials and arcaded toprail, on turned legs carved with lotus leaves and ball feet, 74in. wide.
(Christie's)   £3,300

A rare Irish pearwood Art Nouveau three-piece suite by James Hayes, comprising; a two-seat sofa and two side chairs, each upholstered with brown leather, the frames carved with naturalistic forms, the shaped legs with carved feet reminiscent of cloven hooves.
(Christie's)   £6,050

An Empire mahogany and ormolu mounted salon suite, comprising: a canape and four fauteuils, the upholstered and slightly arched carved backs with neo-Classical decorated toprails. (Phillips London)   £6,000

A pair of early Victorian rosewood open armchairs, each with a shaped, curved back, the shepherd's crook arms with eagle's head supports, with claw and ball feet and a sofa en suite, 100in. wide. (Christie's London)   £17,380

A mid Victorian carved walnut salon suite comprising a scrolling floral and foliate carved sofa with shaped crested toprail, on cabriole legs, and four side chairs with pierced balloon back. (Christie's)   £3,520

A 19th century suite of Louis XV-style giltwood seat furniture, comprising a canape and four fauteuils, upholstered in 19th century Aubusson tapestry.   £2,250

An Art Deco burr-walnut and satinwood bedroom suite, comprising: a 'Lit Double', a pair of
bedside cabinets, a dressing mirror and a wardrobe with overhanging rectangular top.
(Christie's)   £1,650

Part of a suite of George III mahogany seat furniture comprising eight side chairs,
each with arched rectangular back and serpentine seat covered in pink striped material
with plain moulded frames, the sofa 77in. long. (Christie's)   £9,900

Early 20th century German suite of furniture consisting of: a round table, four chairs
and a cupboard, in cherrywood with teak inlay, the cupboard with three glazed doors,
190cm. wide, the table on four sided base with corner columns. (Kunsthaus am Museum)
                                                                         £1,087

A French Aubusson-upholstered salon suite, Paris, circa 1880, in Louis XVI style, comprising four armchairs, a pair of bergères and a settee, the settee 187cm. long.
(Sotheby's)   £28,600

Cloud back suite, 1930s, comprising settee, three armchairs, two footstools, figured veneer, simulated leopard skin upholstery.
(Sotheby's)   £4,400

A French tapestry upholstered salon suite, circa 1900, of generous proportions comprising a settee and four armchairs, the gilt wood frames elaborately carved with foliage acanthus, the settee 158cm. wide.
(Sotheby's)   £13,750

ARCHITECTS TABLES

The architect's table was a product of the upsurge of popular interest in architecture and building design which occurred in the 18th century, the amateur enthusiast requiring a surface on which he could execute and study his inspirations. These tables come with many variations, but all incorporate leaves and some sort of adjustable top, under which there are usually drawers and partitions for storing pens, brushes and the like. Some have pillar bases, while others are supported on four legs and resemble a writing table.

George III mahogany architect's portable table.   £450

A mid Georgian walnut architect's table, the frieze drawer with leather lined slide and swivelling ink drawer, 33in. wide.   £5,

A George III mahogany architect's table with adjustable top above a pull-out front section fitted with compartments, 37½in. wide.   £3,800

An early George III mahogany architect's table with crossbanded hinged and ratcheted rectangular top above a frieze drawer, on square chamfered legs. 34in. wide.
(Christie's)   £5,500

A George III mahogany architect's table, the rectangular moulded top with easel support and mechanical book rest, 3ft. wide.
(Russell Baldwin & Bright)   £4,

Early 18th century architect's walnut veneered table, with hinged adjustable top, 31in. wide.   £7,250

A mid Georgian mahogany and rosewood crossbanded architect's table, 37in. wide.   £3,900

An early George III mahogany architect's table, the mitred adjustable top above a frieze drawer, 42in. (Lawrence Fine Arts)   £2,5

A special form of table for breakfasting seems to have existed at least since Tudor times, when it appears in inventories of the day. During the Stuart period gateleg and flap types were often used for this purpose, but the 18th century habit of rising late and breakfasting upstairs led to the introduction of a small table designed to match the bedroom furniture. These are often of a flap type, with a cupboard or shelf under.

In the Regency period, the breakfast table once again descended the stairs and popularly consisted of a pedestal base with splayed legs.

A George III fiddleback mahogany breakfast table with well-figured rounded rectangular tip-up top, on turned stem and splayed feet, 68³/₄in. wide.
(Christie's)   £11,550

A mid Victorian walnut breakfast table with quarter-veneered shaped oval tip-up top on four splayed scroll legs, 57in. wide.
(Christie's)   £1,760

George IV rosewood breakfast table, circa 1825, the circular top with a panelled frieze tilting above a fluted shaft raised on fern-leaf carved and moulded quadruple supports, 4ft. 2¹/₄in. diameter.
(Butterfield & Butterfield)   £4,496

A George III mahogany breakfast-table, the crossbanded oval tilt-top inlaid with fruitwood stringing, on turned shaft and quadripartite base, 59¹/₂in. wide.
(Christie's)   £3,080

George III mahogany breakfast table, first quarter 19th century, on a high arched moulded quadruple base ending in foliated and shell-cast gilt-bronze cappings on castors, 4ft. 2¹/₂in. wide.
(Butterfield & Butterfield)   £1,012

Regency rosewood brass mounted and inlaid breakfast table of large size, the circular snap top with a border of stylised foliate cut brass marquetry, 4ft. 5¹/₂in. diameter.
(Phillips)   £6,500

A George III mahogany breakfast table on baluster turned shaft and ribbed splayed legs, 43in. wide.
(Christie's)   £880

A satinwood breakfast table, the canted tip-up top banded in tulipwood, on turned simulated fluted shaft and four splayed legs, 42¹/₂in. wide.
(Christie's)   £1,100

A coromandel breakfast table, William IV, circa 1830, the circular hinged top with a crossbanded border, 4ft. diameter.
(Sotheby's) £2,012

A Regency rosewood breakfast table, with rounded rectangular banded tip-up top, 60¼in. wide.
(Christie's) £2,750

A Regency rosewood and brass inlaid breakfast table, the circular tip-up top with foliate scroll border above trefoil shaft, 52in. diameter.
(Christie's) £4,950

A George III mahogany breakfast-table with oval tilt-top crossbanded overall upon a turned tapering columnar quadripartite base, 54in. long.
(Christie's) £2,070

A Regency mahogany breakfast-table with rounded rectangular tilt-top, on turned shaft and reeded downswept legs with brass caps, 64in. wide.
(Christie's) £5,175

A Regency oval mahogany breakfast table with banded tip-up top above a turned columnar stem and downswept tripod base, 63in. wide.
(Christie's) £2,860

A mahogany breakfast table, George IV, circa 1820, the hinged top with round corners on a ringed pillar, a platform and four sabre legs.
(Sotheby's) £4,600

A George III mahogany and plum-pudding breakfast-table, on turned fluted spreading base and quadripartite base with fluted downswept square tapering legs and brass caps, 42in. diameter.
(Christie's) £9,350

A George III mahogany breakfast-table, with oval top on turned spreading shaft and channelled downswept legs and brass caps, probably adapted from a section of a dining table, 71¼in. wide.
(Christie's) £6,050

A good English satinwood breakfast table, early Victorian, circa 1840, the octagonal tip-top on a square column, 4ft. ½in. wide.
(Sotheby's) £3,450

A George III mahogany oval breakfast-table with moulded tilt-top crossbanded overall and inlaid with boxwood and ebonised lines, 52¾in. wide.
(Christie's) £4,600

A Scottish rosewood and marquetry breakfast table, Victorian, by Deans of Melrose, circa 1845, 4ft. 5in. wide.
(Sotheby's) £3,335

A George IV rosewood breakfast table, the rounded rectangular tilt-top crossbanded with thuyawood, on a part spirally-twisted and reeded turned shaft, 60¼in. wide.
(Christie's) £2,750

A George III mahogany breakfast-table, with associated rounded rectangular twin-flap top above a double-ended frieze drawer, on a concave-fronted platform, octagonal legs and rounded block feet, 41in. wide.
(Christie's) £3,080

A Regency mahogany breakfast-table, the rounded rectangular tilt-top crossbanded with rosewood, satinwood, boxwood and ebonised borders, 53in. wide.
(Christie's) £2,300

A walnut circular breakfast or library table, by Howard of Berners Street, London, circa 1860, on tripod support overlaid with gilt bronze acanthus, 4ft. 6in. diameter.
(Sotheby's) £6,600

A Regency mahogany breakfast-table, the oval tilt-top crossbanded and inlaid with boxwood and ebonised lines, late 19th century, 54¾in. wide.
(Christie's) £3,000

A Regency giltmetal-mounted rosewood and parcel-gilt breakfast-table, the circular tilt-top banded in satinwood and on turned spreading shaft with gadrooned base, 50¾in. diameter.
(Christie's) £4,180

As the design of card tables progressed, tops tended to become square in shape, but with circular projections on the corners which were dished to hold candlesticks and which also had oval wells for money and chips.

The legs became progressively bolder, the earlier spade and club feet giving way to lions' paws or ball and claw designs. In about 1720, mahogany superseded walnut as the most widely used wood in the construction of gaming boards, though, occasionally, more exotic woods, such as laburnum, were used.

Prior to this time, carving had generally been rather limited – perhaps a shell motif on the knee – but with the introduction of the harder mahogany, more intricate designs, such as lion masks, were added and hairy lions' paw feet employed.

By the 1770's, gambling had reached such a peak that King George III felt it necessary to forbid the playing of cards in any of the Royal Palaces and Horace Walpole, that indefatigable commentator on the fashions of his time, is reported to have remarked that the gaming at Almacks, where young blades were losing as much as £15,000 in a night, was "... worthy of the decline of the Empire".

Although the Prince of Wales, who was later Prince Regent and finally King George IV, extolled the virtues of games of cards, it would appear that the popularity of the pastime had waned somewhat, for 19th century cabinet makers were producing far fewer card tables than their predecessors.

A George II red walnut tea table with circular fold-over top, two quadrant frieze drawers and on shell-carved cabriole legs, 30in. wide.
(Bearne's) £1,600

A Victorian walnut card table with serpentine-sided fold-over top, on four splayed 'S'-scroll legs carved with strapwork and foliage, 35¹/₂in. wide.
(Bearne's) £7

George I inlaid walnut concertina action games table, circa 1720, the burled walnut veneered top within narrow featherbanded and rosewood crossbanded borders, 32³/₄in. wide.
(Butterfield & Butterfield) £2,730

One of a pair of George III painted and satinwood card-tables crossbanded with rosewood and decorated overa with swags of flowers, scrolling foliage and husks, on square tapering legs, 36in. wide.
(Christie's) (Two) £11,5

A half-round mahogany card table inlaid with boxwood lines, on square tapering legs headed by oval fan medallions, late 18th century and later, 3ft. 2in. wide.
(Phillips) £1,300

A William IV rosewood D-shaped tea table on turned lotu carved shaft with gadrooned base and four acanthus carved splayed legs, 36in. wide.
(Christie's) £1,4.

An early George III mahogany card table, the baize-lined interior above frieze drawers on club legs, restored, 30in. wide. (Christie's S. Ken) £825

A Regency rosewood card table with reeded panelled and roundel decorated frieze on U-shaped support, 26in. wide. (Christie's) £605

A George III mahogany card-table with hinged eared serpentine top, the beaded edge carved with paterae, 36in. wide. (Christie's) £3,300

A Dutch hardwood tea-table with eared serpentine top, the waved frieze carved with C-scrolls and rockwork, on cabriole legs headed by acanthus, mid-18th century, 34in. wide. (Christie's) £4,400

A Regency brass-inlaid rosewood and simulated rosewood card-table, on turned spreading partially-fluted shaft, gadrooned socle and circular quadripartite platform base, 36in. wide. (Christie's) £1,430

One of a pair of George III satinwood and marquetry card-tables, each with D-shaped hinged top crossbanded in rosewood and inlaid with oval panel with musical and martial trophies, 36in. wide. (Christie's) (Two) £14,300

A fine antique English George I concertina action walnut tea table of desirable small size, on shell-carved cabriole front legs, circa 1720, 28in. wide. (Selkirk's) £2,668

A mid Victorian walnut card table with serpentine eared swivelling top and scroll carved frieze on four scroll uprights, 36½in. wide. (Christie's) £1,210

An early George III 'red walnut' or mahogany half-round tea table, the double fold-over top enclosing a well, on turned legs with pad feet, 1ft. 11in. wide. (Phillips) £1,500

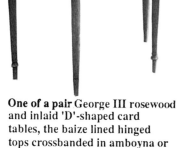

A fine classical carved mahogany swivel-top card table, labelled *Stephen and Moses Youngs*, New York, circa 1815, 36in. wide.
(Sotheby's) £3,970

A Regency rosewood 'D'-shaped tea table, on sabre legs headed by panels of brass marquetry and terminating in castors, 3ft. wide.
(Phillips) £1,600

One of a pair George III rosewood and inlaid 'D'-shaped card tables, the baize lined hinged tops crossbanded in amboyna or burr walnut with purpleheart and rosewood borders, 3ft. wide.
(Phillips) £12,000

A George III red ebony, rosewood, amaranth and burr-yew card-table of semi-circular shape, the hinged crossbanded top centred by a half fan medallion, enclosing a green baize-lined playing-surface, 37³/₄in. wide.
(Christie's) £3,520

One of a pair of Regency rosewood card tables inlaid overall with boxwood lines, each with canted rectangular hinged green baize-lined top crossbanded in mahogany, on square tapering legs, 36in. wide.
(Christie's) (Two) £3,300

A Federal inlaid mahogany card-table, 1790–1810, with hinged D-shaped crossbanded top with inset rounded corners opening to a baize-lined playing surface over a conforming frieze, 35³/₄in. wide.
(Christie's) £4,275

A George II mahogany harlequin games table with rounded rectangular triple-flap top, crossbanded overall, on turned tapering legs and pad feet, 29³/₄in. wide.
(Christie's) £5,500

A marquetry, satinwood and rosewood D-shaped card-table, the hinged flap inlaid with garlanded laurel suspended between opposing classical urns, 39in. wide.
(Christie's) £4,950

One of a pair Regency mahogany, crossbanded and ebony strung card tables, the baize lined hinged tops crossbanded in rosewood with canted corners and friezes centred by panels.
(Phillips) £3,200

A Louis XVI brass and ebony-inlaid mahogany card table, the rotating rectangular hinged top above a well, enclosing a green baize-lined playing surface with four sunburst dishes, 33½in. wide.
(Christie's) £7,920

A Louis XVI brass-mounted and brass-inlaid mahogany table à jeu with triple D-shaped flap and panelled frieze, 43in. wide.
(Christie's) £2,200

An extremely fine and rare Chippendale carved mahogany card table, Boston-Salem, Massachusetts, circa 1765, the oblong top with squared outset corners, width 31¼in.
(Sotheby's) £88,487

One of a pair of Regency brass-inlaid rosewood scissor-action card-tables, each with D-shaped folding top inlaid with a running stylised foliate and anthemion border supported by scrolled S-shaped legs, 35½in. wide.
(Christie's) (Two) £7,150

A Chinese export padoukwood triple-flap harlequin games, tea and writing-table, the rounded rectangular top enclosing a green baize-lined playing surface with candle-stands and counter-wells, mid-18th century, 31½in. wide.
(Christie's) £1,980

One of a pair of Regency rosewood card-tables, crossbanded with satinwood and tulipwood and inlaid with boxwood and ebonised lines, each with hinged D-shaped top enclosing a red baize-lined interior, 35½in. wide.
(Christie's) £7,700

One of a pair of William IV mahogany tea-tables, each with rounded rectangular hinged top above a plain frieze with flowerhead angles, 36in. wide.
(Christie's) (Two) £3,520

A Federal satinwood and mahogany card-table, New York, 1790–1810, the hinged clover-shaped top with crossbanded edges above a conforming apron centring a raised rectangular inlaid reserve, 35½in. wide.
(Christie's) £4,275

One of a pair of Regency mahogany card-tables, each with hinged D-shaped top banded with an ebony line enclosing a green baize-lined playing surface, 35¼in. wide.
(Christie's) (Two) £3,520

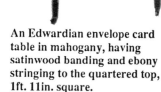

An early George III mahogany concertina-action card-table, the hinged green velvet-lined rectangular top with foliate-carved rim, on channelled cabriole legs, 36in. wide.
(Christie's) **£10,450**

A Regency rosewood card-table, the rounded rectangular baize-lined swivel-top inlaid with a band of scrolling foliage on four scrolled downswept legs, 36in. wide.
(Christie's) **£2,640**

An Edwardian envelope card table in mahogany, having satinwood banding and ebony stringing to the quartered top, 1ft. 11in. square.
(Russell Baldwin & Bright) **£1,1**

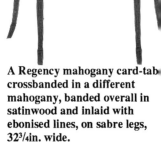

A Regency kingwood scissor-action tea-table with hinged D-shaped top crossbanded in satinwood on four downward-scrolling legs with brass caps, 36in. wide.
(Christie's) **£2,750**

Early George III later japanned games table, the interior centred by a painted chequerboard and inset with four oval counter wells, 31½in. wide.
(Butterfield & Butterfield) **£607**

A Regency mahogany card-tab crossbanded in a different mahogany, banded overall in satinwood and inlaid with ebonised lines, on sabre legs, 32¾in. wide.
(Christie's) **£2,09**

A mid-Georgian mahogany card-table with canted rectangular top enclosing a green baize-lined interior with candle-rests, on cabriole legs headed by acanthus, 29in. wide.
(Christie's) **£4,180**

A Victorian walnut and marquetry inlaid serpentine card table, on a reeded tapering shaft and foliate lappeted quadruple splayed legs, 35in. wide. (Christie's S. Ken) **£660**

A good Federal inlaid mahogan serpentine card table, attribute to Bryant & Loud, Boston, Massachusetts, circa 1815, the shaped top with lunette-inlaid edge, 35¼in. wide.
(Sotheby's) **£1,65**

A William IV mahogany 'D'-shaped card table, the turned shaft with leaf carving on a quadripartite platform with outscrolled carved feet, 3ft. wide.
(Phillips) £820

An Arts and Crafts inlaid oak card table, attributed to William Birch, the square top with four hinged triangular panels above arched aprons and plank legs, 74.6cm. high.
(Christie's) £715

A Regency brass inlaid rosewood card table with fold-over swivel top inlaid with a continuous band of trailing flowers and leaves, 36in. wide.
(Lawrence Fine Art) £2,090

A boulle serpentine card table of Louis XV design, the fold-over top with central figure playing a lyre flanked by caryatids, urns and butterfly motifs, 19th century, 34¼in. wide.
(Christie's) £1,870

A Regency rosewood and simulated rosewood and brass strung card table, on dual turned columns, platform and on scroll headed splayed legs, 3ft. wide.
(Phillips) £1,200

A George II mahogany tea-table with D-shaped twin-flap top enclosing a semi-circular well, with panelled frieze and gateleg action, on cabriole legs, 27¼in. wide.
(Christie's) £4,400

A mahogany concertina action card table, the shaped rectangular top inlaid with Dutch marquetry, 34½in. wide, basically 18th century.
(Bearne's) £3,000

Sheraton Revival period mahogany fold top card table, the top inlaid with musical instruments and music and satinwood crossbanded, 1ft. 8in. wide.
(G. A. Key) £290

A French ormolu-mounted tulipwood and kingwood card-table with rectangular banded quarter-veneered top with foliate edge, late 19th century, 32½in. wide.
(Christie's) £1,100

These were tables designed to be free-standing and were often circular. Italian examples dating from the 15th century are often elaborately decorated, and the form became increasingly popular through the 16th century. In the 17th century examples are usually of oak or walnut, but from around 1750 mahogany came to be commonly used in both England and America. During the Directoire and Empire periods, marble-topped centre tables were popular.

A good French marquetry centre table, Napoléon III, circa 1860, on fluted tapering legs, 136cm. wide.
(Sotheby's) £4,620

A regency rosewood and parcel-gilt table centre table, the circular top on bold acanthus-carved turned shaft, 53½in. diameter.
(Christie's) £9,775

A Continental marquetry centre table, Swiss or Austrian, circa 1860, the top etched and inlaid with hunting scenes and a man defending himself from an eagle, 92cm. diameter.
(Sotheby's) £2,750

A giltwood centre table, in the Louis XVI style, with a breche violette marble rectangular top, the frieze centred by an Apollo sunburst mask, flanked by panels of scrolling foliage, the tapering fluted legs each with a Corinthian capital, second half 19th century, 38½in. wide.
(Christie's) £2,200

A good English and Italian pietra dura centre table, the Derbyshire top with a Florentine base, circa 1860, 85cm. diameter.
(Sotheby's) £10,450

A 19th century Sorrento walnut and marquetry centre table, by Luigi Garguilo, inlaid with classical figures after the Antique, 2ft. 5in. wide.
(Phillips) £13,000

A fine Italian micro-mosaic and giltwood circular centre table, Rome, circa 1860, 88cm. diameter.
(Sotheby's) £23,100

An impressive bronze centre table, the design after the Antique, and possibly by Gottfried Semper, circa 1860, the circular marble top on three lion monopodia, 3ft. 5in. high.
(Sotheby's) £23,100

A South German burr walnut veneered table on gadrooned baluster column and tripartite base, 115cm. diameter. (Kunsthaus am Museum) £1,758

A fine French circular gilt-bronze jardinière table, Napoléon III, cast by Ferdinand Barbedienne, Paris, circa 1860, 86cm. high. (Sotheby's) £9,680

A French circular ormolu-mounted kingwood and marquetry table, Paris, circa 1890, in flower-inlaid quarter-veneered wood, 77cm. diameter. (Sotheby's) £2,750

A Gothic Revival oak centre table, New York, second quarter 19th century, the octagonal top with green baize lining and moulded edge above a conforming frieze with ebonised moulding above an octagonal pedestal carved with ogee arches, 48$^{1}/_{2}$in. wide. (Christie's) £5,919

A rare Queen Anne carved walnut slab-table, Philadelphia, 1730–1750, the rectangular thumbmoulded marble top above a conforming walnut apron with shaped multiple lobed skirt, 36$^{1}/_{2}$in. wide. (Christie's) £276,233

A bronzed and ebonised centre table with associated circular painted marble top decorated with figures on rocks in a Mediterranean coastal scene within a border of oak leaves and acorns on a black ground, 19th century, 33$^{1}/_{4}$in. diameter. (Christie's) £2,420

An unusual German oval porcelain mounted elm centre table, circa 1850, the top with one hexagonal and six circular Sèvres-style plaques, top 129 x 94cm. (Sotheby's) £2,200

A Chinese export black and gilt lacquer centre table, the circular tilt-top decorated with a chinoiserie battle scene within a foliate border with mythical monsters, first half 19th century, 36in. diameter. (Christie's) £2,420

An unusual North Italian burr walnut table, inlaid all over with fruitwood marquetry, with serpentine moulded border, 117cm. diameter, 19th century. (Finarte) £18,365

A late Victorian satinwood and marquetry table, the circular top centred by a sun-burst with radiating fan-pattern and green-stained demi-lunes, 54in. diameter.
(Christie's)   £4,620

Flemish baroque carved oak centre table, the flattened oval top above a deep scalloped frieze fitted with a geometrically-fronted drawer, 40¹/₄in. wide.
(Butterfield & Butterfield)
                              £1,080

Italian rococo style carved, silvered and giltwood and scagliola centre table, raised on a baluster and ring-turned standard, 31¹/₂in. high.
(Butterfield & Butterfield)
                              £2,531

Italian Empire walnut centre table, circa 1800–1810, the circular top veneered in radiating section of Circassian walnut above a plain deep frieze fitted with a single drawer, 27¹/₂in. diameter.
(Butterfield & Butterfield)
                              £1,445

A Victorian rosewood and marquetry centre table, the circular top segmentally veneered, each segment centred by a cartouche incorporating birds and foliage, 48¹/₂in. wide.
(Bonhams)   £2,300

Biedermeier inlaid mahogany centre table, Austrian, second quarter 19th century, on a hexagonal line-inlaid pedestal supported by six C-scroll brackets terminating on a six-sided flanged base, 30in. wide.
(Butterfield & Butterfield)
                              £2,025

An early Victorian mahogany centre table with circular Italian specimen marble top on three scrolled supports headed by carved dragons, 23in. diam.
(Christie's London)   £6,050

A late George II mahogany centre table, the plain frieze with gadrooned edge and cabriole legs carved with foliage and cabochons ending in claw-and-ball feet, 33¹/₄in. wide.
(Christie's)   £35,200

An early Victorian mahogany marble-specimen centre table, the circular top with various marbles including verde antico and Siena, 27in. wide.
(Christie's)   £2,200

A 19th century walnut and marquetry centre table, with geometric fruitwood inlay, on a turned baluster column and quadripartite base, 89cm. diameter, Sorrento.
(Finarte) £918

An early Victorian mahogany, ebony and marquetry centre table attributed to E.H. Baldock, the octagonal tilt-top with simulated rosewood leather-lined rim, 56in. wide.
(Christie's) £10,120

A Victorian mahogany centre table, the moulded foliate carved and fluted baluster shaft supporting four scrolled columns, stretching to foliate carved scrolled toes, 37in. wide.
(Christie's) £880

An Italian grey-veined Carrara marble centre table, the circular top inlaid with various marbles with central radiating motifs and borders with butterflies, birds and flowers, 35^1/$_2$in. wide.
(Christie's S. Ken) £3,850

An ebony and marquetry centre table, the octagonal tilt-top profusely inlaid with ribbon-tied stylised Medici foliate panels heightened with mother-of-pearl, 19th century, 49^1/$_2$in. wide.
(Christie's) £8,800

Italian baroque carved walnut centre table, the octagonal top raised on a faceted attenuated baluster standard flanked by four inverted dolphins, 31^3/$_4$in. high.
(Butterfield & Butterfield) £742

An early 19th century Dutch mahogany and marquetry centre table, the circular top with cornucopia, birds and butterflies, on a splayed trefoil pedestal, 3ft. 4in. diameter.
(Phillips) £2,800

An Empire mahogany centre table surmounted by a circular dished grey marble top with a veneered frieze, raised on five cylindrical columns with ormolu capitals, 4ft. 5in. diameter.
(Phillips) £6,400

A burr walnut and ormolu mounted centre table, with white marble top, on concave triangular column and paw feet, 118cm. diameter, early 19th century.
(Finarte) £4,591

Console tables are so named for the console, or bracket, which is used to support them against the wall in the absence of back legs.

Perhaps surprisingly, their development came later than that of most other tables for they did not appear until the early 18th century, when house interiors became more sophisticated, with furniture being designed to blend into the entire decorative scheme. It was not, in fact, until about 1730 that eagle console tables achieved real popularity following their appearance in the court of Louis XIV where, as a rule, they were placed beneath a pier glass and sported superbly figured tops of Italian marble.

On the original tables, the marble tops were regarded as being by far the most important features (console tables were described as 'marble slab frames' in early inventories) and they were carefully selected for fine grain and exquisite colour gradation and harmony from such notable suppliers as Signor Domenico de Angualis. The Victorians, having rather less flamboyant tastes, tended to go more for plain white tops in preference to the pinks and greens of the earlier examples and were inclined to build up the rococo ornamentation with gesso.

Later still in the Victorian period, the original marble and gilt materials were often abandoned in favour or a much more prosaic style, made either of mahogany or walnut. These are generally about three and a half feet wide, though a smaller example exists with a single cabriole front leg support.

One of a set of four Continental parcel gilt corner console tables, probably French, circa 1880, in Louis XV/XVI Transitional manner, 75cm. wide.
(Sotheby's) (Four)   £4,620

One of a pair of Louis XV giltwood console tables each with serpentine-moulded brown breccia marble top above a pierced frieze with central scallop shell, 46^{1}/$_{4}$in. wide.
(Christie's) (Two)   £18,700

A pine console table with portor rectangular marble top above a Vitruvian scroll frieze supported upon a splayed eagle resting on a rockwork base, 29^{1}/$_{2}$in. wide.
(Christie's)   £3,300

One of a pair of Louis XVI ormolu-mounted white-painted and parcel-gilt corner consoles each with eared bowed honey alabaster top, 36in. wide.
(Christie's) (Two)   £22,000

A late 17th/early 18th century carved giltwood console table, the legs and stretchers heavily carved with foliate and shell motifs, with yellow marble top, Neapolitan.
(Finarte)   £6,308

A rare French 'Boulle' pier table, Louis-Philippe, Paris, circa 1845, the inverted breakfront frieze above four square tapering legs, 113cm. wide.
(Sotheby's)   £3,410

An 18th century Italian baroque giltwood console table with a later rectangular Siena mottled marble veneered top, 5ft. 3in. wide.
(Phillips) £3,800

A George II carved giltwood 'eagle' console base, in the form of a four winged bird, one claw resting on an orb, 3ft. 7in. wide.
(Phillips) £3,400

One of a pair of Bolognese giltwood console tables each with later serpentine green marble top above a moulded frieze and pierced apron, mid-18th century, 68in. wide.
(Christie's) (Two) £22,000

One of a pair of ormolu and verde antico console tables, each with moulded rectangular top above a plain frieze mounted at each end with a patera, possibly North European, 35½in. wide.
(Christie's) (Two) £8,800

A Louis XVI brass-inlaid mahogany console desserte with rectangular grey marble top with pierced three-quarter gallery, on later toupie feet, 34¼in. wide.
(Christie's) £2,860

A marble top pier table, attributed to Charles-Honore Lannuier, New York, 1819, the rectangular white marble top with canted corners above a conforming frame centring applied ormolu trophies and foliage, 43in. wide.
(Christie's) £7,235

A Swedish giltwood console table attributed to Burchardt Precht with moulded rectangular green and white Swedish Tolmards granite top, early 18th century, 39¾in. wide.
(Christie's) £22,000

A George III giltwood console table in the manner of Thomas Johnson, the top of arc en arbalette outline with a later marble slab, 2ft. 6in. wide.
(Phillips) £6,500

An early Louis XV oak console table, with later-rounded-rectangular mottled red-marble top, 34in. wide.
(Christie's) £3,080

A 19th century German rosewood and oak console table, of demi-lune form, the deep frieze applied and carved with heraldic crests, 4ft. 3in. wide. (Spencer's) **£800**

One of a pair of grained pine console tables with marble tops on carved eagle supports, 42¼in. wide. **£3,150**

One of a pair of Louis XVI white-painted consoles, the pierced fluted friezes carved with foliage on fluted scrolli⸱ supports edged with ropetw⸱ 21¼in. wide. (Christie's) (Two) **£5,2⸱**

One of a pair of Milanese ebonised console tables, each supported by a kneeling blackamoor and scrolling back panel, mid 19th century, 40¼in. wide. (Christie's) (Two) **£4,180**

A Louis XV giltwood console table with moulded eared serpentine brèche violette top, the waved apron carved with interlocking chain pattern and centred by a pair of ribbon-tied bagpipes, 34in. wide. (Christie's) **£19,800**

One of a pair of George II styl⸱ parcel-gilt mahogany eagle-for⸱ consoles each with rectangular⸱ salmon marble top within a parcel-gilt and floral-carved border, 4ft. wide. (Butterfield & Butterfield) **£3,7⸱**

An 18th century carved giltwood console table, in the Louis XV taste, surmounted by a later simulated marble top of arc en arbalette serpentine outline, 3ft. 2in. wide. (Phillips) **£5,000**

An 18th century Italian baroque blackamoor console table, supported by a crouching figure with strained expression holding a cloth on his lap. **£5,571**

Régence style carved giltwood console table, 19th century, wit⸱ an acanthus carved frieze, raise⸱ on foliate carved scroll support⸱ 33½in. high. (Butterfield & Butterfield) **£2,6⸱**

Mid 18th century German giltwood console table with grey marble eared serpentine top, 37in. wide.
(Christie's)   £12,100

One of a pair of giltwood console tables with serpentine moulded white tops, 40in. wide.   £3,750

One of a pair of brass inlaid rosewood console tables, each with a verde antico marble top on displayed eagle support, 43½in. wide. (Christie's S. Ken)   Two   £7,700

A Swedish Empire giltwood console table with rectangular grey marble top above a lappeted frieze, on scrolled dolphin supports and stepped base, early 19th century, 30¾in. wide.
(Christie's)   £2,970

A Southern Italian giltwood console table with moulded eared serpentine white marble top, the pierced frieze carved with flowerheads, acanthus and rockwork, mid-18th century, possibly Neapolitan, 46in. wide.
(Christie's)   £3,520

Italian rococo parcel-gilt and polychromed console table, mid 18th century, the blue marbleised top of shaped outline with inswept sides above a conforming frieze carved with rocaille, 40½in. wide.
(Butterfield & Butterfield) £3,212

A William IV rosewood console table with rectangular white marble top above foliate carved scroll uprights and mirrored back, 29in. wide.
(Christie's S. Ken)   £660

A pine console table with rectangular white marble top, now painted to simulate verde antico, 32in. wide. (Christie's)   £4,950

George III inlaid mahogany console table, circa 1790–1800, raised on fluted and reeded turned tapering supports, 36in. wide.
(Butterfield & Butterfield) £2,193

DINING TABLES

Dining tables, of course, come in many shapes and sizes, several of which, gateleg, dropleaf and large, have their own sections in this book. The circular, tilt top table is another variant, having much in common with the loo table.

No, we are still in the dining room ... Loo tables are named for the three to five handed variety of whist which became a fashionable craze in the mid 19th century. The tables had a circular top and central pillar design, which meant that all players could sit round them in comfort, unhindered by distant corners and constricting table legs.

Usually made of mahogany or rosewood, they have reeded or turned central columns on a platform base with either bun, claw or lion's paw feet. In Victorian times they became more elaborate, with superbly carved bases and often figured walnut tops which have a useful tip up action operated by two screws underneath, enabling them to be stood to one side when not in use. Later too, they often became more ovoid in shape, and the central pillar was enlarged into a cage of four columns. During the Regency period extending, pillar dining tables became popular. These were extremely versatile, and the Victorians were quick to see the advantages in having a table which could stretch or contract to accommodate the number of guests on the night. Their styles however tended to be very much more massive, of the leg-at-each-corner-type, and having centre leaves which could be added by turning a handle to open the table.

A Louis XVI mahogany extension dining-table, with demi-lune drop ends above a plain frieze on canted square tapering legs ending in casters, 77¼in. long. (Christie's) £13,869

A mahogany centre table, probably French, late 19th century with oval white and grey-veined carrara marble top, 87cm. wide. (Sotheby's) £2,300

A Charles X bois clair extension dining-table, circa 1825, with demi-lune drop ends above a plain frieze, on ring-turned baluster legs ending in casters, 72in. long extended. (Christie's) £17,000

A Louis XVI style ormolu-mounted mahogany extension dining-table, with demi-lune drop ends above a plain frieze, on tapering legs headed by engine-turned capitals, 88in. long, extended. (Christie's) £8,000

A Regency brass-inlaid rosewood breakfast-table, the circular tilt-top inlaid with a band of scrolling foliage and with a gadrooned edge, 52in. diam. (Christie's) £7,820

An extending dining table, with rounded rectangular top on foliate-headed line-inlaid baluster-turned legs with brass cappings and castors, 201½in. wide extended. (Christie's) £4,000

A Regency brown oak centre table, the geometrically veneered circular tilt-top inlaid with ebonised lines, 54¼in. diameter.
(Christie's)   £13,225

A Regency mahogany extending breakfast table, on a baluster-turned shaft and hipped reeded downswept legs, 66½in. wide, including leaf.
(Christie's)   £2,760

A good Victorian rosewood dining table with quatrefoil shaped top, 59 x 43in.
(G. E. Sworder)   **£1,200**

A 19th century mahogany 7 leaf extending table, the central standard in the form of columns on a quadripartite base and paw feet, 153cm. diameter unextended, each leaf 30.5cm.
(Finarte)   £5,050

A mid-Victorian rosewood, mahogany and marquetry dining table, the circular tip-up top with central radially-veneered circular panel, 52in. diameter.
(Christie's)   **£2,500**

A George IV rosewood breakfast-table, the circular tilt-top with bead-and-reel edge and plain frieze on a panelled triangular shaft centred by a flowerhead and stylised foliage, 56¼in. diam.
(Christie's)   £4,830

Regency mahogany extending dining table on tapering spiral turned legs with brass terminals, 48 x 88in.
(Ewbank)   **£3,400**

Regency rosewood round dining table on turned gadrooned central pillar and platform base with lion's paw feet, 53in. diameter.
(Ewbank)   **£2,000**

A late Louis XVI mahogany travelling drop-leaf table, with demi-lune drop ends above a plain frieze and gates on circular tapering stop-fluted legs, 59½in. wide.
(Christie's)   £5,008

A Regency circular mahogany and brass inlaid breakfast or dining table.
£1,400

Late 19th century amboynawood octagonal breakfast table with ebonised borders, 48in. wide. £1,250

A 19th century exhibition centre table, the top within a chequered ivory and ebony surround, 45in. diam. £7,250

A mahogany circular extending dining table with foliate carved and ribbon-twist frieze, on foliate carved turned legs, 120in. wide.
(Christie's) £1,430

A Louis XIV walnut refectory table, the detachable rectangular top pegged and fitting onto a cross frame, on ring-turned columns with bun feet, 1.1m. x 89cm.
(Phillips) £1,300

Gustav Stickley dining table, no. 632, circa 1904, overhanging round top with apron on five square tapering legs, 49in. diameter.
(Skinner) £1,241

A large William IV rosewood veneered loo table, the triform base on knurled toes with tulip scrolls, 4ft. 5in. diameter.
(Woolley & Wallis) £1,250

A Killarney yewwood pedestal table inlaid with satinwood stringing, circa 1840, 5ft. wide. £1,750

A Victorian circular snaptop burr walnut veneered breakfast table, with cabriole legs, 4ft.6in. diam.
£1,000

DINING TABLES

An early Victorian mahogany veneered circular snap-top breakfast table, 4ft.7in. diam. £1,100

A George II mahogany tripod table with rectangular needlework top, 2ft.8½in. wide, circa 1750. £6,000

A Regency circular breakfast table in rosewood with a beaded edge, 52in. diam. £8,750

A late George III mahogany D-ending dining table on square tapered fluted legs each headed by a fanned oval, 84½in. wide, including an extra leaf. (Christie's S. Ken) £1,650

A William IV mahogany breakfast table, the circular tip-up top with arcaded frieze hung with finials, 48in. diameter. (Christie's S. Ken) £1,980

An early Victorian mahogany extending dining table with rounded rectangular top on turned tapered legs, 127in. extended. (Christie's) £1,540

A George IV loo table, the circular tilt top veneered in figured rosewood, with a band of brass marquetry and a gadroon edge, 4ft.2in. diameter. (Woolley & Wallis) £3,800

A George III satinwood and inlaid breakfast table, crossbanded in tulipwood, with oval snap top, 1.23m. £10,000

A rosewood veneered loo table, the grained base with a turned stem and three splay legs with shaped knees, 4ft. diameter. (Woolley & Wallis) £1,000

Large dressing tables complete with mirrors were, if we are to judge from the design catalogues, made in profusion throughout the eighteenth century and some, Chippendale's in particular, were very fine indeed.

Designers of the period vied with each other to see who could cram in the greatest number of ingenious little fitments, each designer claiming every innovation as his own and decrying all others for having pinched his ideas. Sheraton, in particular, was fascinated by the challenge and his designs became more and more complex as he progressively widened the scope of his ideas until, toward the end, it would seem that he was attempting to develop the ultimate, all-purpose item of furniture. One of his later creations was a superbly eccentric construction incorporating hinged and swing mirrors, numerous drawers, a washbasin, compartments for jewellery, writing materials and cosmetics, not to mention the commode.

By far the most popular dressing tables to come from the second half of the eighteenth century were described by Shearer as 'dressing stands'. These were usually of quite small size, standing on fine, elegant legs.

During the Victorian period, there were a few small dressing tables but, as a rule, the Victorians preferred them rather more solidly proportioned. The Edwardians, on the other hand, seem to have taken to them with a little more enthusiasm and reproduced a number of styles of the late eighteenth century.

A French gilt-bronze mounted dressing table, by Krieger of Paris, circa 1900, 110cm. wide, fitted for electricity.
(Sotheby's) £3,910

A fine and rare Queen Anne mahogany block-front kneehole dressing table, Boston, Massachusetts, circa 1760, on scroll-cut bracket feet, width 36in.
(Sotheby's) £59,539

A North Italian walnut crossbanded and strung bombé kneehole dressing table of serpentine form, on cabriole legs, 3ft. 6in. wide.
(Phillips) £2,600

A German ormolu-mounted burr elm, burr thuya and mahogany dressing-table of Empire style, early 19th centur 40³/₄in. wide.
(Christie's) £4,0?

A William and Mary black-painted pine and maple dressing-table with baluster and trumpet-turned legs joined by flat serpentine X-stretchers, 32¹/₂in. wide.
(Christie's) £4,76

An Arts and Crafts dressing table, circa 1900, oak, copper handles, lockplates and repouss panels, 4ft. wide.
(Sotheby's) £93

DRESSING TABLES

A George III mahogany kidney-shaped dressing table crossbanded overall and with a central frieze drawer, on square tapering legs, 42½in. wide. (Christie's) **£4,025**

An Empire mahogany and ormolu mounted dressing table, with arched swing frame plate on columns with urn finials, 2ft. 2in. wide. (Phillips) **£1,500**

A fine George III mahogany Rudd's dressing chest, with a moulded edge centred by a fitted drawer, having carrying handles to the sides, on bracket feet, 3ft. 6in. wide. (Phillips) **£6,000**

An Anglo-Chinese white-metal-mounted padouk dressing-table with part-hinged tripartite serpentine top banded in ebony and with boxwood stringing, enclosing a central mirrored section within an ebony frame, mid-18th century, 33in. wide. (Christie's) **£9,350**

A Queen Anne maple dressing table, Massachusetts, 1740–1760, the rectangular top with thumbmolded edges above a conforming case fitted with one long thumbmolded drawer above three short thumbmolded drawers, 33½in. wide. (Christie's) **£4,932**

A Louis XV ormolu-mounted mahogany and tulipwood poudreuse by Roger Vandercruse Lacroix (RVLC), the banded waved eared rectangular tripartite top inlaid à quatre faces with key-pattern corners, 36¼in. wide. (Christie's) **£8,800**

A George III ormolu-mounted rosewood, sycamore and marquetry serpentine dressing-table attributed to Mayhew & Ince, 33in. wide. (Christie's) **£35,200**

An Edwardian satinwood, crossbanded and decorated bowfront lady's dressing table, painted with floral and drapery swags and sprays, 1ft. 10in. wide. (Phillips) **£1,600**

The Samuel Morris Chippendale carved mahogany dressing table, Philadelphia, 1760–1780, on shell-carved cabriole legs with ball-and claw feet, 36in. wide. (Christie's) **£17,100**

An Edwardian satinwood and inlaid dressing table, the oval plate above two small drawers, the lower section with five drawers around the kneehole. (Bonhams) £750

A rosewood bow front dressing chest fitted with a rectangular rising mirror and splayed supports, 19th century, 140cm. (Lawrence Fine Arts) £616

A classical mahogany dressing table with mirror, attributed to the workshop of Duncan Phyfe & Sons, New York, circa 1845, 47^7/₈in. wide. (Sotheby's) £4,632

An Empire mahogany and giltmetal mounted dressing table, the arched rectangular swing-plate above a single frieze drawer, 32in. wide. (Christie's S. Ken) £1,760

A George III fustic dressing-table crossbanded in kingwood, the stepped rectangular top with hinged central section enclosing a formerly fitted interior, 40in. wide. (Christie's) £4,950

A Dutch mahogany and marquetry bombé dressing chest, the rectangular plate on shaped supports, above four long graduated drawers, on paw feet, 35in. wide. (Bonhams) £3,800

A fine Federal carved mahogany swivel-top card table, New York, circa 1810, on waterleaf-carved reeded and ring-turned legs, 36^3/₄in. wide. (Sotheby's) £1,489

A Federal carved mahogany dressing table with mirror, New York, circa 1815, the rectangular mirror plate pivoting between two scrolled supports, 36^1/₂in. wide. (Sotheby's) £1,985

A Chippendale carved mahogany dressing table, Philadelphia, circa 1770, the rectangular thumb-moulded top above one long and three short moulded drawers, 35in. wide. (Sotheby's) £12,571

An Arthur Simpson of Kendal dressing table, with three quarter galleried top, on square section tapering legs, stool en suite, 114cm. wide. (Christie's London) £715

Federal mahogany dressing table, New England, circa 1825, 33in. wide. (Skinner) £373

A George III mahogany dressing table, the divided hinged rectangular top enclosing a fitted interior with adjustable mirror, with block feet and leather castors. (Bearne's) £3,100

A Biedermeier mahogany pedestal dressing table mounted with brass and inlaid with bands of scrolling foliage heightened with mother-of-pearl, with conforming stepped base, 18¾in. wide. (Christie's London) £2,420

A Louis XV ormolu mounted kingwood, tulipwood crossbanded and marquetry poudreuse or coiffeuse with cartouche shaped panels of floral sprays veneered à quatre faces, 3ft. 2in. wide. (Phillips) £10,500

A Louis XVI-style mahogany and marquetry dressing table applied throughout with gilt brass mounts, the hinged rectangular top with projecting corners and inlaid with musical trophies, 26in. wide. (Bearne's) £1,350

A parquetry and marquetry dressing table, the folding rectangular top part lined in maroon leather and enclosing three compartments, 35in. wide. (Christie's London) £1,650

An early Victorian satinbirch dressing table with two swing-frame mirrors fitted with ten drawers on rounded rectangular plinth base, 63in. wide. (Christie's S. Ken) £825

A late Regency oak dressing table, in the manner of George Bullock, on bulbous turned legs tied by a concave platform stretcher, 34¼in. wide. (Bonhams) £770

A small kingwood veneered necéssaire, possibly English, circa 1900, various hallmarked silver gilt fittings, 82.5cm. high. (Sotheby's) £2,640

A Queen Anne walnut dressing-table, Massachusetts or Rhode Island, 1740-1760, the over-hanging moulded top with indented front corners, 34¼in. wide. (Christie's) £24,650

A Victorian satinwood and gilt-metal-mounted dressing table, of inverted form applied with Sevres-style porcelain plaques, 45in. wide. (Christie's) £4,500

A Louis XVI mahogany dressing table with moulded rounded rectangular hinged top with mirror on the reverse, the interior with later marble base, 32½in. wide. (Christie's) £2,200

An inlaid toilet table attributed to Luigi Gargiulo, the surface with a mythological scene within a foliate border, Sorrento, 1840, 72cm. wide. (Finarte) £9,409

A George III mahogany and marquetry dressing-commode inlaid with boxwood lines, the concave-fronted canted rectangular top inlaid with a central oval panel of floral sprays, 43in. wide. (Christie's) £2,070

A Chippendale carved mahogany dressing table, Philadelphia, 1760-1780, the rectangular top with moulded edge and indented corners above a cavetto moulding, 38½in. wide. (Christie's) £45,895

A mahogany dressing-table with hinged, rounded rectangular top enclosing a fitted interior with six variously-sized lidded compartments, 38¾in. wide. (Christie's) £1,495

A Chippendale walnut dressing table, Philadelphia, 1760-1780, the rectangular top with pinched corners above a fitted case with three thumbmoulded graduated drawers, 35½in. wide. (Christie's) £19,250

From about 1750 until the end of the 18th century, furniture designers strove to break away from traditional styles in the attempt to create something completely different and this period saw a multitude of legs, flaps and movements built into tables which extended, opened, hinged, turned and folded up in order to achieve the maximum possible surface area in the smallest practicable space.

One of the simpler designs to emerge from this orgy of inventiveness was the envelope table – obviously so called from the triangular shape of the flap – which has all the attributes of a good Georgian table, being made of nicely grained mahogany and having cabriole legs.

Another form of drop-leaf table has rectangular flaps which sometimes reach almost to the ground. Though essentially country made and of simple design, with straight, square legs chamfered on the inside edge, units of this kind were often used to form part of the large extending tables so popular throughout the 18th century.

Made from about 1850 and continuing in popularity until the end of the 19th century, Sutherland tables were manufactured in a variety of woods; earlier examples are usually of rosewood and burr walnut, later ones employing walnut or mahogany.

This little table, named after Queen Victoria's Mistress of the Robes is ideal for the small dining room for it will seat six when fully open yet, closed, will stand quite comfortably out of the way.

A classical carved and inlaid mahogany breakfast table, attributed to Duncan Phyfe, New York, 1805–1815, 49½in. wide open.
(Christie's) £3,850

A Regency mahogany Cumberland-action breakfast-table, the rounded rectangular twin-flap top on ring-turned supports and channelled downswept legs, 53½in. wide.
(Christie's) £4,830

A William IV brown oak work-table with twin-flap rounded rectangular top above a mahogany-lined beaded panelled frieze drawer, on downswept legs and foliate feet, 31¾in. wide.
(Christie's) £3,300

An elegant Regency calamander and satinwood banded sofa table, in the manner of George Oakley, outlined in brass stringing, 58in. wide.
(Bonhams) £8,500

A Chippendale mahogany drop-leaf table, Newport, Rhode Island, 1740-1760, the rectangular top with similarly shaped drop leaves above a conforming case, 47¾in. wide.
(Christie's) £2,300

A Federal inlaid mahogany drop-leaf table, Boston, Massachusetts, 1800-1815, the rectangular top with hinged rounded drop leaves, 39¼in. wide.
(Christie's) £4,235

A Chippendale mahogany
dining table with two drop-
leaves, Phila., 1765-85,
55in. long.   £1,200

A Victorian walnut Sutherland
table with quarter-veneered
burr-walnut oval top, on splayed
legs, 42in. wide.
(Bearne's)   £600

A Chippendale mahogan
card table with scalloped
front skirt, Mass., circa
1770, 31½in. wide, open
£5,65

A late 18th/early 19th century
Dutch mahogany and
marquetry drop-leaf table, with
all over profusion of floral and
riband twist inlay, on square
tapering legs, 3ft. 6½in.
extended.
(Phillips)   £1,100

A Victorian walnut Sutherland
table with well-figured quarter-
veneered shaped oval top, 41in.
wide.
(Bearne's)   £720

A Queen Anne maple drop-leaf
dining table, New England, circ
1775, the cyma-shaped skirt
continuing to cabriole legs
ending in pad feet, length 53in.
(Sotheby's)   £1,9

A mahogany drop-leaf table
with rounded rectangular twin-
flap top above a plain frieze with
ogee-shaped apron, on later
cabriole legs headed by acanthus
knees, part 18th century, 38½in.
wide.
(Christie's)   £495

A good Chippendale walnut
drop-leaf breakfast table,
Boston, Massachusetts, circa
1760, the oblong top with two
hinged D-shaped leaves, 35¾in.
long.
(Sotheby's)   £1,985

A George II Cuban mahogany
oval drop leaf dining table, fitte
an end frieze drawer with a
brass ring handle, the plain
turned legs on hoof feet,
4ft. 10in. wide.
(Woolley & Wallis)   £2,00

A good Queen Anne maple drop leaf dining table, Rhode Island, circa 1765, on angular cabriole legs ending in pad feet, width extended 52½in.
(Sotheby's) £2,194

An early 19th century Dutch inlaid mahogany drop leaf dining table, raised upon turned and tapering fly leg supports with foliate inlay, 3ft. 7in. wide.
(Spencer's) £900

Chippendale walnut dining table, Pennsylvania, 1770–90, with two end thumb-moulded drawers, 49¼in. wide.
(Skinner) £2,648

Edwardian rosewood Sutherland table with marquetry and bone inlay, on turned ring legs with baluster bottom stretcher, 24in. wide.
(G.A. Key) £390

A Queen Anne walnut drop-leaf table, Pennsylvania, 1740–1760, the oval top with two drop leaves above a shaped skirt, on cabriole legs with slipper feet, 65½in. wide.
(Christie's) £5,590

A Dutch mahogany and floral marquetry triangular drop-flap table on foliate carved cabriole legs with claw and ball feet, 33in. wide.
(Christie's S. Ken) £1,100

A Napoleon III amboyna, parcel ebonised and marquetry table à volets, the rectangular top with elliptical leaves, 43in. wide.
(Bonhams) £1,100

A George II mahogany drop leaf table, circa 1740, on circular tapered legs with pad feet, 39in. diam. £502

Gustav Stickley round drop leaf table, circa 1912, demi-lune drop leaves, paper label, 32in. long.
(Skinner) £915

These rather elegant tables are also known as 'library' or 'rent' tables, and first appeared in the second half of the 18th century. They remained popular throughout the Regency period and well into the Victorian era.

Most earlier examples are of mahogany, while those dating from the Regency period may also be of rosewood. The Victorians used both these woods, but seemed on the whole to prefer burr walnut.

Drum tables were often used in estate offices and commonly had revolving tops.

A mid-Victorian mahogany library table, the octagonal moulded top with a frieze fitted with four drawers and four false drawers, 57in. wide. (Christie's)   £3,250

A classical carved mahogany drum table, New York, 1815-1825, on four sabre legs with panel carved knees and brass paw castors, 27in. diameter of top.
(Christie's)   £2,700

A late George III mahogany and satinwood-banded library drum-table, on a ring-turned support and three splayed legs, 40in. diameter.
(Christie's)   £3,750

A Regency rosewood library drum table banded overall in tulipwood, the frieze with four mahogany-lined drawers and four hinged doors simulated as drawers, 29¾in. high.
(Christie's)   **£11,000**

A Regency mahogany library drum table inlaid overall with ebonised lines, on a turned shaft and panelled tripod base, 35in. diameter.
(Christie's)   £4,370

A Regency mahogany drum table, the crossbanded circular top above four hinged triangular mahogany-lined drawers, on a ring-turned baluster support, 18¾in. diam.
(Christie's)   £3,450

A Regency brass-mounted and brass-inlaid rosewood library table, the circular top inlaid with a foliate arabesque border, 48in. diameter.
(Christie's)   £8,050

A Maltese fruitwood centre table, circa 1825, the top inlaid with an ebonised Maltese cross, 54cm. diam.
(Sotheby's)   £1,840

A Regency mahogany drum top table, on turned column and quadruped splayed legs with foliate carved ornament, 4ft. diameter.
(Phillips) £4,000

A George III mahogany rent table, on a cupboard base enclosed by a panel door, on a plinth base, 3ft. 7in. diameter.
(Phillips) £3,800

A George III circular mahogany drum table with inset grey tooled leather top, with four reeded splay legs, 42in. diameter.
(Anderson & Garland)
£2,500

A Regency mahogany drum top library table, on a baluster turned column and quadruped reeded splayed legs, brass cappings and castors, 3ft. 1in. diameter.
(Phillips) £3,400

A Regency mahogany library table with circular green leather-lined top above a panelled frieze with eleven mahogany-lined segmental drawers, on turned spreading shaft and quadripartite base, 54½in. diameter.
(Christie's) £4,180

A George III mahogany drum table, the circular top with inset green leather above two long and two short drawers lettered *B/R/M/L* and four simulated drawers, 40¾in. diameter.
(Christie's) £8,250

A Regency maplewood drum table inlaid with ebonised lines, the circular green leather inset top above eight frieze drawers, 2ft. 8in. diameter.
(Phillips) £3,500

A Regency mahogany library drum table, the circular leather inset top above four frieze drawers, 3ft. 5in. diameter.
(Phillips) £3,000

A Regency mahogany and yew-wood drum table, the circular banded top centred by a circle, the frieze with two cedar-lined drawers, 30in. diameter.
(Christie's) £6,000

DRUM TABLES

A Victorian mahogany drum-top library table, the revolving top with tooled leather insert, on a scroll-carved tripod base with brass castors, 48in. diameter.
(Bearne's) £1,550

A Regency mahogany drum-table, on gadrooned baluster shaft and quadripartite support with fluted leaf-headed scroll legs, 27¹/₄in. diameter.
(Christie's) £16,500

A George III rosewood drum-table, the frieze with four mahogany-lined drawers and four simulated drawers, 39in. diameter.
(Christie's) £13,7

A William IV carved mahogany drum-top library table, the revolving crossbanded top inset with a panel of green tooled leather containing four short and dummy drawers in the frieze, 3ft. 6in. diameter.
(Phillips) £4,500

A Maltese olivewood drum-top table, the circular top centred by a Maltese cross above four true and four false frieze drawers, first quarter 19th century, 26in. wide.
(Christie's S. Ken) £1,760

George IV mahogany drum table, second quarter 19th century, the cross-banded circular revolving top above a frieze fitted with alternating drawers and false drawers, 4 diameter.
(Butterfield & Butterfield)
£2,0

A mahogany drum table, the circular green leather-lined top with four drawers, and four simulated drawers, on downswept legs with scrolled ends and paw feet, 42in. diameter.
(Christie's) £4,400

A satinwood drum table banded in walnut with circular red leather-lined top, the frieze with four drawers and four false drawers, 23in. diameter.
(Christie's) £1,320

A good George IV mahogany drum table, the tooled leather inset top within an ebony inlai border of scrolling foliage, up a plain turned lotus capped column and tri-form base wit scroll feet, 49³/₄in. diameter.
(Tennants) £1,8

322

DUMB WAITERS

Dumb-waiters were extremely fashionable during the final quarter of the 18th century and throughout the Regency period, although there is evidence that they were available as early as 1727, when Lord Bristol purchased one from a cabinet maker named Robert Leigh.

It was Sheraton, with a turn of phrase as elegant as one of his own chairlegs, who described the dumb-waiter as "a useful piece of furniture to serve in some respects the place of a waiter, whence it is so named".

A William IV mahogany dumb waiter with three rectangular tiers on lotus carved side supports, 39½in. high. (Bearne's) £1,700

A Regency mahogany two-tier dumbwaiter, 36½in. high. £875

A Regency mahogany dumb-waiter with two circular tiers on brass column supports and spirally-reeded baluster stem, 21¼in. diameter. (Christie's) £1,210

A late Regency mahogany dumb waiter, the two rectangular tiers each with a pierced brass gallery, 46in. wide. (Christie's) £4,400

A George III mahogany twin tier dumb waiter with revolving dished tops and reeded edges, on tripod splayed legs, 2ft. diameter top. (Phillips) £700

A Regency ormolu mounted mahogany dumbwaiter, 26¼in. diam., 45¼in. high. £6,500

A William IV mahogany three tier dumb waiter with serpentine acanthus and gadrooned rectangular galleried top, on brass castors, 50½in. wide. (Christie's S. Ken) £1,045

A Regency ormolu mounted mahogany dumbwaiter, 27in. diam., 42¾in. high. £7,250

A mid-Georgian mahogany three-tier dumb waiter with ring-turned baluster shaft, arched base and pad moulded feet, 47in. high.
(Christie's)   £893

A George III mahogany two-tier dumb waiter, the circular hinged tiers on downswept legs with brass caps and castors, 2ft. 8in. high.
(Phillips)   £1,000

A George II mahogany three-tier dumb waiter, each circular shelf on baluster-turned shaft and chamfered tripod base and pointed pad feet, 43½in. high.
(Christie's)   £2,420

A Regency mahogany triple folding three-tier dumb waiter with hinged tops, on column and tripod splayed legs.
(Phillips)   £1,500

A pair of mahogany and brass-mounted two tier dumb waiters, each circular tier with pierced Greek key gallery, each 22½in. diameter.
(Christie's)   £1,540

A George III mahogany dumb waiter of good colour, with three dished circular tiers, 40in. high.
(Bonhams)   £3,000

A mahogany three-tiered dumb-waiter with circular dished tiers on laurel-carved baluster shaft and downswept legs carved with acanthus, 18th century, 26in. diameter.
(Christie's)   £1,760

One of a pair of brass-mounted mahogany dumb-waiters, on turned spreading shaft and tripod base with channelled downswept legs, block feet and casters, 45½in. high.
(Christie's)   £6,050

A George III mahogany two-tier folding dumb-waiter, each double-hinged tier with rounded rectangular swivelling support, on turned urn-shaped shaft, 23in. wide.
(Christie's)   £638

GATELEG TABLES

The gateleg table has remained one of the most popular styles ever since its introduction during the 17th century, even those being made today having the same basic design and movement as the originals.

Usually made of oak, though occasionally of more exotic woods such as yew or walnut, the majority of gateleg tables have tops of round or oval shape and the legs are braced with stretchers which, like the main frame, are cut to take the pivoting 'gate' leg. (Larger tables are constructed with two gatelegs on each side.)

Although these tables have been made since the 17th century, the vast majority date from the late 19th and early 20th centuries.

As a rule, prices reflect top size and, when the length of the closed table is greater than four feet, they really begin to soar into large figures.

The cabriole leg is so called from its likeness in shape to the leg of an animal (it's derived from the French word meaning "goat's leap") and implicit in the meaning is the suggestion of a free, dancing movement which would obviously be destroyed if stretchers were employed.

The change from gateleg to gate tables was a direct result of the switch in fashion towards cabriole legs and, once free of encumbering stretchers, the table's movement could be simplified in that two of the actual legs could now be swung out to support the flaps. This cleaned up the lines of the leg section by allowing the omission of the two extra 'gatelegs'.

A burr-walnut Sutherland table, Victorian, circa 1850, with shaped oval top, 117cm. open. (Sotheby's) £977

A mahogany gateleg table, the oval oval twin-flap top with moulded edge, on turned legs and fluted scroll feet, 35¼in. wide. (Christie's) £3,680

A George II mahogany oval drop-leaf table with moulded top above a frieze drawer on cabriole legs carved with rockwork C-scrolls, 60in. wide. (Christie's) £4,000

A mid-Georgian mahogany drop-leaf table, the oval twin-top with moulded edge and on club legs, 70in. wide. (Christie's) £5,175

A mid-Georgian laburnum spider-gateleg table, the twin-flap rectangular top with re-entrant corners and moulded edge, 30in. wide. (Christie's) £3,335

A William and Mary turned walnut and yellow pine gateleg dining table, American, probably Southern, 1720–50, width extended 51in. (Sotheby's) £6,053

A William and Mary maple gate-leg dining-table, probably Massachusetts, 1730–1745, with oval drop-leaf top above an apron with single end drawer, 45$\frac{1}{2}$in. deep.
(Christie's) £3,083

A mahogany and walnut gateleg dining table, the rounded rectangular top crossbanded in satinwood, on baluster turned supports tied by similar stretchers, the top 18th century.
(Bonhams) £850

A Charles II oak oval gateleg table with a boldly figured top, frieze drawer and slender turned legs, joined by moulded stretchers, 59$\frac{1}{2}$ x 46in.
(Tennants) £1,500

A walnut gateleg table with oval twin-flap top and single end-drawer on fluted column legs and splayed feet joined by plain stretchers, 30in. wide.
(Christie's) £825

A Chinese Export huali miniature gateleg table inlaid overall in mother-of-pearl with foliage and domestic utensils, the circular twin-flap top inlaid with birds in trees, bats' wings and butterflies, late 18th/early 19th century, 26in. diameter.
(Christie's) £3,080

An oak gateleg table, the oval top with single flap on baluster legs joined by squared stretchers, 34in. wide.
(Christie's London) £1,265

A late 17th century oak gateleg table with oval top, frieze drawer, the baluster legs joined by square stretchers, 28$\frac{1}{4}$in. high.
(Bearne's) £380

A George III mahogany spider gateleg-table with eared serpentine twin-flap top, on turned legs joined by turned stretchers on claw-and-ball feet, 35$\frac{3}{4}$in. wide.
(Christie's) £13,200

An oak gateleg dining-table, the oval twin-flap top with single later frieze drawer on baluster and square legs joined by square stretchers, early 18th century, 49in. wide.
(Christie's) £2,530

An oak gate-leg table with oval twin-flap top with one drawer to the end, on spirally-twisted legs joined by square stretchers on bun feet, 63½in. wide.
(Christie's) £3,080

Drop leaf maple and pine trestle base table, New England, 18th century, refinished, 37½in. open.
(Skinner) £1,980

An oak gate-leg table, the rectangular top with two hinged leaves on baluster turned legs joined by stretchers, 17th century, 69in. long.
(Christie's S. Ken) £990

A Charles II walnut gateleg table, previously with a drawer, on baluster-turned legs joined by square stretchers, on turned feet, 32¼in. wide.
(Christie's) £7,150

A mid-Georgian mahogany gateleg table, the folding triangular top with a small frieze drawer, on club legs, 39in. (Christie's) £770

A German walnut gateleg table, the hinged rectangular top inlaid with flowers, scrolls and geometric bands, basically late 17th century, 33½in. wide.
(Christie's) £3,300

A George II mahogany gate-leg dining-table on turned tapering legs joined by turned and square stretchers, on pad feet, restorations to underside and top, 48in. wide.
(Christie's) £4,950

An oak gate-leg table with oval hinged top on bobbin-turned supports joined by stretchers, 58in. wide.
(Christie's S. Ken) £1,760

An oak gate-leg table, the demi-lune fold-over top on baluster column supports joined by stretchers, 37½in. wide.
(Christie's S. Ken) £1,430

A William and Mary maple gate-leg table, New England, 1700–1730, with rectangular top and two hinged rectangular leaves, 36in. wide open.
(Christie's) £3,067

One of a pair of satinwood Sutherland tables, circa 1900, with banded tops and shaped flaps on square cut legs with splayed feet, 65cm wide.
(Sotheby's) £1,380

19th century mahogany Sutherland table on a central reeded pillar and quadruped base with matching supports, 32in. wide.
(Ewbank) £50

A fine and rare French marquetry occasional or Sutherland table, attributed to Joseph Cremer, Napoléon III, Paris, circa 1855, 103cm. wide open.
(Sotheby's) £33,350

A very fine and rare Queen Anne maple 'butterfly' tavern table, New England, 1730–60, the oblong top with two hinged D-shaped leaves, width extended 37¼in.
(Sotheby's) £5,624

A William and Mary gumwood trestle drop-leaf table, New York, 1720–1735, the oval top with hinged drop leaves above baluster and ring-turned legs, 33¾in. wide.
(Christie's) £10,65

A Queen Anne mahogany drop-leaf table, Rhode Island or Pennsylvania, 1740–1760, the hinged oval top with D-shaped drop-leaves, 43¾in. open.
(Christie's) £5,350

A Federal mahogany dining table, New York, 1805-1810, the demi-lune ends above a conforming apron with inlaid tablets, on twelve reeded tapering legs, 88in. wide open.
(Christie's) £9,250

A Queen Anne mahogany drop-leaf table, Salem or Boston, Massachusetts, 1740–1760, with two rounded drop leaves, 30½in. wide.
(Christie's) £24,533

Named after the monastic dining rooms in which they were originally used, refectory tables are based upon a very old design.

The name is now given to virtually any long table with legs on the outside edge although it originally applied only to those having six or more legs joined by stretchers at ground level.

Widely used until the end of the Jacobean period (1603–1688), refectory tables dwindled in popularity after that time, though they have been made in small numbers ever since.

The design of tables changed at the beginning of the 19th century from the rectangular and D-ended styles to tables which were either round or sectional.

The latter were extremely practical tables for, besides allowing ample leg room, they could by the simple addition of more units be extended at will from four seaters to a length more suited to a banquet.

Bases had plain or turned columns with three or four splayed legs which were either plain or reeded, terminating in brass castors.

Another large table is the Victorian extending dining table which, being heavy and massive, most people instinctively associate with the Victorian period. This type of table, usually made of mahogany, though sometimes of oak, extended by means of a worm screw operated by a handle in the centre and allowed the addition of one or two extra leaves. Occasionally the centre leaf was equipped with drop-down legs as a means of providing extra stability when the table was fully extended.

A William IV mahogany extending dining-table attributed to Miles and Edwards with mounted D-shaped ends and ten leaves, on turned legs carved with lotus leaves, 263in. long.
(Christie's)   £13,800

A mahogany two-pedestal dining-table with two D-shaped end-sections and a central leaf, on turned spreading columnar supports and downswept legs with anthemion-cast brass caps, the top early 19th century, 111¼in. long, fully extended. (Christie's)   £4,600

A Regency mahogany extending dining-table, with two D-shaped end sections and three extra leaves, one associated, with plain frieze and on removable broad-reeded turned baluster legs, 113in. long, overall.
(Christie's)   £6,440

A George III mahogany three-pedestal dining-table with two tilt-top D-shaped end-sections, a central tilt-top rectangular section and two further leaves, with moulded rounded rectangular top on waisted turned baluster supports, 141¾in. long, fully extended.
(Christie's)   £23,000

A large and early refectory table, the massive three-plank top supported on solid trestle ends joined by two 'beam' stretchers, 119in. long. (Tennants) £5,000

An Edwardian mahogany extending dining table with rounded rectangular top on foliate-headed cabriole legs, 152in. wide extended. (Christie's) £2,420

A George IV mahogany extending dining table with D shape pedestal ends, each on three sabre shape leaf capped supports, 126in. long. (Lawrence Fine Art) £2,970

Italian Renaissance walnut refectory table, on a baluster trestle support joined by a plain stretcher, 57in. wide. (Skinner Inc.) £1,236

A brass-mounted William IV mahogany wine table, the semi-circular top with a hinged semi-circular removable section and two hinged flaps, on turned tapering reeded legs, 73in. wide. (Christie's) £4,400

An oak dining table, designed by M.H. Baillie-Scott, of rectangular shape on two trestle supports, each composed of twin turned baluster columns on square plinths and shaped transverse base, circa 1897, 183cm. long. (Christie's) £3,520

An oak refectory table with rectangular plank top on baluster-turned uprights joined by stretchers, the top 18th century, 121in. wide. (Christie's) £2,640

A George III mahogany D-end dining table in three sections, the centre with two flaps above a plain frieze on square tapering legs, 106in. £3,000

A mahogany extending dining table, on four rectangular supports, each with two reeded splayed legs with giltmetal paw feet, 214½ x 50¼in. (Christie's) **£6,050**

A late Regency mahogany extending dining table with two rounded ends, raised on four reeded tapering supports, 274cm., extended. (Lawrence Fine Arts) **£5,060**

Flemish baroque oak drop-leaf table, the moulded base raised on turned supports on flattened bun feet, 63¹/₂in. long. (Skinner Inc.) **£1,854**

A Regency twin pedestal D-end dining table, each pedestal with two rectangular supports and quadripartite splayed base, 118½in. long. (Christie's) **£44,000**

A George IV oak dining-table by Alexander Norton, with rectangular central section and two rectangular end-sections, on turned tapering arcaded legs carved with acanthus and headed by paterae, 216in. long. (Christie's) **£4,950**

A Regency mahogany extending dining-table with two D-shaped end-sections, one with hinged section and gateleg action, with two extra leaves, on turned tapering reeded legs with brass caps, 95¹/₂in. wide. (Christie's) **£3,520**

A George IV mahogany extending dining-table with two D-shaped end-sections, on turned ribbed legs and giltmetal caps, 103in. wide. (Christie's) **£6,050**

A late Federal mahogany three-part dining table, New York, circa 1820, on ring and spirally turned legs on brass casters, length 9ft. 6in. (Sotheby's) **£3,972**

A Regency mahogany extending dining-table with two D-shaped end-sections and five extra leaves of which two are later, on turned tapering legs, 199in. wide.
(Christie's)   £5,500

An early Victorian mahogany extending dining-table with two D-shaped end-sections and four extra leaves, on turned tapering legs carved with acanthus leaves, with brass caps stamped *COPE COLLINSON PATENT*, 149in. wide.
(Christie's)   £3,520

A Regency ormolu-mounted oak, brown oak and ebonised four-pedestal dining-table attributed to George Bullock, inlaid overall with ebony lines, the crossbanded top inlaid with linked beads, and comprising two D-shaped end-sections and five leaves all of which slide on, 227in. wide, fully extended. (Christie's)   £209,000

A Regency mahogany twin-pedestal dining-table with two D-shaped end-sections with tilt-top, the quadripartite base with reeded downswept legs and brass paw feet, 92½in. wide.
(Christie's)   £5,720

A Regency mahogany twin-pedestal Cumberland-action dining-table with two twin-flap rounded rectangular end-sections and one later extra leaf, 125in. wide.
(Christie's)   £23,100

A Federal mahogany accordion-action dining table, New York, 1790–1810, the rounded rectangular top extending to include five extra leaves over a straight apron and baluster and ring-turned supports, on downswept moulded sabre legs, 147in. wide, extended.
(Christie's)   £12,760

An oak and elm refectory table with square top and plain end-supports joined by a plain stretcher on downswept legs, late 17th century, 94½in. wide.
(Christie's)   £12,100

A George III mahogany extending serving-table, the frieze carved with a rosette edged with fluting flanked by flowerhead swags and fluttering ribbons with foliate lower border, 32in. high.
(Christie's)   £49,500

A set of four Regency oak Gothic tables in the manner of George Bullock, each banded in brown oak and an ebonised line, each inlaid on three sides, two with one detachable end-moulding.
(Christie's)   £9,900

An early Victorian mahogany three-pedestal dining-table with two D-shaped end-sections and three extra leaves, each banded in relief with mythical animals, birds and figures within scrolling foliage, 184in. wide.
(Christie's)   £52,800

A George III mahogany serving-table in the manner of Robert Adam, the fluted frieze centred by a ram's mask hung with acanthus scrolls and paterae, 80in. wide.
(Christie's)   £18,700

A Regency mahogany extending dining table with two D-shaped end-sections, a central swivel-section and two extra leaves, on eight ring-turned tapering legs and brass caps, 101in. wide.
(Christie's)   £5,280

An Anglo-Indian solid satinwood dining table with two D-shaped gateleg end-sections and three central sections, on turned legs, early 19th century, 87^{1}/$_{2}$in. wide.
(Christie's)   £2,750

An Elizabeth I walnut draw-leaf table, the later rectangular top above a frieze carved with scrolling foliage and screaming masks, each panel centred by a smiling mask within scrolls, 87^{1}/$_{2}$in. wide.
(Christie's)   £18,700

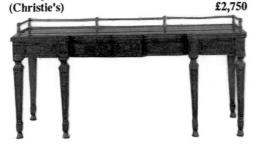

A Regency brass-inlaid mahogany serving-table with inverted-breakfront rectangular top inlaid with ebonised stringing, the back-rail with two later supports, 88^{1}/$_{2}$in. wide.
(Christie's)   £4,400

A Regency mahogany serving-table with rectangular top, on leaf-carved scroll legs and paw feet, with plain panelled back-supports, 84in. wide.
(Christie's)   £2,640

A Regency mahogany drinking table, the semi-circular top with associated D-shaped inner section and two side flaps, on turned tapering reeded legs, 86in. wide.
(Christie's) £4,180

Italian baroque walnut refectory table, with a central long drawer flanked by drawers, raised on scrolling supports joined by a stretcher, 80½in. long.
(Skinner Inc.) £1,096

A William and Mary oak and pine stretcher-base table with moulded edge over four block and baluster-turned supports, on baluster feet joined by moulded box stretchers, 67¾in. long.
(Christie's) £1,569

A Regency mahogany patent extending dining table, the hinged 'D'-shaped reeded top with two extra leaves, on concertina action turned and ribbed legs, 6ft. 11in. long.
(Phillips) £3,500

A William IV mahogany and brass mounted extending dining table with concertina action, the D end folding over and extending to take three additional leaves, 132in. long.
(Lawrence Fine Art) £5,500

A George III mahogany dining table in three parts inlaid with boxwood and ebonised lines, with a central drop-leaf section and 'D'-shaped ends, 8ft. 6in. x 3ft. 6in. wide.
(Phillips) £4,200

An early 19th century mahogany twin pillar dining table with a moulded edge on ring-turned columns and reeded splayed quadruped supports, 6ft. 2in. long.
(Phillips) £2,400

George III mahogany three-part dining table, late 18th century, D-shaped end flanking a rectangular centre section, inlaid with stringing, 98¾in. wide.
(Skinner Inc.) £1,350

A Regency mahogany extending dining table in two sections, in the manner of Gillows, the reeded D-end top on ring turned and reeded legs, 2.85m. long.
(Phillips London)   £5,500

A George III style mahogany D-end dining table on triple turned tapering shafts and fluted quadruple splayed legs, extending to 124in. x 46½in. including two extra leaves.
(Christie's S. Ken)   £2,310

A classical mahogany three-pedestal dining table, American, circa 1825, comprising a rectangular centre section and two D-shaped end sections, length approximately 15ft. 7in.
(Sotheby's)   £9,079

A George IV mahogany dining table with two D-shaped end-sections and one extra leaf, on fluted turned tapering legs and giltmetal caps, 79in. wide.
(Christie's)   £1,540

A Charles II oak bench with moulded rectangular top and arcaded frieze, on splayed turned baluster legs joined by stretchers, 80¾in. wide.
(Christie's)   £2,640

A fine Federal mahogany three-part dining table, American, probably Boston, circa 1810, on turned and reeded tapering legs ending in ball feet, length extended 13ft. 3½in.
(Sotheby's)   £4,632

An oak refectory table, designed by Margaret Butterfield, for the Choir School, All Saints, Margaret Street, London, 1850–1859, 90cm. wide, 152cm. long.
(Christie's)   £1,650

A French Provincial walnut centre table, the rounded rectangular top with central star inlay above waved scroll frieze, late 18th century, 76in. wide.
(Christie's)   £2,200

A poplar and pine trestle base dining table, possibly North Carolina, early 19th century, the rectangular top with two chamfered cleats tilting above two trestle supports, 118½in. long. (Christie's) £17,875

A 17th century rectangular walnut table, having three frieze drawers, on three turned legs ending in plinth feet, 252cm. wide, Emilian. (Finarte) £8,878

A Tuscan walnut refectory table with rounded rectangular top, on waisted square supports joined by a square stretcher, 138in. long. (Christie's) £7,150

A Regency mahogany four-pedestal dining-table with four tilt-top pedestal sections and three leaves, the rounded rectangular top on turned baluster supports, 175½in. long, fully extended. (Christie's) £12,100

A good and large oak library or centre table, circa 1850, on trestle supports, guarded by lions couchant, the stretcher supporting quatrefoils and gothic tracery, 6ft. 11½in. wide. (Sotheby's) £4,290

A Regency mahogany three-pedestal dining-table with reeded top with two D-shaped ends and central section on turned columnar shafts and channelled downswept legs and casters, 106in. long. (Christie's) £9,350

A George IV mahogany dining-table with two D-shaped end-sections, central twin-flap gateleg section, plain frieze and reeded turned tapering legs with brass caps, 122¾in. long overall. (Christie's) £4,400

A Regency Irish triple-pillar mahogany dining table, each pillar with a turned baluster column and leaf carved and grooved quadripartite foot, 163½in. long. (Christie's) £23,826

An oak and elm refectory table, the rectangular top with mitred angles above a plain frieze with moulded border, 17th century and later, 152in. long.
(Christie's) £4,400

A large and unusual Continental console table, circa 1900, of double serpentine outline with parcel-gilt and silvered frieze, 335cm. long.
(Sotheby's) £8,140

A mahogany triple-pedestal D-end dining table, on turned columns and downswept splayed legs, late 18th century, 127^1/$_2$in. extended.
(Christie's) £4,620

A mahogany three-pedestal dining-table with two D-shaped end-sections, a central quadripartite pedestal and two extra leaves, early 19th century, 138^1/$_2$in. extended.
(Christie's) £6,050

An Irish mahogany oval drop-leaf hunt table, on double gate-leg supports, 19th century, 106in. long.
(Christie's) £6,949

An oak and ash refectory table, the rectangular ash top with two shaped end-supports now joined by two later stretchers, 18th/19th century, 84in. wide.
(Christie's) £4,400

A fine Regency mahogany extending telescopic and twin pedestal dining table, in the manner of Gillows, comprising a pair of 'D' ends, and a pair of telescopic section with rounded frieze, 5ft. 6in. wide.
(Phillips) £7,500

A George III mahogany five-pedestal dining-table with two D-shaped end-sections and three rectangular central sections, each with reeded edge, turned shaft and downswept channelled legs with brass caps, 187^1/$_2$in. long.
(Christie's) £7,700

Tables have come a long way from the mediaeval board and trestle variety, and as social life became more sophisticated so tables of various designs were devised for all relevant activities.

It is perhaps with the Restoration that the age of specialised tables really begins and many distinct varieties were made for the requirements of a luxurious and pleasure loving society. Centre tables, similar to consoles, but with decoration on all four sides, became popular, and huge sums were also paid for silver tables which were quite the dernier cri of the time – if you could afford them.

Decoration was a common factor however in all types of occasional tables. They could be intricately carved, decorated with scagliola, particularly towards the end of the 17th century, or painted with gilt gesso or lacquer.

By the later 18th century, many craftsmen were concentrating on the ingenuity of their designs, and patents were taken out for all types of collapsible or extending devices. People, it seemed, loved 'the facility of changing the flaps at pleasure'.

In the Regency period, the new exotic woods such as zebrawood and mahogany became popular for occasional tables, the decoration often being of ormolu. Animal supports with classical and Egyptian motifs were also favoured for centre and side tables at the time. By the mid 19th century other forms of decoration, such as papier mâché were becoming popular and found application also on occasional tables.

A mahogany tripod table with circular piecrust top and birdcage action, on baluster shaft with foliate splayed base, 29¹/₂in. wide.
(Christie's) £1,588

A giltwood stand table of Charles II design, with pierced scrolling acanthus leaves and foliage centred by a pair of cherubs, on foliate moulded cabriole legs, late 19th century, 42¹/₂in. wide.
(Christie's) £495

A set of 19th century mahogany and rosewood quartetto tables, the rounded rectangular tops on dual turned splayed end supports, 2ft. wide.
(Phillips) £1,500

A French marquetry **etagère** the concave top inlaid with birds on flowering branches, on scroll supports, inlaid signature Gallé, 30¹/₂in. wide
(Christie's) £1,54●

A late 18th/early 19th century North Italian rosewood, marquetry and bone inlaid poudreuse, all over decorated with formal scrolling bands an● panels with foliage masks and mythological beasts, 2ft. 6in. wide.
(Phillips) £1,200

A fine Queen Anne walnut single-drawer tavern table, Pennsylvania, circa 1780, the rectangular top above a single moulded drawer, 35¹/₄in. wide.
(Sotheby's) £2,812

A Gordon Russell walnut occasional table, twelve-sided moulded top above octagonal section legs with ebony feet, 53.3cm. high.
(Christie's)   £605

A mid Victorian papier mâché and gilt decorated occasional table, with central painted panel depicting figures in a landscape, 24in. wide.
(Christie's)   £1,210

An Egyptian carved wood and shell-inlaid occasional table, the rectangular top intricately carved with scrolling foliage and a geometric design, 27$\frac{1}{2}$in. wide.
(Bearne's)   £400

A Gordon Russell oak table, the rectangular overhanging top with chamfered edges, above plain frieze enclosing single drawer, with ebony chamfered feet, 80cm. wide.
(Christie's)   £1,320

An ormolu-mounted amaranth, harewood and stained beech tricoteuse inlaid overall with ebonised and boxwood stringing, inlaid with lozenges, the rectangular top with D-shaped ends and hinged front, 30in. wide. (Christie's)   £6,050

A William and Mary black-painted trestle-base table, New England, 1730–1750, with oval top above double baluster-turned legs, 28$\frac{1}{4}$in. wide.
(Christie's)   £10,650

Fine 19th century satinwood two tier occasional table, with painted detail in the style of Vernis Martin, the bottom tier measuring 34in. x 21in.
(G. A. Key)   £1,350

A table with glazed, brass framed, hide top supported on elephant feet, 27in. wide.
                    £650

One of a pair of Spanish walnut-kingwood and marquetry corner tables, late 18th century/early 19th century, possibly Majorca, 32in. wide.
(Christie's)   £6,600

A mid-Victorian polished granite occasional table with circular segmentally-inlaid specimen marble top edged with polished slate, on a baluster shaft, 20¾in. diameter.
(Christie's) £4,400

A rare Queen Anne cherrywood slate-top mixing table, Pennsylvania, 1730–1750, on tapering cylindrical legs with pad feet, 26¼in. wide.
(Christie's) £10,010

A Regency rosewood and brass mounted octagonal wine table, on foliate reeded column circular trefoil base with ball ornament, with scroll feet, 1ft. 3½in. wide.
(Phillips) £2,00

An Empire mahogany and brass inlaid and mounted bouillotte table with pierced galleried breche d'Alep marble circular top fitted with slides and drawers, 2ft. 1½in. diameter.
(Phillips) £1,900

A 19th century Belgian black and micro mosaic round table top, the centre with Pliny's doves within a lapis band, surrounded by panels with Roman scenes, 75cm. diameter.
(Finarte) £26,168

A rare William and Mary painted and turned cherrywoo stretcher table, New York or Connecticut, 1710–50, painted grey over red, length 21¾in.
(Sotheby's) £9,07

An early 19th century decorated occasional table, the top depicting a seascape with rounded corners, the frieze with classical grisaille figures, 2ft. 7in. high.
(Phillips) £1,500

A William and Mary cherrywood slate-top table, the rectangular top with inset slate panel above an elaborately scalloped apron, 25in. wide.
(Christie's) £3,083

A painted papier mâché tripod table, circa 1840, the circular tip-top with a monk surveying the day's game, entitled *Bolton Abbey*, 62cm. diameter.
(Sotheby's) £5,50

OCCASIONAL TABLES

A fine George III sabicu envelope-top tripod table, the cross-banded harewood-veneered top set with a yewwood circular reserve centred by a sunburst motif, 28in. high.
(Bearne's) £43,000

A mid 19th century walnut veneered table, richly inlaid with fruitwood and mother of pearl, on a carved column and four carved legs ending on paw feet, Umbrian, 82cm. high.
(Finarte) £8,878

A fine George III painted and parcel-gilt specimen marble top occasional table, in the manner of Robert Adam, the circular top veneered with a trompe l'oeil design, 2ft. 4in. high.
(Phillips) £5,200

A walnut and palisander veneered circular table, inlaid with fruitwood, the central medallion flanked by female figures in regional costumes, Piedmont, mid 19th century, 102cm. diameter.
(Finarte) £5,252

A George III mahogany architect's table, the rounded rectangular hinged rising top with re-entrant corners and spring-loaded book-support, with two hinged brass candle-slides, on canted square legs and scrolled-carved block feet, 37³/₄in. wide.
(Christie's) £3,850

A George III mahogany tripod table, the galleried hexagonal tilt-top with egg-and-dart edge and on birdcage support and turned spreading shaft with cabriole legs and lion-mask feet, 26in. wide.
(Christie's) £4,180

A George III mahogany piecrust tripod table, with later scallop-edged circular top above a bird-cage support on turned spreading urn-shaped shaft, 26in. diameter.
(Christie's) £4,400

A very fine and rare early Chippendale carved mahogany piecrust tilt-top tea table, Philadelphia, circa 1745, height 27in.
(Sotheby's) £28,372

A Regency rosewood circular specimen marble top occasional table with beaded ornament, the top inset with a specimen marble panel including lapis, porphery, malachite and portor, 2ft. 7in. high.
(Phillips) £5,000

A good figured maple oval-top tavern table, New England, 1750–80, on circular turned and tapered legs, 26¼in. wide. (Sotheby's) £5,624

A satinwood and amaranth tricoteuse inlaid overall with trellis and dot pattern, on splayed legs, 29¼in. high. (Christie's) £5,280

A George II mahogany tripod table, the waved tip-up top on swivelling birdcage support, 31in. diam. (Christie's) £20,900

A Victorian mother-of-pearl inlaid black lacquer night table, mid 19th century, with a serpentine rectangular moulded-top above a conforming shaped frieze, 30in. high. (Christie's) £3,000

Louis XIV beech occasional table, raised on shaped moulded supports joined by an undulating H-form stretcher, 32³/₈in. wide. (Butterfield & Butterfield) £2,531

A Louis XV style kingwood and marquetry inlaid table en chiffoniere of oval form, the inset rouge royale top with a pierced three quarter gallery above, 19½in. wide. (Christie's S. Ken) £968

A mahogany tripod table, the shaped square top with a spindle gallery on an associated bird-cage support above a baluster-shaped acanthus carved stem, 23in. wide. (Christie's) £3,300

Spanish baroque walnut table, late 17th/early 18th century, on double baluster-turned and blocked supports joined by incised tied stretchers, 43¼in. wide. (Butterfield & Butterfield) £2,025

An oak inlaid two-tiered occasional table, supported on four shaped legs each decorated with a band of chequered ebonised and fruitwood inlay, 56.5cm. high. (Christie's) £440

A Gallé mahogany and marquetry two-tier etagère, signed in the marquetry Gallé, 59.3cm. wide.
(Christie's) £1,836

A Gothic Revival invalid's table, the top on adjustable slide with two reading slopes on a hexagonal four-footed pedestal base, 90cm. long. (Phillips) £850

A George II mahogany tripod table, the top with pierced fretwork gallery, 15in. diam., 24½in. high. £2,150

Italian micro-mosaic occasional table in the rococo taste, the base Alpine, third quarter 19th century, the black circular top centred by a spray of flowers, 30in. high.
(Butterfield & Butterfield) £1,350

A Carlo Bugatti ebonized, inlaid and painted vellum table, the octagonal top with central vellum panel, painted with Arabic script, 74cm. high. (Christie's London) £7,480

A 'Two-All' burr olive ash and hickory table, by John Makepeace, square overhung top over two shelves, each inset with a burr olive panel supporting two leather-lined drawers, 64.5cm. wide.
(Christie's) £1,980

An ormolu mounted kingwood etagère crossbanded with tulipwood, on tapering cabriole legs with foliate clasps reaching to pieds de biche sabots, 37in. wide.
(Christie's) £2,860

A Regency ormolu-mounted mahogany occasional table, the square top banded in maple, the baluster shaft on concave-sided triangular base with scrolling feet, 17³/₄in. wide.
(Christie's) £1,650

Quaint Furniture spindle-side occasional table, circa 1908, overhanging rectangular top, square tapering legs with three vertical spindles at each side, 30in. wide. (Skinner) £395

A mahogany tripod table with piecrust tilt-top and bird-cage support on fluted shaft with downswept legs, 27¹/₂in. high. (Christie's) **£1,870**

A Louis XV/XVI Transitional tulipwood and kingwood serpentine table en chiffoniere inlaid with lines, the hinged top quarter veneered and enclosing a velvet lined interior, 1ft. 5in. wide. (Phillips) **£1,400**

A George II mahogany tripod table with circular piecrust tilt-top on spirally-fluted baluster shaft with downswept legs, 26¹/₂in. high. (Christie's) **£10,450**

A Napoleon III bronze gueridon after the monument to Henri II, with circular specimen marble top inlaid with various marbles including brocatelle, green and red porphyry, verde antico and Siena, 26¹/₂in. high. (Christie's) **£1,980**

An Italian scagliola top signed by *Mannelli* and dated *1702*, centred by a roundel decorated with a seated figure in 17th century costume with a parrot and a dog, on an associated part-17th century oak base, 32in. high. (Christie's) **£82,500**

A mahogany tripod table, with baluster gallery inlaid with a brass line and pierced at the centres with carrying-handle motifs, mid-18th century, 28³/₄in. high. (Christie's) **£7,150**

A mid-Georgian fruitwood tripod table inlaid overall with bands of walnut squares, the circular tilt-top on bird-cage support and turned spreading shaft, 27¹/₄in. diameter. (Christie's) **£1,870**

A late George II mahogany árchitect's table, the rectangular moulded top with re-entrant corners and book rest, adjustable ratchet and with hinged brass candlestands at the sides, 3ft. wide. (Phillips) **£4,000**

A Chippendale birch tilt-top tea-table, New England, circa 1760–1780, the serpentine top with outset corners tilting above a ball and column-turned pedestal and tripartite base with cabriole legs, 26¹/₄in. wide. (Christie's) **£1,403**

A brass and mahogany tripod table on scrolled channelled supports joined by a circular stretcher on paw feet, first half 19th century, 22in. diameter.
(Christie's) £2,420

A George III mahogany tripod table with circular tip-up top with raised piecrust scalloped border on later birdcage and partly-fluted foliate baluster support, 28in. high.
(Christie's) £46,200

A mid-Victorian rosewood tripod table, the shaft carved with lotus leaves with fluted cluster columns on downswept legs with pointed feet, $29\frac{1}{2}$in. high.
(Christie's) £1,980

A fine Chippendale carved mahogany tea table, Philadelphia, 1760–1780, with circular dished and moulded rim top revolving and tilting above a tapering columnar and compressed ball-turned pedestal, $27\frac{1}{2}$in. high.
(Christie's) £15,400

A Roman circular micro-mosaic table-top inlaid with flowers including roses, a tulip, violets and lily-of-the-valley, mid-19th century, $26\frac{1}{2}$in. diameter.
(Christie's) £13,200

A George III mahogany tripod table with chamfered square tip-up top and curved gallery pierced and carved with running foliate scrolls, $29\frac{1}{2}$in. high.
(Christie's) £77,000

A mahogany tripod table, the shaped rectangular tilt-top with brass-inlaid spindle gallery on turn shaft carved with a pagoda roof, $25\frac{1}{4}$in. high.
(Christie's) £1,210

A Louis XV kingwood, crossbanded and marquetry tric trac table, by Pierre Migeon II, the rectangular detachable top inset with a panel of tooled leather, 2ft. 8in. wide.
(Phillips) £23,000

A mahogany urn table of George III style with pierced square galleried top, the frieze carved with blind fretwork and with candle-slide, 24in. high.
(Christie's) £1,320

PEMBROKE TABLES

This useful table, introduced during the 1760's, was, according to Sheraton, named after the Countess of Pembroke, who was the first to place an order for one.

Essentially, the Pembroke table has a rectangular top with a drawer and small flaps that are either squared or oval in shape. Beyond this, there are any number of different bases, ranging from elegant centre columns with tripod splay feet to bulbous, turned pine legs as on the late Victorian examples.

From 1770, Pembroke tables were often made of inlaid satinwood and painting was often also used for their embellishment. They served for meals and, according to Sheraton, "were suitable for a gentleman or lady to breakfast on."

Towards the end of the 18th century, the Harlequin Pembroke was introduced. This ingenious variation comprised a box-like structure fitted with drawers or small receptacles which were concealed in the table body and made to rise by means of weights. Great numbers of small Pembroke-type tables were made in the last decade of the 18th century.

A George III mahogany Pembroke table in the French taste with twin-flap serpentine top, 38½in. wide. (Christie's) £5,720

A George III mahogany, tulipwood crossbanded and boxwood strung oval Pembroke table, 79cm. x 1m. (Phillips) £2,200

A fine George III satinwood and marquetry Pembroke table, attributable to William Moore of Dublin, on square tapering legs inlaid with paterae hung with husk chains united by an undertier with gaitered feet, 2ft. 9in. long. (Phillips) £9,200

A George III satinwood Pembroke table, the rounded rectangular twin-flap top crossbanded with kingwood, on square tapering legs with kingwood block feet, 41½in. wide. (Christie's) £3,960

A George IV mahogany Pembroke table, the hinged rounded rectangular top with a frieze drawer on ring turned tapering legs, 3ft. 4in. wide. (Phillips) £260

A Regency rosewood and brass inlaid occasional table of serpentine outline, 26¾ x 37½in. extended. £9,250

A George III mahogany Pembroke table with moulded edge to the rectangular top, frieze drawer and on tapering square legs, 37½in. wide. (Bearne's) £920

A George III mahogany
Pembroke table with twin-
flap top and frieze drawer,
42in. wide, open. (Christie's)
£660

**A George III mahogany
Pembroke table, the oval flap top
banded in harewood with
stringing, 30in. wide.
(Woolley & Wallis)** £1,000

A George III mahogany
Pembroke table, the oval
twin-flap top crossbanded
in satinwood, 36½in. wide,
open. £2,000

An attractive early 19th century
style satinwood Pembroke table,
raised upon square tapering
supports terminating in brass
spade feet and leather castors,
2ft. 10in. wide.
(Spencer's) £650

A George III satinwood
marquetry, white-painted and
parcel-gilt Pembroke table, the
top possibly by Thomas
Chippendale with serpentine
moulded twin-flap top with
central ammonite flower and
conch shell-medallion, 37¼in.
wide. (Christie's) £12,100

**A Regency ebony Pembroke
table inlaid with brass lines, the
rectangular twin-flap top edged
with milled brass border, on
spirally-turned tapering legs,
38in. wide.
(Christie's)** £29,700

A George III mahogany
Pembroke table, of oval shape, a
single drawer to the end, on
tapered legs with reeded
corners.
(Bonhams) £480

A George IV mahogany
Pembroke table, the frieze with
two drawers and two simulated
drawers, on turned pedestal
carved with acanthus, 38in.
wide.
(Christie's) £4,620

A late George III 'plum
pudding' mahogany Pembroke
table with kingwood
crossbanding and boxwood and
ebonised stringing, 44¼in. wide.
(Bearne's) £2,900

A painted satinwood Pembroke table, the oval twin-flap top banded in rosewood and centred by an oval painted with lovers in a woody glade, part 18th century and later, 38in. wide. (Christie's) £2,860

A George III mahogany breakfast table after a design by Thomas Chippendale, the rectangular undertier enclosed with chinoiserie fretwork with recessed door, 43½in. wide. (Christie's) £3,850

A George III satinwood and kingwood crossbanded Pembroke table, the oval top above a bowed frieze drawer on square tapering legs with casters, 3ft. 3in. x 2ft. 6in. (Phillips) £1,200

A George III satinwood decorated and tulipwood crossbanded oval Pembroke table, the radially veneered top with a central guilloché and paterae roundel with vine leaf border, 2ft. 6½in. x 3ft. 5in. (Phillips) £6,000

A George III satinwood Pembroke table, on square tapering legs headed by rosewood panels, and brass caps, 37¾in. wide. (Christie's) £8,250

A George III satinwood and painted small Pembroke table, the panels possibly by Henry Clay, the oval twin-flap top inset with pale-blue-painted panels centred by a circle depicting a goddess in her chariot, 32in. wide. (Christie's) £5,500

A George III satinwood Pembroke table banded and crossbanded overall in tulipwood, the oval twin-flap top above a mahogany-lined frieze drawer, 39½in. wide. (Christie's) £6,600

A George III satinwood and marquetry Pembroke table crossbanded overall with tulipwood, the oval twin-flap inlaid with a central scrolling shell within an oval, 41½in. wide. (Christie's) £30,800

A George III mahogany and marquetry oval Pembroke table, containing a crossbanded bowfront drawer in the frieze, on square tapered legs headed with oval inlaid paterae and terminating in brass cappings and castors. (Phillips) £4,800

A George III satinwood Pembroke table inlaid overall with ebonised lines, the rounded rectangular twin-flap top crossbanded with tulipwood, on square tapering legs and brass caps, 37¼in. wide.
(Christie's) £3,520

A George III pearwood and mahogany fiddleback Pembroke table crossbanded in rosewood and inlaid with boxwood lines, on square tapering legs and brass caps, 41in. wide.
(Christie's) £4,180

A George III satinwood, marquetry, white-painted and parcel-gilt Pembroke table, the top possibly by Thomas Chippendale, on cabriole legs headed by ribbon-tied flowers, 37¼in. wide. (Christie's) £8,250

A Federal inlaid mahogany Pembroke table, Rhode Island, 1790–1810, the hinged oval top with moulded edge decorated with stringing over a bowed frieze drawer with lightwood banding, 31in. wide.
(Christie's) £8,316

A George III rosewood, satinwood and marquetry oval Pembroke table, the crossbanded and quarter veneered top with oval satinwood panel with radiating wavy fan medallion, 3ft. 1in. x 2ft. 4½in. (Phillips) £7,000

A George III yew-wood Pembroke table in the manner of Mayhew and Ince with rectangular twin-flap top crossbanded with mahogany, on square chamfered legs, 37¾in. wide (Christie's) £7,150

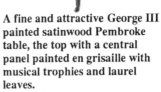

A George III satinwood Pembroke table crossbanded overall in rosewood and inlaid with fruitwood and ebonised lines, on square tapering legs headed by panels, 39in. wide.
(Christie's) £4,950

A Federal mahogany Pembroke-table, New York, 1790–1810, on square tapering legs joined by serpentine X-stretchers, 31in. wide.
(Christie's) £3,080

A fine and attractive George III painted satinwood Pembroke table, the top with a central panel painted en grisaille with musical trophies and laurel leaves.
(Tennants) £4,200

Federal mahogany inlaid
Pembroke table, New York City,
1785–1800, with inlaid flutes
and shaded husks and
overlapping ovals, 19¹/₈in. wide.
(Skinner)   £8,827

A Regency mahogany Pembroke
table, on a ring turned vase
shaped column support, circular
plinth and hipped reeded
outswept legs, 36in. wide.
(Bonhams)   £800

A Federal inlaid mahogany
Pembroke table, New York,
circa 1800, the oblong top with
two line-inlaid hinged leaves,
length 30³/₄in.
(Sotheby's)   £2,194

A mahogany oval   Pembroke
table, the top with rosewood and
satinwood bands edged with
stringing, fitted with one drawer
and on four square tapering
supports, 18th century.
(Lawrence Fine Art)   £1,045

A George III   satinwood
Pembroke table with moulded
serpentine twin-flap top inlaid
with three amboyna oval panels,
on square tapering mahogany
legs with satinwood panels and
pendant husks, 36³/₄in. wide.
(Christie's)   £7,700

A Chippendale carved
cherrywood Pembroke table,
Connecticut River Valley, circa
1800, on square tapering legs
joined by an X-stretcher with
incised scrolling vines, width
extended 36in.
(Sotheby's)   £1,437

A mahogany Pembroke
table with twin-flap top
and one frieze drawer on
cabriole legs, 34¼in. wide,
open. (Christie's) £770

A George III mahogany
Pembroke table, on associated
quadripartite base with turned
spreading shaft, the downswept
reeded legs with brass caps,
48in. wide.
(Christie's)   £1,760

A George III mahogany
Pembroke table banded overall
in kingwood with oval twin-flap
top and single frieze drawer,
37in. wide.
(Christie's)   £1,870

An early Victorian mahogany Pembroke table, the rounded rectangular top above a square section column, on a concave plinth and scroll feet.
(Bonhams) **£450**

A well figured mahogany Pembroke table banded in satinwood, above square tapering legs to brass castors, 31in. long.
(Woolley & Wallis) **£1,200**

A George III mahogany serpentine Pembroke table with narrow rosewood crossbanding, on four square section cabriole legs.
(Lawrence Fine Arts) **£3,960**

A Chippendale mahogany Pembroke table, Massachusetts, 1760–1780, the hinged serpentine top with serpentine drop leaves above a cockbeaded bowed frieze drawer, 27$^{1}/_{2}$in. high.
(Christie's) **£2,125**

A George III mahogany and marquetry Pembroke table, with oval twin-flap top centred by an oval inlaid with a stylised flowerhead with a satinwood border inlaid with entwined ribbon and flowerheads, 42in. wide. (Christie's) **£6,380**

A George III sycamore, satinwood and marquetry oval Pembroke table, containing a drawer in the bowed frieze with shell, palm and anthemion headed angles, 3ft.2in. x 2ft.4½in. (Phillips) **£9,000**

A George III plum-pudding mahogany Pembroke table with butterfly top, on square tapered legs, 3ft. x 2ft.6in. (Phillips) **£2,000**

A mid Georgian mahogany Pembroke table, one end with a drawer with a writing slope and pen and ink drawer, 21in. wide.
(Lawrence Fine Arts) **£2,310**

A George III mahogany butterfly top Pembroke table, raised upon box strung square tapering supports terminating in ogee spade feet, 2ft. 6in. wide.
(Spencer's) **£500**

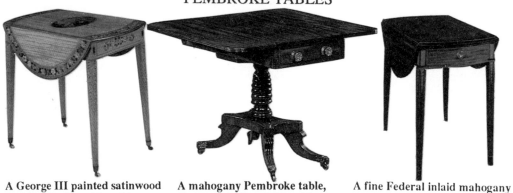

A George III painted satinwood oval Pembroke table, with overall rosewood bands and boxwood and ebony lines, 39in. wide.
(Christie's)   £4,400

A mahogany Pembroke table, George IV, circa 1820, with round corners, a drawer at each end, 96cm. open.
(Sotheby's)   £1,150

A fine Federal inlaid mahogany Pembroke table, Newport, Rhode Island, circa 1800, the oblong top with hinged D-shaped leaves, width extended 38½in.
(Sotheby's)   £24,589

A George III satinwood decorated and tulipwood crossbanded oval Pembroke table, the radially veneered top with a central guilloché and paterae roundel with vine leaf border, 3ft. 5in. overall extended.
(Phillips)   £3,500

One of a pair of George III mahogany serpentine Pembroke tables, each with crossbanded twin-flap top inlaid with ebonised and boxwood lines above a mahogany-lined frieze drawer and a simulated frieze drawer to the reverse, 39½in. wide.
(Christie's)(Two)   £14,300

One of a matched pair of Regency mahogany and ebonised Pembroke-tables, each with rounded rectangular twin-flap top above a panelled frieze with a blue paper-lined drawer, 28in. high.
(Christie's) (Two)   £4,400

A George III plum-pudding mahogany Pembroke table, the serpentine twin-flap top crossbanded and inlaid with a geometric line, 37in. wide.
(Christie's)   £4,400

A George III mahogany butterfly Pembroke table, after designs by Chippendale, of rich colour with a deep grain, 2ft. 4in. high.
(John Nicholson)   £3,600

A George III mahogany Pembroke-table, the serpentine twin-flap top above a waved frieze with a drawer to one end and a dummy drawer to the other, 32¼in. wide.
(Christie's)   £1,760

A George III green and polychrome-painted wood and papier-mâché Pembroke table, the panels possibly by Henry Clay, 32¼in. wide. (Christie's) £3,300

A mahogany Pembroke work table, William IV, 1834, stamped *Thomas Bartram, 1834*, with crossbanded top, 67cm. open. (Sotheby's) £1,800

A very fine Federal satinwood-inlaid mahogany Pembroke table, Baltimore, Maryland, circa 1795, on inlaid square tapering legs ending in brass caps, width extended 41¼in. (Sotheby's) £16,425

An inlaid mahogany Pembroke table, Baltimore, Maryland, 1790–1810, the line-inlaid oval top with drop leaves above a conforming apron with line inlay flanked by inlaid paterae on ring-and-flower and line-inlaid square tapering legs, 41½in. wide. (Christie's) £11,839

A George III painted satinwood Pembroke table, inlaid overall with ebonised lines and banded in tulipwood, the rounded rectangular twin-flap top with central oval mahogany panel painted with a fruit basket flanked by foliate scrolls, 42¾in. wide. (Christie's) £11,550

A George III satinwood Pembroke table, the tripartite oval top with two hinged flaps, banded overall with tulipwood and rosewood above a mahogany-lined frieze drawer and simulated frieze drawer to the reverse, 45in. wide. (Christie's) £4,400

A George III satinwood and mahogany Pembroke table, decorated with fruiting floral trails, the rectangular twin-flap top crossbanded and inlaid with a central oval panel, 39¾in. wide. (Christie's) £4,290

A mahogany 'Spider-leg' Pembroke table, English, late 18th century, with oblong top and slender turned legs and stretchers. (Sotheby's) £1,437

A late George III plum-pudding mahogany, rosewood crossbanded and marquetry Pembroke games table, 39in. extended. (Christie's) £4,950

SIDE TABLES

Side tables are the root from which occasional tables grew, dating from the 15th century and resembling, in their earliest form, a kind of chest of drawers under a table top. They were used in large households only, for storage of cutlery, linen and condiments in the dining room and, true to the fashion of the time, were made of oak. Few of these have survived and as such command exceptionally high prices.

From about 1850 fine tapering legs gave way to massive turned ones with heavy brass cup castors.

One of a pair of parcel gilt and bronzed side tables with mottled green marble tops, 34½in. wide. £8,400

A William and Mary oak side table banded with walnut and inlaid with boxwood lines, 25¾in. wide. £1,75

A Victorian gilt-metal mounted walnut and marquetry side table, the serpentine top inlaid with a foliate marquetry in fruitwoods, 30in. wide.
(Christie's) £825

A Majorelle side table, the top inlaid with floral marquetry, having three curved and sinuous moulded legs, with further leaf below, 90cm. high.
(Phillips) £2,200

An oak side table, the rectangular top with a single drawer, on baluster turned legs joined by an 'X'-stretcher, bun feet, 2ft. 6in. wide.
(Phillips) £58

A William Burges ebony sidetable inlaid with ivory, the rectangular top with shaped edges above rectangular shelf and arched end supports.
(Christie's) £16,500

A Regency black painted and gilded side table in the Brighton Pavilion taste, 38in. wide. £5,500

An early George II walnut and feather banded side table, the quarter veneered rectangular top with re-entrant corners above a drawer, 2ft. 6in. wide.
(Phillips) £3,2

An oak side table with rectangular top above a frieze drawer on turned baluster legs, late 17th/early 18th century, 36in. wide. (Christie's) £770

A Dutch oak side table, with two drawers on cabriole supports and pointed pad feet, 19th century, 21in. wide. (Christie's) £385

An Italian grey-painted side table with moulded rectangular mottled yellow and pink marble slab, 39½in. wide. (Christie's) £2,640

A George III mahogany side table, the rounded rectangular top with moulded edge above two long drawers and on club legs and pad feet, 31½in. wide. (Christie's) £1,320

A George I burr walnut side table with quartered and crossbanded rectangular top, on cabriole legs and pad feet, 30in. wide. (Christie's) £4,950

A Louis XIV oak side table, the flowerhead-and-trellis apron and sides carved with a palmette and scrolling acanthus, 37in. wide. (Bearne's) £720

A 19th century Chinese hardwood half round table, the four legs with carved knees and floral carved feet, 36in. wide. (David Lay) £500

A 17th century oak side table, the D-shaped top with a flap at the back, 37¼in. wide. £5,750

A German mahogany side table with serpentine eared top above three frieze drawers, on carved cabriole legs and scroll feet, 19th century, 46in. wide. (Christie's) £660

A gilt-gesso and pine side-table of George II style with rectangular black fossil marble top, the frieze decorated with acanthus scrolls above a cartouche with female mask, 58in. wide.
(Christie's)   £3,300

A George III mahogany side table, the rectangular top above a geometric blind-fretwork frieze, on canted square legs with pierced fretwork angles and on block feet, 60in. wide.
(Christie's)   £4,400

Late 18th century Italian mahogany side table with rectangular yellow marble top on lyre shaped supports joined by stretchers 156.5cm. wide.
(Finarte)   £4,4

A fine 18th century Florentine scagliola panel table top, possibly attributable to Lamberto Gori, inset into a Regency ebonised and parcel gilt base, the top panel 3ft. 7in. x 2ft. 2in.
(Phillips)   £19,000

One of a pair of George III harewood, sycamore and marquetry side tables possibly by Thomas Chippendale Senior or Junior, banded overall in mahogany and amaranth, on square tapering legs, 44in. wide.
(Christie's)   (Two)   £33,000

A fine George III mahogany inlaid and crossbanded side table, raised on slender cabri legs with simple leaf-carved spandrels and stiff acanthus to the feet, 28¾in. wide.
(Tennants)   £4,

A George III mahogany side table with rectangular top, the rim carved with entrelac, above a beaded moulding, on square tapering fluted legs, 46in. wide.
(Christie's)   £4,620

Italian walnut and burr walnut and marquetry side table, with one long drawer, on cabriole legs, Turin, early 18th century.
(Finarte)   £23,810

A George III mahogany and marquetry side table, the ear serpentine top crossbanded i tulipwood and inlaid with a geometric pattern centred by oval floral pattern, 42in. wide
(Christie's)   £9,

A George III giltwood side table attributed to George Brookshaw, with demi-lune white marble top decorated with bands of urns linked with anthemia and scrolling foliage, 60^1/$_2$in. wide.
(Christie's) £24,200

A George III mahogany side table banded overall in satinwood and inlaid with ebonised lines, on turned tapering feet, 56in wide.
(Christie's) £6,820

A George III satinwood, marquetry and white-painted and parcel-gilt side table, the serpentine top crossbanded in tulipwood and banded with scrolling foliate inlay divided by paterae, 44^3/$_4$in. wide.
(Christie's) £13,200

A George III mahogany side table, the serpentine moulded top with a flap at the back, on tapering cabriole legs mounted with gilt-lacquered brass foliage, 32in. wide.
(Christie's) £13,750

A classical green-painted and gilt-stencilled side-table, attributed to John Needles, Baltimore, early 19th century, on a quadripartite base with foliate bracketed X-shaped supports, on turned tapering feet, 37in. wide.
(Christie's) £3,696

A French brass-mounted floral marquetry side table, the rectangular top with moulded edge and inlaid with a vase of flowers, with two frieze drawers and on panelled square tapering legs, second half 19th century, 48in. wide.
(Christie's) £3,960

A George III mahogany side table with rectangular top, the frieze with three drawers divided by projecting panels carved with berried laurel wreaths, 52^1/$_2$in. wide.
(Christie's) £126,500

A William and Mary rosewood and kingwood oyster-veneered side table, the rectangular top inlaid with a star-pattern within circles, 26^1/$_2$in. wide.
(Christie's) £3,520

An early Georgian green and gilt-japanned side table decorated overall with chinoiserie scenes with people, birds and buildings in a landscape, 35^3/$_4$in. wide.
(Christie's) £5,500

357

A cream painted side table of early Georgian design with rectangular crimson top above a frieze carved with shells on two massive shell supports, 54in. wide.

(Christie's) £5,060

A scarlet and gold lacquer side table, basically late 17th century, 32½in. wide. £1,850

A Regency rosewood and crossbanded side table, the rounded rectangular top above two long drawers, on ring turned legs headed by brass banding, 2ft. wide.

(Phillips) £950

A mahogany side table with mottled rectangular breccia marble top above a moulding carved with flowerheads, the frieze applied with scrolling acanthus and strapwork, 48in. wide.

(Christie's) £3,520

A fine Federal mahogany two-drawer side table, New York, circa 1810, on reeded tapering legs ending in ebonised vase and ball feet, 20¹/₂in. wide.

(Sotheby's) £2,481

An 18th century Irish mahogany side table with associated moulded rectangular carrara marble top, the waved frieze carved with acanthus and centred by an eagle, on cabriole legs, 35¹/₂in. wide.

(Christie's) £3,300

A Charles II oak side table, the moulded rectangular top above a panelled frieze drawer, on bobbin-turned legs joined by a conforming front stretcher, 34¹/₄in. wide.

(Christie's) £2,200

A Piedmontese giltwood half-round side table with contemporary breche d'Alep top above a frieze applied with anthemia and lozenges, late 18th century, 37in. wide.

(Christie's) £2,420

A burr-elm side table inlaid overall with kingwood feather-banding, on baluster turned legs joined by a stylised X-shaped stretcher, basically late 17th century, 29¹/₂in. wide.

(Christie's) £2,090

A Flemish oak side table with planked rectangular top, on turned and squared legs joined by a rectangular under tier, 17th century, 35½in. wide. (Christie's London) £4,180

An oak credence table, with folding semi-circular top, the frieze applied with lozenges and fitted with a drawer, 48½in. wide. (Christie's London) £2,530

A giltwood side table with later terracotta and white veined marble top, on cabriole legs with leafy scroll feet, early 18th century, re-gilded, 37in. wide. (Christie's London) £5,500

Spanish baroque walnut side table, the rectangular top with breadboard ends overhanging a deep frieze fitted with a pair of quadruple-fronted drawers, 4ft. 2in. wide. (Butterfield & Butterfield) £2,891

A walnut and marquetry side table, the moulded rectangular top inlaid with a songbird amid floral sprays with one frieze drawer, on spirally turned legs, 17th century and later, 31½in. wide. (Christie's London) £3,190

One of a pair of George III mahogany side tables with D-shaped tops, the friezes carved with classical urns and ribbon-tied swags of berried foliage, 45¾in. wide. (Christie's) (Two) £1,787

A William and Mary giltwood side table with later inset green-painted white marble top above a pierced vigorous acanthus-carved frieze centred by putti, 46in. wide. (Christie's) £1,650

A George III mahogany serpentine side table, with boxwood stringing and a single frieze drawer with pressed brass oakleaf and acorn handles, 40in. wide. (Christie's) £794

A French ormolu-mounted polychrome and tortoiseshell boulle marquetry side table inlaid overall in contra-partie with foliate scrolls, third quarter 19th century, 27½in. wide. (Christie's) £3,080

An Italian giltwood side table, the rectangular top above a panelled frieze carved with foliate scrolls within lotus-leaf borders and centred by vestal masks, late 18th century, 60in. wide.
(Christie's) £3,080

A Louis XV walnut side table with serpentine rectangular variegated red languedoc moulded marble top above a waved pierced panelled frieze, 47in. wide.
(Christie's) £25,300

A satinwood and marquetry side table crossbanded overall in kingwood and inlaid with ribbon-tied husk swags, the demi-lune top centred by a half fan medallion, 50in. wide.
(Christie's) £3,300

A Florentine serpentine specimen marble table top with a central verde antico oval medallion flanked by radiating Siena, portor, jasper and specimen marble wedges within a black marble border, third quarter 18th century, 35½in. wide.
(Christie's) £3,300

A Regency mahogany side table, in the manner of Gillows, with a rectangular top and rounded corners, on projecting reeded tapered legs with turned feet, 3ft. 3in. wide.
(Phillips) £1,700

A Regency mahogany side table attributed to Thomas Chippendale Junior, with rectangular white marble top above a panelled frieze supported by Egyptian caryatids above turned tapering reeded columns and human feet, 33½in. wide.
(Christie's) £8,800

A George III mahogany marquetry and parquetry side table, on stop-fluted square tapering legs and blocks inset with painted roundels, above shaped feet, 47in. wide.
(Christie's) £5,500

A good French marble-topped giltwood serpentine side table, Paris, circa 1880, in Louis XV style, with a later moulded mottled purple green and white marble top, 141cm. wide.
(Sotheby's) £3,960

A Régence giltwood side table with later rectangular alabaster top with black marble border, on angled scrolled legs headed by scallop shells, 44in. wide.
(Christie's) £11,000

A giltwood side table with later simulated verde antico scagliola top above a boldly scrolled pierced acanthus-carved frieze centred by a Vesta head, on naturalistic scrolled legs headed by bold eagles, 61¹/₂in. wide.
(Christie's)   £6,380

A George II mahogany side table, the rounded rectangular top above a plain frieze centred by a pendant boss, on cabriole legs headed by scallop shells and on paw feet, 54in. wide.
(Christie's)   £2,530

An Italian giltwood side table with later veined rectangular white marble top, on cabriole legs carved with trailing foliage, rockwork and C-scrolls, 62in. wide.
(Christie's)   £3,850

A George III satinwood and inlaid pier table of small size, the top of bowed and broken outline crossbanded in tulipwood and harewood, 3ft. wide.
(Phillips)   £3,000

An Italian red-painted and parcel-gilt side table with serpentine moulded top above a pierced frieze with scrolling foliage and confronting C-scrolls, mid-18th century, 44in. wide.
(Christie's)   £1,540

One of a pair of gilt lead-mounted satinwood, marble and simulated tortoiseshell side tables of George III style, on square tapering legs and tapering block feet, 32¹/₂in. wide.
(Christie's) (Two)   £11,000

A satinwood D-shaped side table, the radiating top centred by a stylised fan medallion terminated by bell husks, the mahogany-banded edge with stylised flowerhead and oval running motif, 52¹/₄in. wide.
(Christie's)   £8,250

An early George III mahogany serving table, the frieze carved with blind fretwork, on pierced fretwork and ring-turned legs with spade feet, 62in. wide.
(Christie's)   £9,431

A George III mahogany serpentine serving-table, the shaped rectangular top above a panelled frieze and central baize-lined fitted frieze drawer divided by marquetry panels of flowers in an urn, 69³/₄in. wide.
(Christie's)   £8,800

SIDE TABLES

A classical brass inlaid mahogany marble top pier table, N.Y., circa 1810/30, 41½in. wide. £2,150

One of a pair of George II giltwood pier tables, each with D-shaped white marble top, 35in. wide. £125,000

A Regency mahogany demi-lune pier table with veined white marble top, and mirrored back flanked by giltwood semi-columns, 23½in. wide. (Bearne's) £620

One of a pair of giltwood side tables, each surmounted by an eared top of verde antico marble above a beaded and meander frieze centred by a tablet hung with husk swags, on cabriole legs, late 19th century, each 47in. wide. (Christie's S. Ken) £4,070

A Baltic grained beech mahogany and parcel-gilt pier table with rectangular top above a gilt foliate frieze on scroll supports, mid 19th century, 37in. wide. (Christie's S. Ken) £770

A George I gilt-gesso pier table attributed to James Moore and John Gumley, the removable rectangular top with re-entrant corners decorated in low relief with ribbon-tied laurel around the ensigned *RC* cypher of Richard Temple. (Christie's) £220,000

A neo-classical Italian cream painted and parcel gilt half-round pier table, surmounted by a volute moulded top with projecting angles, 4ft. 2½in. wide. (Phillips) £1,700

One of a pair of satinwood, marquetry and giltwood demi-lune pier tables, each with a top centred by classical urns on tapering fluted legs with turned foliate carved feet, each 39in. wide. (Christie's S. Ken) £9,900

An Adam period satinwood and marquetry pier table, with similarities to the work of Ince and Mayhew, the elliptical top crossbanded in rosewood and tulipwood with central radiating fan lunette, 3ft. 9in. wide. (Phillips) £8,000

SERVING TABLES

A late Regency mahogany serving table with rounded rectangular ledge back top above a frieze drawer on reeded tapering legs.
(Christie's) £1,210

A Federal carved mahogany serving table with D-shaped top, 1810-15, 36in. wide. £2,450

An Irish mahogany serving table with rope carved borders, on rope carved tapering legs with paw feet, 72in. wide. (Christie's S. Ken) £3,300

Lifetime Furniture buffet server, circa 1915, plate rail on overhanging rectangular top, single long drawer with brass pulls, 39in. wide.
(Skinner) £254

A good Federal mahogany three-drawer serving table, New York, dated 1816, on frontal reeded supports joined by a shaped medial shelf, 36½in. wide.
(Sotheby's) £3,308

One of pair of Louis XVI mahogany and ormolu mounted console dessertes, by Conrad Mauter, with concave canted sides surmounted by contemporary fossilised marble tops, 4ft. 3in. wide.
(Phillips) (Two) £58,000

A Louis XVI mahogany console desserte with brass mounts and grey veined marble top, 34in. wide. £1,900

A Victorian pollard oak serving side table, the serpentined top with an oak leaf carved border above a shaped frieze, 93in. wide. (Christie's S. Ken) £1,540

A rare Federal carved mahogany marble-top two-drawer server, New York, circa 1815, on acanthus-carved ring-turned legs, 29¼in. wide. (Sotheby's) £2,977

The sofa table was originally introduced to the world by Sheraton towards the end of the 18th century. He suggested that the length should be five feet six inches, (with flaps raised) the width two feet and the height 28 inches.

Basically, of course, this is simply the Pembroke table stretched a bit into more elegant proportions and it is interesting to consider how, give the fundamental idea of a table with drawers and flaps, three such successful designs as the Pembroke, sofa and Regency supper tables can be produced.

Earlier sofa tables were made of mahogany or, occasionally, satinwood but later, in the early 19th century, a variety of woods was used including rosewood, amboyna and zebra wood. These are good tables in every sense of the word and, as such, command high prices. Although the 19th century examples are the more flamboyant with their use of exotic woods, inlaid brass and lyre end supports, it is the more austerely elegant late 18th century variety which are the most sought after and, therefore, the most expensive.

The Regency supper table is basically a sofa table with the flaps being hinged from the long sides instead of the short, and having one long drawer in the apron with a dummy front at the opposite end.

Usually made of mahogany or rosewood, the Regency supper table was popular from the beginning of the Regency period through to the start of the Victorian.

A Regency brass-inlaid sofa table with rounded rectangular twin-flap top, the frieze with two mahogany-lined drawers and two simulated drawers, 61½in. wide.
(Christie's)   £3,850

A George III mahogany and tulipwood banded sofa table, inlaid with boxwood and ebonised lines, the rounded rectangular hinged top containing two drawers, 5ft. x 2ft. 4in.
(Phillips)   £4,000

A Regency satinwood and mahogany sofa table inlaid overall with ebony lines, on rectangular end-supports joined by a later turned stretcher, 61½in. wide.
(Christie's)   £2,860

A Regency fiddleback mahogany sofa table inlaid overall with ebony stringing, on vase-shaped end-supports joined by a turned stretcher, 59in. wide.
(Christie's)   £5,500

A late George III rosewood and satinwood banded sofa table, the rounded rectangular top above two frieze drawers opposing two false drawers, 58½in. wide.
(Bonhams)   £5,200

A Regency brass-inlaid sofa table on associated simulated rosewood quadripartite scroll supports and concave-sided platform base, 57in. wide.
(Christie's)   £2,860

A Regency mahogany and inlaid sofa table, the top with 'D'-shaped ends and crossbanded in rosewood, on lyre shaped twin end supports and splay legs joined by an undertier, 75cm. high.
(Phillips) £4,400

A William IV plum pudding mahogany sofa table, the rounded rectangular and crossbanded twin flap top fitted with two frieze drawers to one side, 49in. wide.
(Christie's) £1,800

Mid 19th century mahogany sofa table, the arched pedestals surmounted by giltwood eagle heads, 126cm. wide.
(Finarte) £6,013

A Regency mahogany sofa table, the figured top crossbanded in satinwood and rosewood above two drawers, 58in. wide, extended.
(Bonhams) £3,000

A Regency ormolu-mounted and brass-inlaid rosewood sofa-table, with a shaped rectangular twin-flap top inlaid with a line and fleurs-de-lys, 54in. wide.
(Christie's) £3,740

A Regency rosewood sofa table banded overall in satinwood, the panelled frieze with two mahogany-lined drawers to the front, 56¾in. wide.
(Christie's) £6,050

A Regency roseood, satinwood crossbanded and inlaid sofa table, the hinged top with rounded corners with scroll inlay, supported by lopers with roundels.
(Phillips) £5,000

A satinwood and floral painted sofa table, the rounded rectangular twin-flap top fitted with two frieze drawers to one side, 58in. wide.
(Christie's) £4,000

A George III mahogany sofa table with rounded rectangular two-flap top crossbanded with rosewood and inlaid with ebony and boxwood lines, 58in. wide.
(Christie's) £20,900

A **Regency rosewood sofa table,** outlined in boxwood and ebony stringing, on curved 'X'-shaped end supports, tied by a pole stretcher, 60¹/₂in. wide.
(Bonhams) **£1,400**

A Regency mahogany sofa table, the rounded rectangular twin flap top above a frieze fitted with two drawers, on square tapering sabre legs, 60in. wide, open.
(Christie's London) **£3,080**

A red lacquer and gilt chinoiserie sofa table with rounded rectangular twin-flap top, on down-curved legs, 46in. wide.
(Christie's S. Ken.) **£1,760**

A **Heal & Son oak sofa-table,** designed by Sir Ambrose Heal, the frieze with two short drawers above twin column turned tapering legs, circa 1915, 158.5cm. wide.
(Christie's) **£1,760**

A **Regency mahogany small sofa table** inlaid overall with ebony stringing with rounded rectangular twin-flap top, 30¹/₂in. wide.
(Christie's) **£4,180**

A **Regency mahogany sofa table** with rounded rectangular twin-flap top crossbanded in kingwood and edged with gadrooning, on curved central supports, 56in. wide.
(Christie's) **£2,200**

A **George III mahogany sofa table,** on solid trestle ends joined by a later stretcher and splayed legs with brass caps, 59in. wide.
(Christie's) **£1,925**

A **Regency mahogany, rosewood crossbanded and inlaid sofa table,** the hinged top with rounded corners containing two drawers in the frieze, 5ft. 2in. x 2ft. 3in.
(Phillips) **£2,000**

A **George III mahogany sofa table,** the crossbanded top inlaid with boxwood stringing, above two frieze drawers, 59¹/₂in. wide.
(Bonhams) **£4,800**

A Regency rosewood, ebony banded and brass inlaid sofa table, the rectangular twin flap top with a secrétaire frieze drawer, 4ft. 3in. extended.
(Phillips) £2,200

A mahogany sofa table, on twin turned end-standards with acanthus dog's leg supports and gilt paw feet, 45½in. open.
(Christie's S. Ken) £1,540

A Regency mahogany sofa table, crossbanded in rosewood and satinwood, and inlaid with boxwood and ebony lines, 5ft. extended.
(Phillips) £8,400

A late Regency mahogany sofa table, on twin baluster turned columns and stepped arched downswept legs terminating in brass cappings and castors, 4ft. 10in. wide.
(Phillips) £3,000

A Regency mahogany crossbanded and brass strung sofa table, the hinged, rosewood crossbanded top with cut corners containing two drawers in the frieze, 4ft. 11in. x 2ft. 4in.
(Phillips) £1,800

A Regency rosewood and brass inlaid sofa table, the hinged top with fleur-de-lys inlat to the corners, on rectangular column quatrefoil platform, 4ft. 10in. x 2ft. extended.
(Phillips) £3,400

A Regency rosewood sofa table inlaid with brass lines and cut-brass foliate motifs, 28¼in. high by 58in. wide.
(Bearne's) £1,300

A Regency maplewood and ebonised sofa table, on twin ring turned end standards applied with rams' masks and anthemions and reeded down-swept legs, 55½in. wide.
(Christie's London) £3,300

A classical mahogany sofa table, the working drawer with a brass lion head pull, circa 1810/20, Phila., 42in. wide. £3,550

An Anglo-Chinese padoukwood double-sided twin-flap sofa table, the rectangular twin-flap top crossbanded with satinwood and inlaid with ebony and boxwood lines, 19th century, 59in. wide.
(Christie's)   £3,080

A Regency gilt-brass mounted mahogany sofa table with rounded rectangular twin-flap top inlaid with boxwood lines and crossbanded with rosewood, 60¹/₂in. wide.
(Christie's)   £4,950

A Regency brass-inlaid and giltmetal-mounted rosewood sofa table with rounded rectangular twin-flap top, the panelled frieze with two mahogany-lined drawers to the front, 58¹/₄in. wide.
(Christie's)   £5,72(

A Regency ebony-inlaid amboyna sofa table with rounded rectangular twin-flap top inlaid with ebonised lines above two mahogany-lined frieze drawers, 60in. wide.
(Christie's)   £5,280

A Regency ebony and brass-inlaid specimen wood and parquetry pedestal sofa table, on turned quadripartite baluster-supports and a concave-sided platform centred by a lotus-leaf finial, 63¹/₂in. wide.
(Christie's)   £17,600

A Regency mahogany and ebony-inlaid sofa table, with lin and stellar banded top, two Greek key-decorated frieze drawers and opposing dummy drawers, 59¹/₂in. extended.
(Christie's)   £5,06(

A Regency rosewood sofa table, on standard ends joined by an arched stretcher with dual downswept legs, paw cappings and castors, 4ft. 11in. x 1ft. 1in.
(Phillips)   £3,200

A late George III mahogany sofa table of rounded rectangular form with reeded edge, 61¹/₄in. wide extended.
(Tennants)   £2,300

A Regency mahogany sofa tabl(inlaid with boxwood lines and geometric shapes, the rounded rectangular twin flap top containing two drawers, 4ft. 11in. x 1ft. 11in.
(Phillips)   £3,80(

Well before the introduction of playing cards, in the 15th century, proficiency at chess, backgammon and dice was considered to be an essential part of the education of anyone intending to take his place in society. Indeed, all forms of gaming were so popular that *The Complete Gamester* was felt to be almost compulsory reading and, in the edition of 1674, we find the declaration "... he who in company should appear ignorant of the game in vogue would be reckoned low bred and hardly fit for conversation." Since there were, at that time, dozens of games widely played, including glecko, primero, ombre, picquet, basset, quadrille, commerce and loo, to name but a few, there must have been a considerable number of people wandering about with inferiority complexes.

And another thing, people in society rarely messed about with gambling for loose change; in many of the higher gaming establishments, the dice were rarely thrown for less than £100 a throw.

Early games were played on marked boards (as chess and draughts) which were placed either on the floor or on a table. Towards the end of the 17th century, however, the business of losing a fortune was civilised somewhat by the introduction of beautifully made gaming tables specifically designed for players of particular games.

Although a few earlier pieces do exist, it was during the 18th and 19th centuries that gaming tables really came into their own, often being combined with a workbox.

A William IV rosewood games table, the rectangular top with central detachable panel inlaid with chess board, 45in. wide.
(Christie's) £2,200

A fine Regency mahogany, ebonised and parcel gilt library and games table, by John Maclean, on curved 'X'-frame end supports, 2ft. 9in. x 1ft. 7in.
(Phillips) £36,000

A painted satinwood work-table crossbanded with rosewood, with hinged octagonal top painted with roses suspending leaves and bellhusk chains, 16¹/₂in. wide.
(Christie's) £1,320

A George II mahogany Harlequin tea, card and writing-table with rounded rectangular triple-flap top enclosing a tea-table, 32in. wide.
(Christie's) £5,175

A Regency mahogany work-table inlaid with ebony lines, the canted rectangular hinged top enclosing a fitted interior with lift-out section comprising four satinwood lidded corner compartments, 16¹/₂in. wide.
(Christie's) £1,210

A satinwood marquetry work table, circa 1870, the hinged lid with brass-moulded border and a roundel of musical trophies, 1ft. 10¹/₂in. wide.
(Sotheby's) £3,630

A Regency rosewood work-table with hinged green leather-lined reading-slope above two mahogany-lined drawers, formerly with work-basket, 46in. wide. (Christie's) **£1,540**

A Chinese export black and gold lacquer work table, on ring turned trestle ends joined by a conforming stretcher with claw feet, 25in. wide. (Christie's) **£990**

A Dutch Biedermeier vide poche with oval dished top and mahogany-lined divided drawer above a green silk-lined workbasket, 21¹/₂in. wide. (Christie's) **£1,100**

A George III mahogany work-table inlaid with satinwood and banded overall, with mahogany-lined drawer above a pleated green silk-lined work basket, 24in. wide. (Christie's) **£1,870**

A Regency kingwood games table with rectangular leather-lined twin-flap top opening to reveal a chequerboard, with single frieze drawer above a blue pleated silk work-box, 31¹/₂in. wide. (Christie's) **£1,980**

A Victorian burr-walnut and inlaid work table with rounded rectangular hinged top enclosing a tapering fitted well, above twin baluster-turned end-standards, 23in. wide. (Christie's) **£1,045**

Regency pen-work decorated work table, circa 1810, hexagonal hinged top centred by a painted classical scene, 28¹/₂in. high. (Skinner Inc.) **£1,483**

A mid Victorian rosewood work table, the rectangular shaped top having frieze drawer opening to reveal a maple wood fitted interior, 58cm. wide. (Phillips) **£500**

A William IV rosewood work table with hexagonal hinged top and upholstered well on scroll uprights carved with rosettes, 22in. wide. (Christie's) **£715**

An early Victorian rosewood work table, the rectangular top with wide crossband, above a fitted drawer and a fabric-covered workbag, 23in. wide. (Tennants) **£650**

A Biedermeier maple and ebony work table, the hinged square top enclosing a fitted interior including a silk lined folding pin-cushion, 20in. wide. (Christie's) **£3,300**

A Regency satinwood games and work table with lift-out top crossbanded with rosewood and inlaid on the reverse with a chessboard, 20in. wide. **£4,000**

A Regency rosewood games table, the top with pierced brass gallery to each shaped flap, the sliding reversible central section inlaid with a chessboard, 39in. wide. (Bearne's) **£3,800**

One of a pair of Regency rosewood work-tables inlaid with boxwood lines, each with a rectangular canted twin-flap top, 31in. wide, open. (Christie's) (Two) **£8,250**

A Regency satinwood work table with purpleheart lines to the rectangular top, two long drawers above a false drawer and on lyre supports, 22½in. wide. (Bearne's) **£2,900**

A fruitwood work table, the rounded rectangular grained burr top on U-shaped square support and splayed legs, 26¾in. wide. (Christie's S. Ken) **£1,320**

A William IV mahogany work table, the rectangular twin-flap top above two frieze drawers, the lower enclosing sliding well, 31 x 20¾in. (Christie's S. Ken) **£935**

A Regency mahogany and brass inlaid drop flap work table, quadruped splayed scroll supports, 2ft. 10in. x 1ft. 5in. (Phillips) **£3,400**

A Regency brass-inlaid rosewood games-table, the blue leather-lined top with sliding rectangular section, on paw feet headed by volutes, 55in. wide. (Christie's) £9,900

A Regency coromandel and brass strung combined games and work table, the stellar inlaid rosewood veneered hinged ratcheted top sliding to reveal a backgammon board, 2ft. 4in. wide. (Phillips) £2,600

One of a pair of Regency ormolu-mounted calamander games-tables, each D-shaped to with stylised satinwood border enclosing a baize-lined playing surface, 36in. wide. (Christie's) £14,30

A Regency Chinese export lacquer decorated work table, with pagoda landscapes within a dragon border enclosing a fitted interior with ivory fittings, having a sliding well with armorial appliquéwork below, 2ft. wide. (Phillips) £1,900

A Federal mahogany sewing-table, Salem, Massachusetts, 1790–1810, the serpentine top above a conforming case with a cockbeaded drawer fitted with a velvet-lined writing surface over an additional drawer and sliding work-bag, 19½in. wide. (Christie's) £4,620

A Regency rosewood and painted work-table, with hinge rectangular top with reading-support and concealed fitted mahogany-lined side drawer above a fixed green silk-lined and tasselled tapering work-basket, 19¾in. wide. (Christie's) £3,0

A Regency brass-mounted and inlaid rosewood combined work and games-table inlaid overall with foliage, the top centred by a rectangular glazed panel inset with a painting-on-vellum of a spray of flowers, 27¼in. wide. (Christie's) £5,720

Late 18th century Italian walnut and burr walnut games table inlaid with fruitwood, 101cm. wide. (Finarte) £4,007

A Regency ormolu-mounted rosewood, burr yewwood and simulated rosewood work-tal with round rectangular greer leather-lined pierced brass three-quarter-galleried top, 21in. wide. (Christie's) £2,2

A Regency ormolu-mounted rosewood games-table, the hinged square top sliding to reveal a backgammon board, on lyre-shaped end-supports, 28½in. wide.
(Christie's) £5,720

A Regency ebonised and penwork decorated games table, painted to simulate ivory marquetry in the Indian taste, the top decorated for chess with flowers and foliage, 1ft. 6in. square. (Phillips) £2,000

A Regency Chinese export lacquer card table, the hinged rectangular top with chinoiserie figures in a pagoda landscape within floral and foliate borders, 2ft. 7½in. wide.
(Phillips) £1,500

A Transitional ormolu-mounted tulipwood and marquetry gueridon, the kidney-shaped top decorated with trophies within scrolled and ribbon-tied foliate borders, on cabriole legs headed by simulated fluting joined by a conforming undertier, 22in. wide. (Christie's) £30,800

A George II brass and mother-of-pearl-inlaid padoukwood concertina-action games-tables attributed to John Channon, the brass-inlaid rectangular eared top bordered by cartouches and engraved strapwork, 32½in. wide.
(Christie's) £22,000

An ormolu-mounted, marquetry and lapis lazuli work table, the hinged top centred by a foliate marquetry inlay on a sycamore ground, banded in harewood and boxwood, with a ribbon-tied foliate marquetry panel to each side, late 19th century, 24¾in. wide. (Christie's) £2,200

Late 18th century triangular walnut games table with two small drawers, on tapering legs, Genoese.
(Finarte) £3,369

A Regency rosewood games table, attributed to Gillows, the rounded rectangular top with re-entrant corners and central reversible sliding section inlaid with a chess-board, 34in. wide.
(Christie's) £6,050

An early George III mahogany work-table with rectangular gadrooned top, a slide and partly-divided drawer on chamfered square legs, 28½in. wide. (Christie's) £17,600

A Victorian figured walnut games table, with hinged swivel action to reveal an inlaid draughts and backgammon board, 35³/₄in. wide. (Tennants) £1,300

A George III satinwood games and writing table, crossbanded in rosewood, the rounded rectangular twin flap top with a reversible centre, 34in. wide. (Christie's) £2,420

A late Regency rosewood combined games and reading table, the rounded rectangular top divided into two, 35in. wide, circa 1830. (Tennants) £2,100

A Regency brass-mounted rosewood games table with removable square leather-lined sliding top, the reverse with chequerboard, enclosing a well with later backgammon board, 28in. wide. (Christie's) £3,300

A George IV maple, grained and ebonised work-table, the rectangular twin-flap top banded in mahogany above three mahogany-lined drawers, on bobbin-turned tapering legs with brass caps, 37³/₄in. wide. (Christie's) £2,420

A giltmetal-mounted mahogany work table the superstructure with two shelves on S-scrolled supports, the lower section with rectangular top banded in rosewood above two drawers, first quarter 19th century, 45in. high. (Christie's) £3,850

An early Victorian ebony and ivory games-table with hinged chamfered moulded square top with an ebony border inset with a printed and pencil-drawn chequer-board, 29in. high. (Christie's) £2,090

A classical carved mahogany worktable, New York, 1815–1825, the rectangular top above conforming case with two graduated drawers on reeded tapering legs, 21in. wide. (Christie's) £2,105

A Federal brass-mounted and inlaid mahogany two-drawer work table, Philadelphia, circa 1810, with ring-turned three-quarter-round columns at each corner, width 20in. (Sotheby's) £2,459

A late George III mahogany work-table inlaid overall with boxwood lines, the canted rectangular top crossbanded in satinwood, 22in. wide. (Christie's) £1,100

A George IV rosewood sewing table with velvet-lined swivelling hinged top, with pleated olive simulated-silk basket, 21in. wide. £900

Early Victorian rosewood worktable, circa 1844, octagonal moulded top enclosing a fitted interior, ending in claw and ball feet, 30½in. high. (Skinner Inc.) £571

A Regency rosewood and marquetry work-table inlaid with bands of scrolling foliage with rounded rectangular twin-flap top fitted with central removable panel enclosing silk-lined interior, 30in. wide. (Christie's) £1,320

A George III mahogany games-table, inlaid overall with boxwood and ebonised lines, the sliding reversable featherbanded top lined with a chessboard and trellis-pattern leather, 40¾in. wide. (Christie's) £8,250

A Regency rosewood and parcel-gilt games table with rectangular sliding top, the reverse with a chequerboard enclosing a backgammon board, the D-shaped end-sections with pierced brass gallery, 31½in. wide. (Christie's) £6,050

An Anglo Indian rosewood work table, the rectangular top with lotus-carved edge above scroll brackets and fitted frieze drawer, mid 19th century, 30in. wide. (Christie's) £825

Federal mahogany veneer carved astragal-end work table, New York, circa 1815, the hinged top above a fitted interior, 26½in. wide. (Skinner) £1,086

A Regency pollard oak work-table with hinged canted rec-tangular top enclosing lidded compartments, with down-swept legs and brass paw feet. 26in. (66 cm.) wide. (Christie's) £2,200

Between 1775 and 1825 there were a number of beautifully made desks designed in a delicately feminine manner yet strongly built so that many have survived in good condition to the present day.

There is a fascination in any piece of furniture which has an action like that which is incorporated in some desks, for, when the drawer is opened, the tambour automatically rolls back into the frame to reveal a fitted compartment which may be used for storing paper and envelopes. The drawer also acts as a support for the flap, which can now be lifted from the centre of the desk and folded forward to provide an ample, leather covered writing surface.

Tambours were widely used during this period, both vertically and horizontally, to cover everything from desk tops to night commodes.

Made of thin strips of wood glued on to a linen or canvas backing, they run in grooves on the frame and follow any path the cabinet maker wishes them to take.

Another elegant and highly desirable writing table which was made from the end of the 18th century until about 1825 and then again during the Edwardian period when the styles of this era were revived, is described by Sheraton in his Drawing Book as "a Lady's Drawing and Writing Table". It adopted the name Carlton House table from the residence of the Prince of Wales for whom the design was originally prepared.

Basically a D-shaped table on fine square tapering legs, it has a bank of drawers and compartments ranged round the sides and back.

A brass-mounted mahogany and partridgewood writing-table with ebonised banding, on lyre-shaped end-supports joined by double turned stretchers, 44in. wide.
(Christie's)   £4,400

A 19th century kingwood, mahogany, ormolu mounted marquetry bureau plat, in the Louis XV style, crossbanded and veneered with 18th century panels, 4ft. wide.
(Phillips)   £6,000

A George III ormolu-mounted writing-table, the eared rectangular red leather-lined top with moulded edge, the inverted breakfront frieze with three mahogany-lined drawers, 49in. wide.
(Christie's)   £6,600

A Regency rosewood writing-table with rounded rectangular green leather-lined top with pierced brass three-quarter gallery, on downsplayed end-supports, 41in. wide.
(Christie's)   £6,380

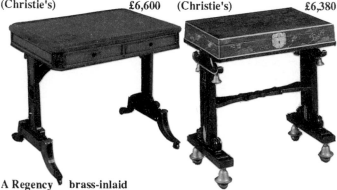

A Regency brass-inlaid satinwood writing-table with rounded rectangular crossbanded top, on solid panelled end-standards centred by a flowerhead medallion and joined by an arched stretcher, 33¼in. wide.
(Christie's)   £9,900

A giltmetal-mounted red-and-gilt Japanese lacquer writing-box-on-stand, the detachable box with hinged rectangular lid decorated with buildings and mountains beside a lake, 27½in. wide.
(Christie's)   £1,650

A George III mahogany writing-table in the manner of Mayhew and Ince, on turned tapering legs headed by ovals and with brass caps, 53½in. wide.
(Christie's) **£7,150**

A Regency giltmetal-mounted rosewood and parcel-gilt Carlton House desk, the carved galleried superstructure with later geometric gallery and with six mahogany and cedar-lined drawers, 55in. wide.
(Christie's) **£77,000**

A Regency rosewood and brass-mounted writing table, in the Louis XVI taste, the rectangular crossbanded top inset with a green tooled leather panel, 4ft. 9in. x 2ft. 7in.
(Phillips) **£2,800**

A George III ormolu-mounted mahogany bonheur-du-jour possibly by John Okeley in the style of David Roentgen, the stepped top lifting to reveal a mirror and well flanked by two platforms with solid galleries, 36½in. wide.
(Christie's) **£66,000**

Louis XVI style gilt-bronze-mounted mahogany escritoire, after Weisweiler, circa 1900, raised on tapering square gilt-bronze legs headed by female herms, 33½in. wide.
(Butterfield & Butterfield) **£5,673**

A Napoleon III ormolu and Sèvres-pattern porcelain-mounted, thuyawood and ebonised bonheur-du-jour, on fluted baluster supports joined by two undertiers, 53¼in. wide.
(Christie's) **£3,300**

A Regency amboyna and ebony bonheur-du-jour, the superstructure with shaped rectangular three-quarter galleried top above a central opening and cedar-lined drawer flanked by panelled bowfronted doors, 29¼in. wide.
(Christie's) **£6,050**

An Edwardian satinwood kneehole writing desk, the leather lined top of recessed serpentine outline with shelved superstructure and pierced brass gallery, 48in. wide.
(Christie's) **£3,080**

A French tulipwood, parquetry and ormolu-mounted serpentine bonheur du jour, decorated overall with geometric motifs, the crested and tiered mirror-backed top above two panelled doors, 33in. wide.
(Christie's) **£6,600**

A Louis Philippe burr-walnut and tulipwood table à ecrire with brass bound top, 31½in. wide. (Christie's) **£2,200**

A good George III mahogany writing table, on moulded square section legs headed by open 'C'-scroll brackets, 39in. wide. (Bonhams) £4,500

One of a pair of George III serpentine tables in the manner of John Cobb, 2ft. 6in. wide, circa 1770. **£22,000**

A late Victorian amboyna and calamander writing table, the tambour roll top enclosing a fitted interior, with square tapering legs and concave platform, 19½in. wide. (Christie's S. Ken) **£660**

An unusual oval amboyna writing table, circa 1850, in the French Louis XV manner, quarter-banded in tulipwood and with a curved brass gallery, 4ft. wide. (Sotheby's) **£4,950**

An elegant George III mahogany lady's writing table, the crossbanded rectangular top inlaid with a boxwood oval, on ring turned tapered legs, 21³⁄₄in. wide. (Bonhams) £2,700

A George III mahogany writing table with leather lined, kidney-shaped top, 40in. wide. **£2,950**

A brass mounted mahogany writing desk with a tambour roll-top, 26½in. wide. (Christie's) **£1,320**

A Regency pollard oak and parcel gilt writing table, the top centred by a hinged easel. 31in. wide. **£2,650**

378

A George III mahogany veneered rectangular writing table with inset gilt tooled green leather top, 3ft.3in. long. £1,350

An Edwardian mahogany writing table, interior fitted with a rising stationery rack and drawers, 26in. high. (Christie's) £2,035

A mid Victorian ormolu mounted walnut and tulip-wood writing table with leather lined top, 43in. wide. £7,250

A Regency mahogany writing table, on dual column standard end supports joined by a pair of arched stretchers on outswept square tapering legs, 2ft. 11in. wide.
(Phillips) £2,200

An early 19th century North Italian walnut, pine and ivory marquetry kneehole writing or dressing table, the sides with pictorial scenes, possibly the life of Moses, on square tapered legs and spade feet.
(Phillips) £2,600

A Regency oak and brown oak writing-table with rounded rectangular black leather-lined top above two mahogany-lined frieze drawers and on panelled end-supports, 39³/₄in. wide.
(Christie's) £1,650

A Louis XV kingwood and parquetry writing table on cabriole legs, 26in. wide. £7,150

A George III mahogany writing table with revolving easel top, 25in. wide. £3,750

A walnut writing table by Peter Waals, with barber's pole inlay, on moulded tapering legs, 94cm. wide. (Christie's) £1,870

A Regency mahogany library table, with a crossbanded leather tooled top, the frieze with a pair of drawers to either side, 4ft. wide.
(Phillips)   £2,800

A rare 'boulle' and tortoiseshell writing desk, by Collinson & Lock, circa 1890, in the French Louis XIV manner, on eight square tapering legs, the whole inlaid with brass and pewter foliage, 3ft. 11in. wide.
(Sotheby's)   £2,750

A William IV mahogany writing-table, the rounded rectangular top with hinged sliding red leather-lined central section, the panelled frieze with two mahogany-lined drawers to each end, 61in. wide.
(Christie's)   £7,150

A Louis XV ormolu mounted kingwood, tulipwood, purpleheart marquetry mechanical table à ecrire, by Jean Francois Oeben, 2ft. 10in. x 1ft. 5in. top.
(Phillips)   £48,000

A Bruce Talbert gothic bureau manufactured by Holland & Son, circa 1865, oak with traces of gilding, 64¹/₂in. high.
(Sotheby's)   £3,080

A George III mahogany chamber writing-table in the manner of Gillows, the rounded rectangular top with inset hinged section enclosing three compartments and a pen slide, 36in. wide.
(Christie's)   £2,640

A Regency rosewood and brass inlaid library table, on concave shaped standard end supports, united by a ring-turned stretcher with outswept legs, 4ft. wide.
(Phillips)   £6,500

A solid satinwood simulated bamboo writing table, by Howard & Sons, circa 1875, with shaped rectangular green leather-lined top, 3ft. 10¹/₂in. wide.
(Sotheby's)   £1,485

An ormolu-mounted kingwood and parquetry bureau plat, by François Linke, the serpentine top inset with tooled red leather skiver and banded with a gilt-metal moulded edge, the wavy frieze centred by a female mask head within a foliate scroll surround, late 19th/20th century, 56¹/₄in. wide.
(Christie's)   £12,100

A George III rosewood box-on-writing-stand, the coffered top centred by a mahogany panel and inlaid with geometric banding, repair to stretcher, 15¼in. wide.
(Christie's)   £1,485

A Regency mahogany writing-table with rounded rectangular black leather-lined top, above three frieze drawers to each side, on fluted turned tapering legs and brass caps, 53in. wide.
(Christie's)   £6,600

A George III mahogany reading-table with moulded rectangular adjustable hinged top and fitted reading-stop above two short and one long mahogany-lined fitted frieze drawer, 28in. wide.
(Christie's)   £6,050

A French ormolu-mounted kingwood and marquetry bonheur du jour in the manner of Topino, inlaid overall with a pictoral marquetry including a flower-filled vase, an inkstand and quiver, books and a teapot, second half 19th century, 26½in. wide. (Christie's)   £1,870

A Regency mahogany small writing-table, the rounded rectangular green leather-lined top with brass moulded rim and pierced three-quarter gallery, 30¼in. wide.
(Christie's)   £3,080

A George III satinwood writing-table, the twin-flap hinged top banded in amaranth and each flap centred by an oval thuyawood medallion, 36¼in. wide.
(Christie's)   £3,080

A late George III mahogany writing table in the manner of Gillows, the rounded rectangular leather inset top above two frieze drawers, on turned reeded legs, 4ft. wide.
(Phillips)   £3,000

A George III Irish mahogany two-handled metamorphic writing table, with a leather inset top opening to form library steps, 28in. wide.
(Christie's)   £11,913

A late George III mahogany and ebony strung library table, the leather tooled top with rounded ends and a ratcheted adjustable top, 3ft. 6in. wide.
(Phillips)   £2,100

A Victorian inlaid and parcel gilt centre writing table with leather inset top above a shallow frieze drawer, 53½ x 25in.
(Lawrence Fine Art)   £4,290

A mahogany writing table, the rectangular top with fan inlay and satinwood stringing, on square capped turned legs, 3ft. 4in. wide.
(Woolley & Wallis)   £900

A William IV mahogany writing table, on partly fluted spreading turned trestle ends carved with bands of egg and dart, 63¾in. wide. (Christie's London)   £4,400

A brass-mounted mahogany writing-table with rectangular leather-lined top and frieze drawer on turned tapering legs, 31in. wide.
(Christie's)   £1,430

A George III mahogany cylinder top writing table, inlaid with boxwood lines, the elliptical tambour shutter enclosing four small drawers and pigeonholes above a writing slide, 3ft. 6in. wide.
(Phillips)   £4,000

An ormolu-mounted kingwood and marquetry table à écrire with crossbanded kidney-shaped top inlaid with end-cut marquetry foliage, 24¼ in. wide.
(Christie's)   £1,430

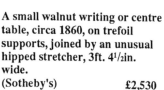

A small walnut writing or centre table, circa 1860, on trefoil supports, joined by an unusual hipped stretcher, 3ft. 4½in. wide.
(Sotheby's)   £2,530

A walnut writing table, circa 1860, with a stepped superstructure, the fluted tapering legs joined by galleried stretchers, 4ft. 2½in. wide.
(Sotheby's)   £2,200

A mid Victorian mahogany writing table, with hinged fitted compartment above two frieze drawers, on fluted tapering legs, stamped *Gillow*, 36in. wide.
(Christie's)   £1,760

A William IV mahogany double-sided writing table with blue tooled leather inset and bead and reel edge to the top, 54½in. wide.
(Bearne's) **£1,700**

A mid-Victorian ormolu-mounted amaranth, bird's eye maple, and marquetry writing-table inlaid overall with mahogany banding and floral bouquets, on cabriole legs with foliate sabots, 57in. wide.
(Christie's) **£3,960**

A Regency ormolu mounted mahogany writing table, on ring turned tapering legs, joined by a galleried platform, 39in. wide. (Christie's) **£11,000**

A Dutch ebonised and lacquer writing table, the top with inset panel of courtly figures boating in a water landscape, 34½in. wide.
(Christie's) **£2,530**

A George III mahogany cheveret with carrying handle and three-quarter solid gallery, 18¾in. wide.
(Christie's) **£1,430**

A mahogany and ormolu mounted writing table with blue leather skiver over one frieze drawer, on turned legs, 19th century, 99cm. wide.
(Finarte) **£4,591**

A walnut and giltmetal mounted writing table, on clasp headed cabriole legs with sabots, restorations, late 19th century, 24½in. wide. (Christie's S. Ken) **£880**

An ormolu mounted king-wood, mahogany, parquetry and marquetry table à écrire, on cabriole legs with foliate clasps, 33½in. wide.
(Christie's) **£2,200**

A mahogany writing table, on shaped end standards and downswept legs with curved stretcher, 39in. wide.
(Christie's London) **£1,375**

A French marquetry Boulle and ebonised wood serpentine bureau plat, Napoléon III, Paris, circa 1850, 150cm. wide.
(Sotheby's)   £5,720

A good French marquetry centre or writing table, Louis-Philippe/Napoléon III, by Gros of Paris, circa 1850, 133cm. wide.
(Sotheby's)   £5,280

A French 'Boulle' bureau mazarin, Napoléon III, Paris, circa 1870, in Louis XIV style, the rectangular top with three drawers in each pedestal, 156cm. wide.
(Sotheby's)   £13,20[

An 18th century Austrian walnut veneered writing desk, inlaid with fruitwood, the raised back with six drawers flanking a central cupboard, on six legs joined by stretchers, 62cm. wide.
(Finarte)   £7,944

A Louis XV style burr-walnut and mahogany bonheur du jour, the raised back having pierced gilt metal gallery over central doors inset with oval floral-painted Sèvres type porcelain panel, 2ft. 9in. wide.
(Russell Baldwin & Bright)
                    £1,600

A fine and rare Federal mahogany lift-top writing table with drawer, labelled *John T. Dolan*, New York, circa 1805, o reeded tapering legs ending in vase-form feet on brass casters, width 33in.
(Sotheby's)   £11,34[

Late 18th century walnut veneered writing desk with one long frieze drawer and two small drawers under, on square tapering legs, Emilian, 99cm. wide.
(Finarte)   £7,221

An Edwardian satinwood, rosewood-banded and line-inlaid Carlton House desk, the leather-lined top with galleried superstructure, 52¹/₂in. wide.
(Christie's)   £10,120

A mid 18th century walnut writing desk with poplar wood inlay and ivory banding, on gol edged cabriole legs, Modena, 117cm. wide.
(Finarte)   £44,39

A George III satinwood and mahogany writing-table inlaid overall with ebonised and boxwood lines crossbanded with tulipwood, the D-shaped top and drawer inlaid in penwork, 41in. wide.
(Christie's) £4,950

A Victorian walnut kidney-shaped writing table with inset top, fitted with two frieze drawers on cheval frame with turned stretcher, 4ft. wide.
(Russell Baldwin & Bright) £1,540

A late Victorian mahogany kneehole writing table inlaid with marquetry, rosewood and zebra wood bands, on square tapering legs and spade feet, 41in. wide.
(Christie's S. Ken) £2,090

An 18th century Italian walnut and gilt copper applied kneehole dressing or writing table, the rectangular top with a hunting scene and palmette ornament to the corners, on later oak cabriole legs, 2ft. 10in. wide.
(Phillips) £1,600

An oak gate-leg writing cabinet designed by M.H. Baillie-Scott, rectangular top above fall-flap with pierced steel hinge plates designed by C.A. Voysey, 91.5cm. wide.
(Christie's) £3,300

An Edwardian mahogany and marquetry writing table, the raised superstructure with broken scroll pediment above a hinged compartment inlaid with fan motif and cornucopiae, 42in. wide.
(Christie's) £2,200

A Napoleon III ormolu-mounted ebonised table milieu, third quarter 19th century, on spirally tapering ormolu legs with foliate cap feet, 36¼ in. wide.
(Christie's East) £15,158

A 19th century amboyna table in French style by W. Williamson & Sons, 31in. wide. £2,500

A Louis XVI ormolu-mounted mahogany and fruitwood marquetry table en encrier in the manner of J.H. Riesener, with shaped rectangular ormolu-moulded top, 42¾ in. wide.
(Christie's East) £8,162

BONHEUR DU JOURS

A satinwood veneered bonheur du jour, Maple & Co. trade label, 28.5in. wide. (Woolley & Wallis) £1,000

A mahogany and satinwood crossbanded bonheur du jour by T. Willson, London, 45in. wide. £1,000

A George III mahogany bonheur du jour, the super-structure with two oval-inlaid doors, 36¼in. wide. £5,000

A George III mahogany bonheur-du-jour, the rectangular top with a tambour-shutter enclosing mahogany-lined drawers and pigeon-holes, on bracket feet, 35¾in. wide. (Christie's) £1,980

A George III mahogany bonheur-du-jour banded in satinwood and inlaid overall with boxwood stringing, the rectangular hinged top with three-quarter gallery enclosing a baize-lined well, on brass paw feet, 36in. wide. (Christie's) £8,250

A mid-Victorian ormolu mounted mahogany burr walnut and marquetry bonheur-du-jour of Louis XVI style, with three-quarter pierced gallery, above a tambour shutter with book-ends, 34in. wide. (Christie's) £3,080

A Regency ormolu mounted rosewood bonheur du jour attributed to John McLean, on turned supports, 32½in. wide. (Christie's) £8,800

A late Victorian ormolu mounted ebonised bonheur-du-jour mounted with Sevres style plaques, 43in. wide. (Christie's) £880

A 19th century French bon-heur du jour, the ebonised ground decorated with panels of foliate scrolls, 38in. wide. £2,000

BONHEUR DU JOURS

A French rosewood and ormolu mounted bonheur du jour, circa 1890, 3ft. 3in. wide. £1,000

A Louis XV style walnut veneered bonheur du jour applied throughout with gilt brass foliate mounts, 48in. wide. (Bearne's) £2,900

A mahogany bonheur du jour surmounted by pierced brass gallery, circa 1780, 3ft.5in. wide. £1,000

Louis Philippe brass and mother-of-pearl inlaid rosewood bonheur du jour, circa 1840, with mother-of-pearl and brass marquetry and gilt-bronze outline, raised on shaped cabriole legs, 31in. wide. (Butterfield & Butterfield) £1,803

A Victorian ormolu-mounted tulipwood bonheur du jour, mid-19th century, with a stepped rectangular three-quarter pierced galleried superstructure, 36³/₄in. wide. (Christie's East) £2,449

A George III mahogany bonheur du jour, inlaid overall with boxwood stringing, the low galleried superstructure with three satinwood veneered drawers, 28¹/₂in. wide. (Bonhams) £1,600

A Regency period rosewood veneered gilt and brass inlaid bonheur du jour in the manner of John McLean, 26½in. wide. £6,150

A Victorian walnut and marquetry bonheur du jour inlaid with foliate arabesques and applied with gilt brass foliate mounts, 48in. wide. (Bearne's) £2,200

A Regency mahogany bonheur du jour with two open shelves above a folding writing flap, 2ft.6in. wide. (Greenslades) £2,300

BUREAU PLAT

An early Victorian ormolu mounted kingwood bureau plat inlaid with mother-of-pearl and polychrome marquetry, on cabriole legs, 45½in. wide.
(Christie's London)   £5,280

Good Louis XVI style gilt-bronze-mounted mahogany and parquetry bureau plat, late 19th/early 20th century, the rectangular top with a leaf-tip cast gilt-bronze border, 45¼in. wide.
(Butterfield & Butterfield)
£6,074

A late Victorian brass-mounted rosewood bureau plat, of Louis XV style, the shaped rectangular red leather-lined top above a waved frieze with three drawers on cabriole legs, 54in. wide.
(Christie's)   £3,0⬛

An ormolu mounted mahogany and marquetry bureau plat in the manner of B.V.R.B., stamped G. Durand, 45½in. wide.
(Christie's)   £2,750

Louis XV style parquetry bureau plat, late 19th century, the rectangular top with gilt-tooled leather writing surface over a central spiral ribbon-inlaid frieze drawer flanked by banks of two parquetry-inlaid drawers, 4ft. 11in. wide.
(Butterfield & Butterfield)
£2,837

A Louis XVI style ormolu-mounted plum pudding mahogany bureau plat in the manner of J.H. Riesener, with shaped rectangular ormolu-moulded top, 78¹/2. wide.
(Christie's East)   £11,0⬛

A Louis XV style kingwood and marquetry inlaid bureau plat applied with gilt metal mounts and borders, on cabriole legs and sabots, 19th century, 45½in. wide.
(Christie's S. Ken)   £3,190

Louis XV style gilt-metal-mounted bureau plat, the shaped rectangular top inset with gilt-tooled leather within a banded reserve applied with a gadroon-cast edge, 5ft. wide.
(Butterfield & Butterfield)
£1,576

A gilt-metal mounted rosewood and parquetry bureau plat, the top inset with a tooled green leather skiver and outlined with a gilt-moulded edge and a scroll cartouche to each corner, 20th century, 64³/₄in. wide.
(Christie's)   £1,⬛

CARLTON HOUSE

A mahogany Carlton House writing table in late George III-style decorated with ebony stringing, 56in. wide. **£3,200**

A figured mahogany and satinwood banded Carlton House style desk, the rectangular top fitted with a superstructure on square tapered legs, 52in. wide. (Christie's) **£1,045**

Edwardian mahogany and satinwood crossbanded Carlton House desk, 4ft. 6in. wide, bearing *Maple & Co.* stamp. (Lawrences) **£2,600**

A mahogany Carlton House desk inlaid with satinwood bands and ebony and satinwood lines, on square tapering legs, 55in. wide. (Christie's) **£4,950**

A painted satinwood and simulated rosewood banded Carlton House desk with leather-lined top and superstructure with drawers and cupboards, 54in. wide. (Christie's) **£2,200**

A satinwood Carlton House desk inlaid with ebonised lines, the D-shaped superstructure with pierced brass gallery with six cedar-lined drawers around a leather-lined reading slope, 41½in. wide. (Christie's S. Ken) **£3,300**

A painted satinwood and rosewood banded Carlton House desk, on square tapering legs, modern, 56in. wide. (Christie's) **£2,640**

A black and gold lacquer Carlton House desk decorated with chinoiserie panels of flowers, landscapes and figures, 59½in. wide. (Christie's) **£2,750**

A mahogany Carlton House desk, with leather lined writing surface, on square tapering legs, 54½in. wide. (Christie's) **£7,700**

A satinwood and inlaid kidney-shape desk, circa 1890, with leather inset top above a central drawer flanked by four small drawers.
(Tennants) £1,550

An Edwardian inlaid satinwood bowfront desk, with ledged back and finials above a frieze drawer between two quarter-veneered panelled doors, 48in. wide.
(Christie's) £825

An oak writing desk, designed by George Walton, the rectangular top above three drawers, on square tapering supports, circa 1900, 37in. high.
(Christie's) £660

A fine and rare walnut schoolmaster's desk, Pennsylvania, circa 1780, the rectangular hinged slant lid with moulded paper stop, 29³/₄in. wide.
(Sotheby's) £4,962

A Carlo Bugatti ebonised and inlaid writing desk inlaid with geometric patterns of bone and pewter together with a chair en suite.
(Christie's) £2,090

A mahogany and marquetry roll-top desk with tambour shutter enclosing a fitted interior of drawers and pigeon-holes, late 18th/early 19th century, 42in. wide.
(Christie's) £2,640

Quaint Furniture oak desk, circa 1910, single drawer flanked by side bookshelves over two vertical side slats, 40in. wide.
(Skinner) £158

An ebonised gilt metal and porcelain mounted desk in the Louis XV style, on four square section cabriole legs, late 19th century, 110cm. (Lawrence Fine Arts) £990

A George III mahogany roll-top desk with tambour shutter enclosing a fitted interior with baize-lined reading-slope, on square tapering legs, 37in. wide.
(Christie's) £2,640

DESKS

An English Arts & Crafts brass mounted mahogany, sycamore and walnut marquetry partner's desk, 129.6cm. wide. (Christie's) £2,484

A Liberty & Co. mahogany desk, the rectangular top having a drawer below flanked with three drawers on each side, 85.5cm. high. (Phillips London) £620

A tortoiseshell veneered and ormolu mounted writing desk, with three frieze drawers, on ormolu mounted cabriole legs, French, 19th century. (Finarte) £2,100

A walnut patent desk, inset with a decorated cast iron letter box inscribed *Manufactured By Wooton Desk Manufacturing Company, Indianapolis, W S Wooton's Patent October 6th 1874*, 3ft. 7in. wide. (Spencer's) £2,400

L. & J. G. Stickley desk and chair, no. 611 and 1313, circa 1910, flat top desk with central letter compartments flanked by single small drawers. (Skinner) £564

German, late 19th century, rosewood roll top desk with neo-gothic style top and two doors on either side of kneehole with three drawers over, 135cm. wide. (Kunsthaus am Museum) £2,174

An early 18th century Piedmontese thuya wood veneered writing desk, on square tapering legs joined by X-stretchers, 103cm. wide. (Finarte) £11,215

A 19th century palisander writing desk, the raised back with two doors flanked by four small drawers, on slender cabriole legs, 110cm. wide. (Finarte) £1,285

Gustav Stickley table desk, similar to no. 430, circa 1903, central drawer flanked by small stacked double side drawers, 36in. wide. (Skinner) £338

An Art Deco oval oak writing table, the oval top inset with green leather supports, the two pedestals enclosing drawers and a shelf, 69.6cm. high. (Phillips London)   £320

Louis XVI style tulipwood and kingwood marquetry desk, 19th century, recessed marble top, raised on sabre legs, 32in. wide. (Skinner Inc.)   £2,025

An Arts & Crafts inlaid oak desk, the rectangular top with bow front, covered in red leather above three short drawers, 149cm. wide. (Christie's)   £1,540

A Quebec pine slope front desk in the George III style, the hinged top opening upwards above a pair of moulded doors with raised panels, on bracket feet, original blue green paintwork, 36in. wide. (Fraser-Pinney)   £3,866

A 19th century mahogany roll top desk opening to reveal an arrangement of drawers and pigeonholes with architectural centre piece, on bracket feet. (Herholdt Jensen)   £1,541

Late 18th century Rhenish carved oak writing desk, the writing compartment behind a slanting board with drawers and pigeonholes, the serpentine commode base with three drawers, 127cm. wide. (Kunsthaus am Museum)

£1,553

A 19th century German mahogany veneer roll top desk, with fall front drawer over, a long drawer and two doors under, on ball feet, 110cm. wide. (Kunsthaus am Museum)   £938

19th century mahogany Louis Philippe roll top desk, some damage to veneer, 132cm. wide. (Auktionshaus Arnold)   £896

Edwardian satinwood and painted cylinder desk. circa 1900, the roll top painted with central medallion, raised on square tapering legs, 36½in. wide. (Skinner Inc.)   £2,295

A Maurice Dufrene semi-circular wooden desk, 31in. high, and a chair upholstered in red velvet, 32in. high, signed and dated 1935. £3,750

A late George III mahogany library desk with pierced gallery and Vitruvian scroll frieze, the plinth base 72in. diam. £27,000

An early John Makepeace, Andaman padouk and leather-covered desk, by M. Doughty, D. Pearson and A. Freeman, 199cm. wide, and a chair.
(Christie's) £1,980

A late Federal mahogany lady's writing desk, attributed to John or Thomas Seymour, Boston, 1800–1820, the rectangular top with hinged out-folding writing slab, 29in. wide.
(Christie's) £1,973

George III mahogany cylinder desk, rectangular top above a roll top opening to a fitted interior, 44½in. wide.
(Skinner Inc.) £549

A Carlo Bugatti ebonised and rosewood lady's writing desk with pewter and ivory inlay, 75.5cm. wide.
(Christie's) £3,850

A Sheraton period faded mahogany roll-top pedestal desk fitted with brass swan-neck handles, 3ft. 10in. wide. £2,550

American Country two-tier writing desk, 19th century, one drawer in base, modern grain-painted decoration, 27½in. wide.
(Eldred's) £133

Victorian cylinder-front writing desk in walnut, fitted cubbyhole interior over four drawers, 34in. wide.
(Eldred's) £342

DESKS

A Makers of Simple Furniture birchwood desk designed by Gerald Summers, the partly hinged rectangular top above two open shelves and single pedestal, 114cm. wide. (Christie's)   £440

Mid Victorian lady's mahogany writing desk on French cabriole supports, 47½in. wide.   £1,000

An Edwardian mahogany and satinwood banded kidney shaped writing desk, on square tapering legs, 42½in. wide. (Christie's)   £3,080

A rococo walnut marquetry lady's desk, bombe and serpentine case with fall-front, Italy, 31in. wide.   £1,300

A mid 19th century mahogany cylinder desk, having satinwood stringing and crossbanding, fitted pierced gilt-metal gallery over three frieze drawers, 4ft. 8in. wide.
(Russell Baldwin & Bright)
£2,700

A German oak green stained writing desk in the style of C. A. Voysey, 110.5cm. wide. (Christie's)   £3,520

A Federal inlaid mahogany writing desk, with hinged lid, 1790-1810, 29.7/8in. wide.   £1,500

George III mahogany double-sided writing desk, circa 1800–1810, the drawers with lion mask ring handles, 42in. wide. (Butterfield & Butterfield)
£1,687

A Chippendale pine standing desk, New England, 1780-1810, 30½in. wide. £1,000

LIBRARY TABLES

A library table with one drawer, by L. & J. G. Stickley, signed with Handcraft label, 42in. wide.
(Skinner Inc.) £513

A Regency mahogany library table, the frieze with two drawers, 46½in. wide.
(Christie's) £1,760

A Renaissance Revival burled walnut library table, labelled by Alex. Roux, N.Y., circa 1860, 48in. wide. £1,950

A George III mahogany library table, the rectangular top with replacement pale green tooled hide, 3ft. 6in. wide.
(Woolley & Wallis) £2,500

A William IV rosewood library table with rounded rectangular leather-lined top above frieze drawers, 42in. wide.
(Christie's S. Ken) £825

L. & J. G. Stickley library table, no. 520, circa 1910, overhanging rectangular top, single drawer with copper hardware elongated corbels inside each leg with medial shelf, 36in. wide.
(Skinner) £367

A Regency mahogany and boxwood strung library table, containing six drawers in the frieze, on standard and dual splayed end supports terminating in brass cappings and castors, 4ft. x 2ft. 6in.
(Phillips) £2,400

A mahogany partners' library table of Regency design with rounded rectangular leather-lined top and sides all carved with Greek-key designs, 19th century, 54½in. wide.
(Christie's) £22,000

A good Regency rosewood and rosewood grained library table, on lyre-shaped end supports, and gilt metal paw feet, 58¼in. wide.
(Bonhams) £7,400

TALLBOYS

The tallboy is essentially a double chest of drawers, one on top of the other, the lower section being, for obvious practical purposes, rather broader and deeper than the upper.

Tallboys were first introduced around 1700, and were surmounted either by a straight, hollow cornice or by a curved and broken pediment. By 1725 they had virtually superseded the chest-on-stand and they remained popular until the mid-Georgian period.

Additional features of the tallboy often include a secret drawer in the frieze and a brushing slide fitted above the oak-lined drawers in the lower section.

Tallboys look cumbersome, and it is a major operation getting up to the top drawers in the upper section. Many were split in half, and their tops veneered to make two smaller chests. Buyers of early walnut chests of drawers should, therefore, beware of any where the top is of a slightly different colour to the rest of the carcase. They could be split tallboys, and as such, worth less than the chests they claim to be.

A Chippendale maple tall chest, New England, circa 1770, 36in. wide. £2,150

A George II walnut tallboy with a cavetto cornice, 40in. wide. £2,500

A George I walnut tallboy chest, with three short and six long drawers, on shaped bracket feet, 5ft.9in. x 3ft.8in. (Phillips) £6,200

A George III mahogany tallboy, the upper section with rectangular key pattern-carved moulded cornice above two short and three graduated long drawers between canted fluted angles, 43in. wide. (Christie's) £3,080

A Country Chippendale cherry tall chest on bracket base, New England, circa 1780, 36in. wide. £3,750

Red painted Chippendale maple tall chest, New England, circa 1780, 36in. wide. (Skinner) £4,414

A mahogany veneered tall-boy chest on bracket feet, 3ft.7in. wide. (Woolley & Wallis) £1,500

A George III mahogany tall-boy with key-pattern cornice, 44½in. wide.   £2,650

Chippendale maple tall chest with six thumb moulded drawers, New England, circa 1770, 38in. wide.   £1,900

A George III mahogany serpentine front tallboy chest on ogee bracket feet, 4ft. overall. £6,250

A George III Welsh walnut and oak tallboy, the later moulded cornice above three short and three long graduated drawers, flanked to each side by fluted angles, 42¼in. wide. (Christie's)   £1,980

An early Georgian walnut tall-boy, the top section with moulded cornice and convex frieze drawer above three short and three long feather banded drawers, 67in. high. (Christie's London)   £6,050

A small George II fruitwood tallboy, with pierced shaped fret brass plate handles and escutcheons, on bracket feet, 3ft. 3in. wide. (Woolley & Wallis)   £1,200

A mid-18th century mahogany tallboy, with original brass handles and escutcheons, on bracket feet with wood castors, 41½in. wide. (Bearne's)   £1,050

A late George III mahogany tallboy with moulded and reeded cornice, satinwood-veneered frieze with shell medallions, on shaped bracket feet, 46½in. wide. (Bearne's)   £720

A George III mahogany secretaire tallboy with two short and three graduated long drawers flanked by fluted canted corners, 43½in. wide. (Bearne's)   £1,600

A walnut and oak tallboy, the moulded cornice above three short and six graduated long drawers, 41½in. wide. (Christie's S. Ken) £4,400

A George III mahogany tallboy chest with dentil moulded cornice and blind fret frieze, on bracket feet, 44in. wide. (Christie's) £1,760

A George I burr-walnut secretaire tallboy crossbanded and inlaid with chevron bands, 42¼in. wide. (Christie's) £16,500

A George III mahogany and crossbanded tallboy chest, the upper part with a moulded cornice, two short and three long graduated drawers, 3ft. 4in. wide. (Phillips) £1,000

A mid-19th century German oak tall chest, the six long drawers inlaid in contra and premier partie with grotesque animal heads and scrolling foliage on bracket feet. (Phillips) £600

A George I walnut and crossbanded tallboy chest with a moulded cornice and fitted with three short and six long drawers, on later bracket feet, 3ft. 5in. wide. (Phillips) £2,000

A George I walnut tallboy, fitted with three short and six long drawers, original brass handles, on bracket feet, 74in. high. (Dreweatt Neate) £6,800

A George III mahogany tall-boy, the top section with a dentilled cornice, the lower section with a brushing slide, 44½in. wide. (Christie's S. Ken) £1,650

A George II walnut-veneered tallboy, the cavetto cornice above three short and six graduated long drawers and on bracket feet, 42¹/₂in. wide. (Bearne's) £2,700

An early George III secretaire tallboy, the base with a well-fitted secretaire drawer, on ogee bracket feet, 48in. wide. (Christie's) £23,100

A George II walnut tallboy, the lower part with a brushing slide above three long drawers, on bracket feet, 41in. wide. (Lawrence) £6,710

A George III mahogany tallboy with a key-pattern cavetto cornice, on bracket feet, 44in. wide. (Bearne's) £1,450

An early Georgian walnut tallboy, featherbanded overall, the upper section with rectangular cavetto cornice above two short and three graduated long drawers, 40½in. wide. (Christie's) £2,530

A George III mahogany tallboy, the moulded rectangular cornice with Greek key decoration above a blind fretwork moulding and two short and three graduated long drawers, on bracket feet, 44in. wide. (Christie's) £1,980

A George I burr-walnut secretaire-tallboy inlaid overall with feather-banding, the base with fitted secretaire-drawer above three graduated long drawers, on bracket feet, 41in. wide. (Christie's) £28,600

A walnut tallboy, the cavetto moulded cornice above five small and five long drawers, on bracket feet, early 18th century, 43in. (Christie's S. Ken) £2,750

A George III mahogany tallboy with moulded cornice above two short and six graduated long drawers on bracket feet, 43½in. wide. (Christie's S. Ken) £880

An early 18th century walnut tallboy chest, with burrwood drawer fronts, the upper part with cavetto moulded cornice, on later ogee bracket feet, 3ft. 7in. wide. (Phillips) £5,800

The word teapoy comes from the Hindi *tin* and *ter*, three, and the Persian *pai*, a foot. It started life therefore as a small tripod table, and only by erroneous association with tea did it arrive at its final form, a small tea chest or caddy standing on a small three-footed stand.

The teapoy is mentioned in inventories as early as 1808, by which time taking tea was well established as an elegant social habit, tea as a commodity still being sufficiently expensive for the hostess to wish to dispense it herself from a locked box.

An early Victorian mahogany teapoy with circular hinged lid, 17½in. £500

An early Victorian rosewood teapoy on bun feet. £450

A Regency mahogany and crossbanded ebony boxwood strung teapoy with brass lion paw feet, 15in. wide. (Christie's) £650

An attractive Regency parquetry decorated rosewood teapoy/work table, on four outward splayed square tapering supports terminating in brass acanthus sheathed caps and castors, 1ft. 4in. wide. (Spencer's) £1,800

A Victorian walnut teapoy, with circular hinged cover, quarter veneered in burr walnut, opening to reveal a foliate carved rosette to the inner cover, 1ft. 4in. diameter. (Spencer's) £160

An attractive William IV mahogany teapoy, the slightly tapering square top with acanthus carved edge, on fluted scroll feet, 14in. square. (Spencer's) £500

A Regency mahogany and satinwood crossbanded rectangular teapoy with canted angles, 12in. wide. (Christie's) £800

Late Regency rosewood brass inlaid teapoy with sarcophagus shaped top, 17in. wide. (Lalonde Fine Art) £1,400

A Victorian burr walnut teapoy with rising lid, 48cm. diam. £700

Victorian rosewood teapoy on scroll feet, 1840. £400

An early Victorian walnut pedestal teapoy, the hinged panel lid enclosing a fitted interior, 19½in.diam. £375

A Regency mahogany teapoy, on baluster shaft and ribbed splayed tripartite base with roundel caps, the sides with lion mask and ring handles, 16½in. wide.
(Christie's) £496

A Biedermeier mahogany teapoy with hinged octagonal lid inlaid with boxwood and ebonised lines enclosing a fitted interior with lidded compartments above a cream-painted silk-lined well, 20½in. wide.
(Christie's) £1,650

A Regency rosewood teapoy with chamfered corners and inlaid with stringing, on four square curved supports joined by X turned stretchers, 48cm. wide. (Lawrence Fine Arts) £2,090

A William IV rosewood pedestal teapoy, the telescopic circular moulded top enclosing recesses and twin boxed caddies, 21½in. diameter.
(Christie's S. Ken) £660

A George III mahogany teapoy with octagonal hinged lid enclosing three lidded boxes, the reeded spreading legs headed by lotus leaves, 16¾in. wide.
(Christie's) £2,640

A Regency specimen wood parquetry pedestal teapoy, the octagonal top with a hinged lid enclosing two caddies and bowl apertures.
(Christie's) £1,980

A Regency rosewood teapoy of sarcophagus design. £500

A Regency brass inlaid rosewood teapoy with Bramah lock and carrying handles, 17½in. wide. £3,150

Regency rosewood teapoy. £2,000

A 19th century Anglo-Indian padoukwood teapoy, the scalloped sarcophagus top enclosing four hinged compartments above a foliate carved frieze. (Bonhams) £450

William IV carved rosewood teapoy, circa 1838, opening to a storage area, raised on a petal-carved baluster-form pedestal on a coved square base on scrolled feet, 32in. high. (Butterfield & Butterfield) £946

A Victorian rosewood teapoy, the hinged domed lid enclosing a divided interior above a turned baluster column, on three 'C'-scroll feet. (Bonhams) £650

A William IV walnut pedestal teapoy, the interior fitted with two canisters and two glass mixing bowls, stamped Gillow, 28½in. high. £925

A Regency mahogany teapoy, the hinged top enclosing a divided interior with later tin liners, 20in. wide. £3,150

A William IV Colonial carved rosewood teapoy with hinged cavetto top with radiating reeded fan panels, 48cm. wide. (Phillips) £800

The coffer, or chest, is one of the earliest forms of furniture.

It was used as a convenient, safe receptacle for clothes and valuables, doubling as a seat and even, in the case of the larger ones, as a bed.

It was Henry II, in 1166, who really started the boom in coffers when he decreed that one should be placed in every church to raise money for the crusades. Despite the holy cause, all those coffers were fitted with three locks whose keys were held separately by the parish priest and two trustworthy parishioners, just in case any insular minded local felt that he could put the money to better use.

On most early coffers, the stiles form the legs but others were made without such refinements, being made to be fastened down to the floor. There were still other designs, which were entirely of plank construction, the front and back being lapped over the sides and fastened with dowels or hand wrought nails. The side planks extend down below the bottom of the coffer to raise it off the damp, straw covered floor.

The 16th century saw a notable advance in the method of construction of coffers. A number of wide upright stiles were joined with mortise and tenon joints on top and bottom rails, muntins (vertical framing pieces) being added to make the panelled framework.

Decoration on these coffers was usually confined to the panels and took the form, particularly in the early models, of a linenfold design.

A cherrywood and pine dough box on stand, Pennsylvania, first half 19th century, the rectangular removable top above a well, length 48in. (Sotheby's) £681

A late 17th century iron bound strong box, the front with a false lock and two hasps, a camouflaged locking device in the lid, 34cm. wide. (Auktionsverket) £1,281

A 17th century iron strongbox, of Armada design, the hinged top with nipple studs to release the key cover to a twelve shutter locking device, 58cm. wide, probably German. (Phillips) £900

A 17th century later decorated chest of Armada type, painted with flowers, the hinged top with pierced interlaced engraved plate concealing a locking mechanism, 2ft. 4$^{1}/_{2}$in. (Phillips) £400

Louis XVI Provincial walnut dough box, late 18th century, serpentine moulded lifting lid opening to a lined interior, 38in. high. (Skinner Inc.) £741

A 17th century rectangular strongbox, iron banded with criss-cross pattern within and without, with two orifices in the base for floor attachment, 66cm. wide. (Duran) £722

An oak blanket chest designed by Gordon Russell, the lid with three wrought-iron strap hinges terminating in 'fleur-de-lys', with carved borders top and bottom, dated 20.6.27, 166.5cm. wide.
(Christie's)   £4,180

A Chippendale pine blanket chest, Pennsylvania, 19th century, the rectangular overhanging top with conforming dove-tailed case, 47³/₄in. wide.
(Christie's)   £286

A painted blanket chest, 19th century, flanked on either side by painted, decorated and braided cloth pulls with hand mounts, probably International Order of Odd-Fellows, 36in. wide.
(Christie's)   £1,118

Salmon grain painted pine blanket chest, New England, late 18th century, 42in. wide.
(Skinner)   £1,019

A Chippendale mahogany blanket chest, labelled by William Savery (1721–1787), Philadelphia, circa 1760, the hinged rectangular moulded top above a compartment fitted with a till and two secret short drawers, 48in. wide.
(Christie's)   £2,499

Country Federal grain and putty decorated blanket chest, Central Massachusetts, circa 1820, 38in. wide.
(Skinner)   £2,648

A William and Mary walnut blanket chest, Pennsylvania, early 18th century, the moulded hinged lid opening to an interior with till with hinged cover, 47¹/₂in. wide.
(Sotheby's)   £1,456

Paint decorated poplar blanket box, probably Pennsylvania or Ohio, early 19th century, 35¹/₂in. wide.
(Skinner)   £4,753

A Heal's oak blanket chest, the rectangular overhanging panelled top above plain panelled sides, on turned legs joined by plain stretchers, 93cm. wide.
(Christie's London)   £605

CASSONES

An Italian walnut cassone, the body elaborately carved with scrolling strapwork motifs around a central cabochon cartouche, part late 16th/early 17th century, 51¹/₂in. wide. (Christie's) £2,640

An Italian walnut cassone, the hinged rectangular lid above fielded front panels and two base drawers, 60 in., late 16th century. (Christie's) £1,155

An Italian walnut cassone, the panelled frieze carved with playful putti baiting a lion flanked by a pair of scrolling cartouches within studded pilaster strips, 19th century, 72in. wide. (Christie's) £3,520

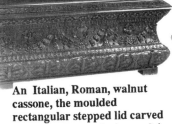

An oak cellaret of cassone form carved with putti, birds, lions and fruit, 34¹/₂in. wide. (Christie's S. Ken) £1,320

An Italian, Roman, walnut cassone, the moulded rectangular stepped lid carved with acanthus enclosing a plain interior with drainage hole, the front and sides of waisted shape carved with flowerheads, late 16th century, 68¹/₂in. wide. (Christie's) £4,400

An 18th century Italian carved walnut cassone, with later hinged top and panelled front with keyhole cartouche between mermaids flanked by caryatids, 2ft. wide. (Phillips) £550

An 18th century Italian carved walnut cassone of small size, with a guilloche decorated hinged top and panelled sides on paw feet, 1ft. 8in. (Phillips) £650

A 17th century walnut cassone, of sarcophagus form, the panelled front carved in high relief with an urn of flowers flanked by winged female figures holding vacant cartouches, 6ft. 2in. wide. (Phillips) £4,200

An 18th century Italian walnut cassone, the front with an armorial shield, grotesque mask and supported by mermen between atlantes and caryatid pilaster stiles, 2ft. 4in. wide. (Phillips) £450

Arts & Crafts veneered cedar chest with strap hinges, 1919, with burled walnut veneer and geometric bronze strapwork, unsigned, 46¼in. wide. (Skinner Inc.) £309

Northwest German 15th century carved oak chest, iron clasps and bands with fleur-delys finials, 189cm. wide. (Kunsthaus am Museum) £1,863

An oak chest with hinged rectangular top and boarded front and sides, the front decorated with horizontal grooves, 17th century, 48in. wide. (Christie's London) £550

A George III mahogany chest enclosed by a hinged coffered rectangular lid above brass side carrying handles, 51in. wide. (Christie's S. Ken) £770

A George III mahogany and brass-mounted campaign medicine chest, on later stand with square tapering legs, 20in. wide. (Christie's S. Ken) £990

An early 18th century South German oak marriage chest, the lid and front decorated with twin inlaid ivory crests and coats-of-arms representing the two families, 53cm. wide. (Phillips) £800

A painted and decorated dower chest, Pennsylvania, circa 1787, the hinged rectangular top with applied moulded trim decorated with three painted floral panels, 48¾in. wide. (Christie's) £4,290

Louis XIII carved oak chest, 17th century, the atlantes carved in the round and forming the front and return of the corner posts and standing on hippocampi, 4ft. 4½in. wide. (Butterfield & Butterfield) £1,606

A painted and punch decorated six-board pine chest, New London, Connecticut, 1700–1730, with rectangular hinged lid above a case with two rows of intersecting punchwork semicircles, 31½in. wide. (Christie's) £7,847

Chippendale walnut inlaid dower chest, Pennsylvania, circa 1774, 49in. wide.
(Skinner)   £951

An oak chest, the front and sides with carved fielded panels on block feet, 17th century, 69in. wide.
(Christie's London)   £2,090

German 18th century, carved oak chest, the base with pierced fretwork border and floral inlay, on bun feet, 145cm. wide.
(Kunsthaus am Museum) £1,553

Louis XIII Provincial oak armour chest, the long rectangular hinged moulded edge top above fielded panelled sides and front, 6ft. 11in. wide.
(Butterfield & Butterfield)
                          £1,967

A large mid-Georgian brass mounted mahogany campaign chest with brass corner mounts and side handles, 49½in. wide.
(Tennants)   £900

Polished oak and marquetry chest, decorated in reserves with birds, with metal fittings, on bun feet, German, 18th century, 117cm. wide.
(Kunsthaus am Museum) £1,087

A 17th century Singhalese hardwood and ebony chest applied with massive brass carrying handles with pierced backplates, 59in. wide.
(Bearne's)   £900

A massive 17th century West-phalian oak chest, the two plank top with hammered iron strap hinges, 70½in. wide.
(Tennants)   £2,600

Japanese bronze mounted lacquered storage chest, 18th century, decorated in hira-makie with the aoi crest of the Tokugawa family, 47½in. wide.
(Skinner Inc.)   £8,750

COFFERS

An early Tudor iron-bound ash coffer, the hinged domed top enclosing an interior with false floor and till, 34½in. wide. (Christie's) **£5,280**

A south German walnut coffer, with hinged lid enclosing a fitted interior, on later bun feet, late 18th century, 38in. wide. (Christie's) **£660**

A Dutch East Indies camphor coffer, the hinged rectangular top with brass studs, the sides with carrying handles, 18th century, 45in. wide. (Christie's London) **£385**

A Charles I oak coffer with hinged moulded rectangular top and frieze carved with foliage and sea-monsters, the front with three panels carved with flowerheads, divided by caryatid mouldings, 48in. wide. (Christie's) **£2,200**

A Venetian cedarwood and penwork coffer with rectangular hinged top enclosing a part-fitted interior decorated with courtly figures in a landscape, 17th century, 27½in. wide. (Christie's) **£1,430**

A Charles II brass-studded leather coffer decorated overall with stylised flowers and scrolling foliage with rectangular domed lid, the front with entwined dolphin and birds, 46in. wide. (Christie's) **£440**

A walnut coffer with slightly domed top and panelled sides inlaid overall with mother-of-pearl flowerheads and foliage, 18th century, near Eastern, 52in. wide. (Christie's London) **£1,210**

A Spanish walnut coffer with hinged rectangular lid, three locks and carrying handles, on plinth base, 40½in. wide. (Christie's) **£495**

A Punjabi oak coffer with hinged rectangular top, the trelliswork front on square supports and wheels, 19th century, 62in. wide. (Christie's) **£825**

COFFERS

A James I oak coffer, the rectangular top above a rosette and null carved front, on trestle supports, 35in. wide.
(Bonhams) £2,600

An ormolu-mounted walnut, kingwood, fruitwood and parquetry coffer, inlaid overall with cube decoration, probably German, mid-19th century, 18in. wide.
(Christie's) £2,310

A Continental walnut coffer, the domed top carved in relief with an armorial flanked by mounted warriors, 46in. wide.
(Bearne's) £680

A giltmetal-mounted walnut coffer, banded overall with ebony, the repoussé mounts with birds among flowerheads and foliage, Flemish or North German, late 17th century, 24in. wide.
(Christie's) £3,520

A Momoyama period rectangular coffer and flat overlapping cover richly decorated in aogai and gold and brown lacquer with a hishigata (lozenge or diamond shape) design, filled alternately with shippo-hanabishi, kikko and other geometric patterns, late 16th century, 107.8 x 65.6 x 73.7cm. high.
(Christie's) £30,800

A 17th century oak coffer, the top divided into three panels, the similarly panelled front with a frieze carved with a repeating foliate design, 39¼in. wide.
(Bearne's) £600

A Charles II oak coffer with moulded rectangular hinged top above a frieze of stylised flowers and a central hobnail-bordered geometric panel flanked by two oval panels, 52in. wide.
(Christie's) £715

A late 16th/early 17th century Continental dome top painted leather and wrought iron bound coffer, of Islamic influence, Italian or Flemish.
(Phillips) £3,400

An Indian padouk and brass bound coffer on stand, with carrying handles to the sides, the stand on ogee bracket feet, 50in., 19th century.
(Christie's) £990

COFFERS ON STANDS

A mahogany chest on stand, with a projecting apron carved with acanthus and centred by a shell, 48in. wide, 19th century. (Christie's) £550

A Goanese hardwood and ivory inlaid box on later stand, inlaid with flowering prunus, late 17th/early 18th century, 21in. wide. (Christie's) £2,420

A Chinese black and gold lacquer coffer-on-stand, the rectangular hinged top decorated with peony, tits and junglefowl within panels of foliage, early 18th century, 53¼in. wide. (Christie's) £5,280

A Flemish giltmetal mounted and kingwood strongbox on stand, the rectangular top with pierced hinges and foliate border enclosing a fitted interior, 17th century, 28in. wide.
(Christie's London) £3,300

A Chinese coffer-on-stand, the rectangular domed top with a central cartouche with Chinese landscapes of pavilions within a border of inlaid mother-of-pearl, with English carrying handles, the coffer 18th century, 39¼in. wide.
(Christie's) £4,400

A Chinese Export red and gilt-japanned coffer-on-stand decorated overall with courtly figures in an extensive watery landscape, late 18th/early 19th century, 39in. wide.
(Christie's) £2,200

A Spanish leather, brass bound and studded coffer chest, the front with fall-flap enclosing two drawers, late 17th century, 42in. wide.
(Christie's S. Ken) £715

A Chinese black-lacquer and chinoiserie chest, on a pine stand profusely carved with dragons and emblems of happiness, 42in. wide.
(Christie's S. Ken) £3,080

An oak domed coffer on stand, the domed hinged top and sides covered in cut floral plush, the base late 17th century, 27in. wide.
(Christie's London) £440

MULE CHESTS

A mid-18th century North
Country oak mule chest with
a rectangular hinged top enclosing a compartment, 62in.
wide. (Bearne's)   £820

A 17th century panelled oak
mule chest, with brass handles,
5ft. wide. (Greenslades)
                        £300

A George II oak mule chest,
the hinged rectangular lid
above fielded front panels,
on bracketed plinth base,
52in. (Christie's)   £825

An early George III mahogany
mule chest, the frieze with
gothic blind fretwork with two
drawers below on shaped
bracket feet, 56½in. wide.
(Christie's London)   £1,210

A Cromwellian oak chest with
moulded rectangular hinged top
enclosing a well above a panel
carved with a coat-of-arms, on
stile feet, with later staining,
52in. wide.
(Christie's)   £3,080

An oak mule chest, the
rectangular hinged lid above
a foliate carved frieze, with
lunette carved apron and
shaped feet, 57in.
(Christie's)   £440

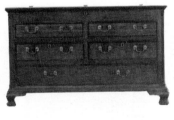

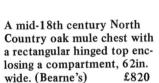

A mid-Georgian oak mule
chest, the front with three
fielded panels above two
drawers crossbanded with
mahogany, on bracket feet,
49¾in. wide. (Christie's
London)   £605

A George III oak mule chest, the
shallow box top with two
dummy drawers above two
short and one long drawer,
raised on ogee bracket feet, 4ft.
11in. wide.
(Russell Baldwin & Bright)
                        £720

Carved and painted oak and
pine chest over drawer, possibly
by Peter Blin (1670–1710), 46in.
wide.
(Christie's)   £7,150

An unusual painted and decorated pine dome-top trunk, Worcester, Massachusetts, circa 1830, with hinged lid opening to a deep well, length 24in.
(Sotheby's)   £4,918

Sculptured hardwood trunk, attributed to Wendell Castle, mid 20th century, domed top on rectangular base, 45in. wide.
(Skinner Inc.)   £2,937

A Malles Goyard cabin trunk, covered in Malles Goyard patterned material, bound in leather and brass, 85 x 49 x 47cm.
(Onslow's)   £400

An Afro-American painted and decorated yellow pine slave's trunk, Southern, 19th century, the rectangular hinged lid opening to a divided well, 24in. wide.
(Sotheby's)   £1,125

A Louis Vuitton gentleman's cabin trunk, bound in brass and leather with leather carrying handle, on castors, 91 x 53 x 56cm.
(Onslow's)   £830

Brass and wood bound Louis Vuitton trunk with fitted interior, 44$^{1}/_{2}$in. high.
(Eldred's)   £1,708

A painted trunk, probably Pennsylvania, late 18th/early 19th century, the hinged rectangular top with thumbmoulded edge lifting to an open compartment lined with portions of Claypoole's Advertiser, 1793 (Philadelphia), 38$^{1}/_{4}$in. wide.
(Christie's)   £478

A Louis Vuitton upright trunk covered in LV fabric and bound in brass, the lid opening to reveal a top compartment with tray, 25 x 16 x 45$^{1}/_{2}$in.
(Christie's)   £5,390

A green painted oak trunk with rounded top and banded in iron, painted with garlands and monogram *CPL 1839 den 13ten May*, 123cm. wide.
(Kunsthaus am Museum)   £586

Wardrobes are, surprisingly, quite close relations to corner cupboards, for both were born in recesses in walls. Wardrobes were late developers, however, failing to break free from their enclosing walls until the second half of the eighteenth century.

Presses with shelves and drawers were in fairly widespread use by the end of the seventeenth century, before which clothes had been stored in trunks and chests. It had sufficed, for a very long time, to store clothes by packing them flat in horizontal containers but, with the advent of a more sophisticated and clothes-conscious society in which both sexes tended to have increased numbers of garments, it became common sense to hang them vertically.

Although the vogue for wardobes of different kinds seems to have dissipated as abruptly as it arose, a few nice examples have remained with us.

All the fashionable decorative quirks found in other pieces of furniture appear on wardrobes, including dentil cornices, applied mouldings and canted front edges. Chippendale favoured serpentine fronts, often with bombé fronted drawers below, while Sheraton and Hepplewhite both featured bow-fronted designs. Adam's hallmark on the other hand, was a frieze decorated with low relief carving depicting classical motifs, or panels inlaid with designs of contrasting woods.

Various styles of feet abound, including bracket, ogee and the superbly sweeping French-style foot.

An antique English Victorian mahogany wardrobe with a tall pair of serpentine-fronted doors with conformingly shaped moulded cornices, circa 1850, 7ft. 4in. high.
(Selkirk's) £1,742

A pine wardrobe designed by E.W. Godwin, the panelled front with two studded brass bands and central cupboard door enclosing single fitted shelf, 241.5cm. high.
(Christie's) £13,200

One of two rare wardrobes inscribed *Thine* and *Mine*, constructed in a rich variety of grain, with similar end panels and fitted interior, each 66in. high.
(Tennants) (Two) £2,000

A Heal & Son mahogany wardrobe designed by Sir Ambrose Heal, from the 'Five Feathers Suite', London circa 1898, 191.5cm. wide.
(Christie's) £1,760

An oak chequered inlaid wardrobe, possibly designed by M.H. Baillie Scott, the moulded cornice above a curved recess flanked by a pair of doors inlaid with flowers, 85in. wide.
(Christie's) £1,870

A Gordon Russell oak wardrobe, the moulded rectangular top above two panelled doors with brass ring drop handles, on rectangular legs, 136.5cm. wide.
(Christie's) £2,530

A stained wardrobe designed by M. H. Baillie-Scott, with carved decoration and green staining, 103.7cm. wide.
(Christie's) £400

Mid 20th century Sellers pollard elm and burr-walnut wardrobe with three panel doors, 82in. wide. £1,000

Victorian mahogany wardrobe, having a centre mirrored door flanked by single doors to either side, 5ft. wide.
(G. A. Key) £210

A bachelor's mahogany wardrobe, the doors opening to reveal four sliding trays, 52in. wide. £1,250

A Victorian mahogany wardrobe, the stepped top with gothic arched centre carved with foliate crockets, on plinth base, 71in. wide. (Christie's London) £1,650

An English Arts & Crafts walnut combination wardrobe with ebony crossbanding, 66in. wide.
(Reeds Rains) £340

An Arts and Crafts oak wardrobe with broad everted top above a central mirrored door flanked by panelled sides, 198.5cm. high.
(Phillips) £300

A Victorian mahogany compactum, the upper central section enclosed by a pair of framed arched panel doors, 6ft.7½in. wide. (Hobbs & Chambers) £520

A Heal & Sons Arts & Crafts oak wardrobe, with central mirrored door enclosing hanging space with single drawer below, 128.3cm. across.
(Phillips London) £529

19th century flame mahogany corner wardrobe with shaped apron. (British Antique Exporters) £400

A Regency mahogany breakfront wardrobe, 102in. wide. £5,850

A Gordon Russell oak wardrobe, together with an oak bed-head and end, 1930's, 138cm. wide. £675

A Robert 'Mouseman' Thompson oak and burr-oak carved panelled wardrobe, with one long cupboard door and one short enclosing two shelves, 119.5cm. wide. (Christie's) £5,720

An Edwardian mahogany breakfront wardrobe with two panelled doors, two short and three long drawers, flanked by full-length mirrored doors, 101½in. wide. (Bearne's) £880

A Regency mahogany breakfront wardrobe in the manner of Gillows, in four sections, the central section with two panelled doors enclosing trays, 99in. wide. (Christie's) £2,420

An impressively large Dutch figured walnut veneered wardrobe, on bracket feet. (Woolley & Wallis) £1,950

An interesting gentleman's teak compactum, circa 1848, fitted with two short and five long graduated drawers with camphorwood linings. (Tennants) £800

A Victorian mahogany and satinwood banded wardrobe, the cavetto banded pediment above two fielded panelled doors and two base drawers, 49¼in. wide. (Christie's S. Ken) £605

An early 19th century Dutch press with brass ring handles and lock plates, 6ft.1in. x 9ft. 8in. high. £5,000

A George III mahogany wardrobe, with two short and six long drawers flanked by a pair of cupboard doors, 95in. wide. (Christie's) £1,980

An 18th century Dutch figured walnut wardrobe, 6ft.3in. wide. £3,600

A Huntingdon Aviation & Co. aluminium wardrobe designed by P.W. Cow, with twin doors and amber plastic pulls, 122cm. across. (Phillips) £150

An 18th century William and Mary walnut schrank, Penn., 74¼in. wide. (Christie's) £4,345

An oak wardrobe by E.P. Gardiner, having a plain cornice above twin panelled doors, raised on square legs, 1.275m. across. (Phillips London) £280

Heal & Sons wardrobe in French walnut with hanging space in the centre section, circa 1930. £700

A Federal inlaid and carved mahogany wardrobe, New York, 1800-1820, on short reeded baluster turned legs, 56½in. wide. (Christie's) £3,573

A late Georgian mahogany breakfront wardrobe with central arched pediment above a pair of doors, 90in. wide. (Spencer's) £600

A 19th century gentleman's mahogany tray wardrobe, 4ft.1in. wide. £1,350

An inlaid mahogany breakfront wardrobe, 88in. wide. £3,000

An Edwardian mahogany wardrobe by Edwards & Roberts, 50in. wide. £2,000

A Gordon Russell oak wardrobe, the moulded rectangular top above two panelled doors with brass ring drop handles, on rectangular legs, 136.5cm. wide. (Christie's) £2,530

A fine Art Nouveau walnut wardrobe, designed by Georges de Feure, with shaped and carved pediment above twin central panelled doors, 200cm. wide. (Phillips) £5,000

A mid-18th century mahogany wardrobe with two doors each with three fielded panels, 54¾in. wide. (Bearne's) £1,250

A George II oak press with moulded cornice above two shaped arched fielded panelled doors divided by a reeded pilaster, 55in. wide. (Christie's London) £1,320

A George II mahogany wardrobe in the style of Giles Grendey, with later broken pediment cornice with dentil moulding centred by a giltwood armorial device, 52¾in. wide. (Christie's) £2,860

A painted wardrobe, coloured in navy blue, red and green with linear decoration, combed wavy banding and roundels, 76cm. across. (Phillips London) £240

A George III gentleman's mahogany wardrobe with gilt brass cast swag handles, 4ft.2in. wide. £840

A mid Victorian mahogany cylinder wardrobe, the drawers with turned handles, 255cm. wide. £875

A Chippendale carved mahogany wardrobe, in two sections, New York, 1760-80, 53in. wide. £3,850

A George III oak wardrobe inlaid overall with mahogany, the lower section with seven false drawers and two long drawers, on shaped bracket feet, 71¼ in. wide.
(Christie's) £1,210

An ebonised lacca povera wardrobe with moulded cornice above a pair of double panelled doors applied with prints of flowers and birds, on bun feet, 19th century, 41in. wide. (Christie's London) £2,200

An important oak wardrobe, by Anthony Salvin, circa 1835, the cornice and four arched doors incised with vases of flowers, acorns, roses and foliage, the lower panels with figures, 8ft. 9in. wide.
(Sotheby's) £4,180

Wardrobe closet, 19th century, in pine with panelled door and drawer in base, 52in. wide.
(Eldred's) £133

A George III satinwood breakfront wardrobe inlaid with narrow bands and stringing, 104in. wide. £4,400

An Aesthetic movement ash combination wardrobe and a similar dressing table, 43in. wide. £425

A Georgian mahogany gent's wardrobe, the interior fitted with brass hanging rail, 51in. wide. **£575**

A gentleman's rosewood, king-wood, parquetry inlaid and ormolu mounted wardrobe, 8ft. wide. **£5,350**

A Charles X burr elm wardrobe, with foliate fruitwood inlay, with moulded pediment and single mirrored door, 86.5cm. wide. (Finarte) **£2,755**

Late Victorian inlaid mahogany wardrobe in the Adam taste, circa 1880, the upper panels inlaid with ribbon-tied wreaths suspending pendant husks, 45in. wide. (Butterfield & Butterfield) **£812**

A Franco-Flemish oak wardrobe with moulded rectangular cornice above a pair of hinged panelled double doors each carved with Romayne busts headed by foliate scrolls, 72in. wide. (Christie's) **£3,850**

A polychrome painted Scandinavian wardrobe, with moulded rectangular cornice above a single door painted with flower sprays, on bun feet, 114cm. wide. (Auktionsverket) **£3,054**

A George III mahogany and satinwood crossbanded gentleman's wardrobe, 4ft. wide, circa 1780. **£1,450**

An early George III break-front gentleman's wardrobe, 5ft.11in. wide, circa 1770. **£3,650**

Gustav Stickley two-door wardrobe, panelled doors opening to pull-out shelves, 1904, 33in. wide. **£1,400**

A fine classical gilt-stencilled mahogany wardrobe, New York, possibly by Joseph Meeks and Sons, circa 1820, with stylised carved paw feet, 54¹/₂in. wide. (Sotheby's) £6,286

A Gillow & Co. 'Stafford' satinwood and walnut wardrobe in three sections, painted in oil depicting Spring and Autumn, enclosing two slides above two short and three long drawers, 258cm. wide.
(Christie's) £4,950

An oak wardrobe designed by Peter Waals, of rectangular form, the two cupboard doors each with four panels and wooden latch, 182.5cm. high. (Christie's) £2,200

A handsome George III mahogany wardrobe, the pair of rectangular panel cupboard doors crossbanded in rosewood and outlined in boxwood stringing, 55³/₄in. wide. (Bonhams) £1,500

A Regency mahogany wardrobe in four sections, the waved cornice centred by an anthemion and divided by turned finials above two panelled doors enclosing five trays, 98in. wide. (Christie's) £2,640

A Regency mahogany wardrobe probably by Gillows, with moulded cornice above two moulded panelled doors enclosing hanging space, 51in. wide. (Christie's S. Ken) £1,430

An Arts and Crafts mahogany wardrobe, attributed to Kenton & Co., possibly to a design by Arthur Blomfield, the doors enclosing drawers and shelves, 149cm. wide. (Phillips) £500

A George III oak wardrobe with moulded rectangular breakfront cornice and Greek-key moulding, on ogee bracket feet, 78¹/₄in. wide. (Christie's) £2,640

A pine Gothic Revival wardrobe inset with quatrefoils above a pair of pointed arched doors, late 19th century, probably French, 71in. wide. (Christie's) £660

Wash basins and ewers were introduced as early as the 16th century when Sir John Harrington deemed it essential to "wash all the instruments of the senses with cold water".

Soap balls had been manufactured since the 14th century; toothbrushes had had to wait until the end of the 17th, but it was not until midway through the 18th century that furniture designers thought to design an article specifically for the housing and use of these essential aids to personal hygiene.

A 19th century enclosed washstand with lift-top revealing a rising mirror. (Lots Road Chelsea Auction Galleries) £550

An early 19th century mahogany cylinder front washstand, later inlaid with intertwined husk chains and foliage, 25½in. wide. £1,000

A George III mahogany wash stand of square shape, the top with raised waved edge, inset with four recesses and basin well, 35in. high. (Lawrence) £1,155

A very fine Federal bird's eye maple veneered mahogany corner basin stand, Boston, Massachusetts, circa 1805, height 40½in. (Sotheby's) £4,161

A 19th century painted pine washstand, painted old pink over other colours, America, 15½in. wide. £600

A George III mahogany lady's toilet stand, the serpentine hinged top enclosing a fitted interior and adjustable plate, 26¾in. wide. (Christie's S. Ken) £605

Victorian marble top oak washstand, 1860. £100

A Federal inlaid mahogany corner washstand, New England, 1790–1810, the shaped splashboards with shelf above a convex top fitted with three holes for basin and dishes, 18¾in. wide. (Christie's) £767

WASHSTANDS

A marble-topped oak wash-stand, designed by A. W. N. Pugin, 108cm. width, circa 1850. £500

An unusual early 19th century mahogany wash basin and stand. (Lawrence Butler) £475

A Regency period faded mahogany veneered toilet stand, 21in. wide. £400

A Liberty & Co. tiled oak washstand, the tapering back and base similarly covered with narrow green tiles, 1.23m. high. (Phillips London) £650

An early 19th century mahogany enclosed washstand, 30in. high. £1,000

Hepplewhite mahogany dressing stand, X stretchered, circa 1800. £550

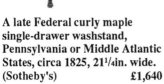

A late Federal curly maple single-drawer washstand, Pennsylvania or Middle Atlantic States, circa 1825, 21¼in. wide. (Sotheby's) £1,640

Shaker pine painted wash stand, circa 1850, retains original chrome yellow wash, 45¼in. wide. (Skinner) £4,000

Victorian mahogany shaving stand, the oval mirror supported on cradle support to a circular centre. (G. A. Key) £310

A George III Sheraton design gentleman's washstand, 28in. wide. £1,150

A late 18th century mahogany corner washstand with splay feet. £275

A 20th century mahogany Sheraton-style dressing table/washstand with serpentine front, 49in. wide. £775

Victorian mahogany and maple, tiled back, marble top washstand, 1865. £400

A George III mahogany washstand with folding rectangular top enclosing basin apertures, on square legs joined by an undertier, 16in. wide. (Christie's) £352

Grain painted chamber stand, New England, circa 1830, 39in. wide. (Skinner) £255

A late 18th century mahogany washstand with side carrying handles, 45cm. wide. (Wellington Salerooms) £800

Victorian mahogany tray top wash stand with centre dummy drawer and two side drawers, 2ft. 6in. wide. (Hobbs & Chambers) £200

A Dutch marquetry and mahogany washstand with rouge royale marble inset top, 2ft.9in. wide, circa 1840. £1,350

A Federal mahogany carved washstand, probably Mass., circa 1815, 20in. wide. £1,900

A mahogany toilet pedestal with enclosed locker top and brass side carrying handles, 1ft.5in. wide. £225

An early 19th century Dutch parquetry walnut bedside cupboard with galleried top, 19.5in. wide. £900

A Dutch mahogany toilet cabinet inlaid with urns and foliate marquetry with folding rectangular top enclosing a telescopic mirror plate, early 19th century, 29in. wide. (Christie's S. Ken.) £2,970

A late George III satinwood and amaranth banded corner washstand with a hinged galleried back enclosing a fitted interior, on splayed legs, 26½in. wide. (Christie's S. Ken) £1,320

A late Regency gentleman's mahogany toilet stand inlaid with satinwood bands and boxwood geometric lines, 24¾in. wide. (Christie's S. Ken) £1,650

A George III mahogany bowfront washstand, the top fitted with three bowl apertures and a three-quarter galleried superstructure, 24in. wide. (Christie's S. Ken.) £1,210

A late Regency mahogany washstand with raised back and sides, on turned supports joined by undershelf, 121cm. wide. (Lawrence Fine Arts) £1,012

Mahogany bow-fronted corner wash stand with tray top, the cupboard enclosed by pair panel doors, 1ft. 10½in. wide. (Hobbs & Chambers) £210

A late Georgian mahogany washstand with gallery back, shelf and single drawer, 18in. wide. £125

A blue and white violin-shaped bidet, Qianlong, 61cm. long, on wood stand. £725

A Regency oval two-tier wash stand, the top tier with open centre, 24½in. wide. £1,000

A George IV mahogany wash stand with a pair of hinged flaps enclosing a pull up swing frame toilet mirror, cut out basin and beaker stands, 33in. x 34in. high. (Anderson & Garland) £640

A Liberty & Co. oak washstand, the shaped superstructure with two tiled panels, above rectangular marble top flanked by two shelves, on bracket feet, 104cm. wide. (Christie's) £400

A George III mahogany gentleman's washstand, the tulipwood crossbanded divided top enclosing a ratchet adjustable mirror and six lidded compartments, 2ft. 5in. wide. (Phillips) £850

A Regency mahogany dressing-commode washstand, the hinged rectangular top with reeded edge, on square tapering legs, 45in. wide. (Christie's) £2,750

A Louis XVI mahogany washstand by Joseph Gengenbach dit Canabas with twin-flap rectangular top enclosing an inset white marble wash surface, 31in. wide. (Christie's) £4,620

A George III mahogany pedestal toilet stand, the folding rectangular top enclosing bowl apertures above a simulated drawer front, 23in. wide. (Christie's S. Ken) £605

WASHSTANDS

A George III mahogany toilet stand inlaid with satinwood bands and geometric boxwood lines, 24¼in. wide.
£600

A French Empire mahogany basin stand with circular dished top, small drawer and on a 'lyre' support, 16in. wide.
(Bearne's)   £270

An early 19th century mahogany washstand in the Gillows manner, on tapering reeded legs, 33in. wide.
(Bearne's)   £430

A George III mahogany bow fronted corner washstand with cut-out for basin and a single drawer on splay legs.
(Abbotts)   £150

A William IV mahogany washstand, the rectangular top with a rising central section and flap ends, 41½in. wide extended.
(Hy Duke & Son)   £350

George III mahogany wash stand with lifting top revealing a central void to house wash basin, 17in. square.
(G.A. Key)   £370

A Classical Revival mahogany washstand, probably Boston, circa 1815, 17½in. diam.
£11,250

Painted decorated washstand, probably England, 19th century, 35in. wide.
(Skinner)   £700

A late George III inlaid mahogany corner washstand 38½in. high, 22in. wide.
£1,350

426

Formerly of French design, the whatnot made its English debut in about 1790 and was enthusiastically received as the ideal display piece for books and bric a brac.

The earlier examples are generally of rather simple designs and usually of rosewood or mahogany. Subsequent styles, late Regency and Victorian, are often found to be quite elaborate with shaped shelves and fretwork galleries, while some of the Victorian whatnots were made to fit into a corner or enlarged up to four feet in length and designed to be placed against a wall. Some were also fitted with a drawer or drawers.

The whatnot is one of those pieces which could have been called anything at all. The original French name was etagère, but this apparently taxed the memory or linguistic talents of our ancestors to the extent that they fell back on just the kind of name we would be likely to use today; thingamebob, oojah or whatsit.

A pair of gilt-lacquered brass-mounted three-tier mahogany whatnots each with ball finials to the corners, 19th century, 15in. wide.
(Christie's) £8,050

A mid Victorian burr-walnut three-tier whatnot, each cartouche-shaped tier joined by spiral-twist uprights and pierced splats to the sides, 32in. wide.
(Christie's) £462

A pair of early Victorian mahogany whatnots, one with a lower part with a cupboard and the other with open top with divisions for magazines, 51in. high. (Lawrence Fine Art) £1,540

A mid-Victorian mahogany whatnot with five graduated tiers, turned uprights and drawer, on turned legs, 24in. wide.
(Christie's) £1,980

A William IV mahogany whatnot of four tiers with a pierced gilt-metal gallery around the top tier, 66in. high.
(Lawrence Fine Art) £3,080

A pair of mid-Victorian ormolu-mounted burr walnut, amaranth and trellis-pattern parquetry three-tier whatnots by Gillows, 20in. wide.
(Christie's) £18,400

A George III satinwood whatnot with four canted rectangular tiers, the top tier with a mahogany and cedar-lined frieze drawer, 16³/₄in. wide.
(Christie's) £11,550

A late Victorian walnut three-tier buffet with pierced fret carved gallery on scroll and spiral twist uprights, 45in. wide.
(Christie's) £880

A Victorian rosewood canterbury/whatnot, the rectangular top with four baluster finials to the corners, 1ft. 11in. wide.
(Spencer's) £600

A serpentine mahogany three-tier whatnot, early Victorian, circa 1840, on turned pillars, 64cm. wide.
(Sotheby's) £1,092

A mid Victorian walnut canterbury whatnot, the serpentine top with a three-quarter fret-carved gallery, 24in. wide.
(Christie's S. Ken) £1,045

An Irish mid-Victorian walnut three tier buffet, on double fluted column supports with turned bun feet, 43½in.
(Christie's S. Ken) £715

An oak Gothic Reform etagère, in the manner of Charles Bevan for Marsh and Jones, circa 1870, with three shelves on trestle supports stencilled with gothic devices, 2ft. ½in. wide.
(Sotheby's) £880

A good walnut three-tier table, Victorian, circa 1850, with fret-pierced end panels and down-curved legs, 67cm. wide.
(Sotheby's) £667

An elegant Regency mahogany whatnot, the upper tier with fretwork gallery, the lowest with a drawer, on lion's paw feet, 35in. wide.
(Bonhams) £1,000

A rosewood whatnot, George IV, circa 1825, with four tiers, the top one hinged and the lowest with a drawer, 51cm. wide.
(Sotheby's) £1,155

Victorian mahogany three tier side whatnot, the bottom and middle tiers supported by swan neck designs, 2ft. 11in. wide. (G. A. Key) £1,300

A George III mahogany whatnot with five tiers, on square end-supports each with splayed finial and brass caps, 48in. high. (Christie's) £3,520

An early Victorian mahogany whatnot of three rectangular tiers, joined by turned supports, 86cm. high. (Lawrence Fine Arts) £825

A mid-Victorian calamander, ebonised and parcel-gilt three-tier whatnot with three-quarter galleried top, on fluted ebonised supports and toupie feet, 20in. wide. (Christie's) £4,400

A George IV rosewood four-tier whatnot, the tiers supported on baluster turned columns, with a drawer to the base, on turned legs, $18^{1}/_{4}$in. wide. (Bonhams) £900

A Victorian burr-walnut canterbury whatnot with pierced scroll galleried oval eared top on spiral-twist supports, on bun feet and castors, $23^{3}/_{4}$in. wide. (Christie's) £1,100

An ebonised and parcel-gilt mahogany whatnot, by Gillows of Lancaster, circa 1875, the two shelves above a drawer. (Sotheby's) £550

A Victorian mahogany three-tier carved and turned buffet. (J. M. Welch & Son) £340

Early 19th century mahogany three tier square whatnot, turned baluster columns and conial finials, 16in. square. (G. A. Key) £530

An early 19th century three-tier mahogany whatnot, 45in. high. £400

A Victorian rosewood serpentine front whatnot of three tiers with pierced gallery and turned supports, 102cm. high. (Lawrence Fine Arts) £748

A Victorian walnut and marquetry four-tier corner whatnot on turned supports. (J. M. Welch & Son) £310

A 19th century canterbury with spiral turned uprights and shaped lower drawer, 22in. wide. (Lots Road Chelsea Auction Galleries) £320

A George III mahogany corner whatnot with three reeded bowfronted graduated tiers, each reeded support crowned by an urn-finial with radially-carved spandrels and paterae, 26¼in. wide. (Christie's) £9,350

A19th century burr walnut canterbury/whatnot, raised on turned columns over a canterbury section set on a drawer set base. £525

Mid Victorian rosewood three tier what-not, with fretwork gallery over turned barley twist supports, 40in. high. (Phillips) £500

A French-style mahogany standing canterbury with lyre supports, 36cm. high. £350

A William IV mahogany five-tier whatnot, with baluster and bobbin-turned uprights, 20½in. wide. (Christie's) £1,210

Victorian figured walnut three tier whatnot, the top tier with a pierced gallery and shaped finials, 2ft. wide.
(G. A. Key) £920

A Regency mahogany what-not with three shelves, 16in. wide. (Christie's) £770

A George III mahogany two-tier whatnot, the reeded rectangular top with two shelves and double-X latticework sides, 13in. wide. (Christie's) £1,540

A Regency mahogany two-tier whatnot with easel top and ribbed supports, 21in. wide. £3,000

A Morris & Co. ebonised mahogany seven-tier whatnot, the design attributed to Philip Webb, on turned and square-section supports, circa 1875, 143.5cm. high.
(Christie's) £1,870

Victorian figured walnut whatnot, three tier, on scroll feet, 2ft.5in. wide. £450

A Victorian mahogany corner whatnot with four graduated bow-front tiers, 80cm. wide. £750

A Victorian figured walnut three tier whatnot, on turned tapered legs terminating in castors, 23in. wide. (Spencer's) £460

A Victorian rosewood four tier corner whatnot, 23in. x 48in. high.
(Dreweatt Neate) £500

A rosewood whatnot, early Victorian, circa 1840, with three tiers, spiral-twist pillars and a drawer, 33cm. square. (Sotheby's) £782

A good 19th century rosewood three tier whatnot, with broken bow front shelves, 40½in. high. £700

A George III mahogany whatnot of three tiers by slender turned supports, 47in. high. (Lawrence Fine Art) £1,870

One of a pair of Regency mahogany whatnots with vase finials, 17¾in. square. £2,600

A mid-Victorian walnut canterbury whatnot with C-scrolling three-quarter galleried rectangular top on open fretwork vase-shaped supports, 24in. wide. (Christie's S. Ken.) £1,650

A Regency mahogany whatnot with four rectangular shelves, 20in. wide. (Christie's) £1,045

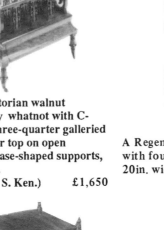

A mahogany four-tier whatnot, with graduated rectangular shelves on turned supports and above one drawer, on brass caps, 18¼in. wide. (Christie's) £3,080

A Regency brass three-tier whatnot with rosewood shelves, 15 x 28in. high. £3,850

A George IV mahogany whatnot, the four tiers on ring turned columns with an apron drawer on turned legs, 1ft. 8in. wide. (Phillips) £1,000

WINE COOLERS

Records indicate that there were wine coolers in use as early as the 15th century, and examples from the following two centuries are to be seen in many a contemporary tapestry or painting.

They were made for cooling the wine in ice or cold water, and were usually of oval or bowl shape, supported on legs and made in a variety of materials including bronze, copper, silver or even marble and other stones. Some of the silver pieces in particular were very extravagant affairs, and one, in the inventory of the possessions of the Duke of Chandos, is recorded as weighing over two thousand ounces.

Wine coolers made of wood with lead liners were first introduced in about 1730, and these were often supported on cabriole legs with finely carved paw feet.

Some have a nice little brass tap on the side for ease of emptying. Others have brass carrying handles so they could be lifted out of the way with minimal risk of slopping the contents over the guest of honour.

Cellarets were introduced in about 1750 and, at first, were usually of octagonal shape, the earliest often having short feet decorated with carved foliage.

Most are made of mahogany with brass bandings, are lined with lead and partitioned to take nine bottles. At first they were of quite large proportions to take the wide green bottles used at the time but, as these slimmed, cellarets followed suit.

Later in the 18th century, cellarets tended towards an oval shape.

A mahogany cellaret, the waved body with detachable tin-liner, 15in. wide. (Christie's) £770

A Regency brass inlaid wine cooler carved overall with gadrooned bands, the stepped rectangular top with re-entrant corners enclosing a later lead lined interior, 28½in. wide. (Christie's London) £2,090

An early 19th century mahogany cellaret, the rect-angular top with ovolo moul-ded edge, raised upon gadroon carved ogee bracket feet, 42cm. wide. (Henry Spencer) £2,500

A brass bound mahogany urn wine cooler on pedestal cup-board, the cover with pine-apple finial. (Lawrence Fine Arts) £3,080

A William IV oak and ebonised wine-cooler with lead-lined interior above a gadrooned body and on spreading fluted shaft and square base, 26in. diameter. (Christie's) £2,200

A Regency mahogany and inlaid cellaret of boat design, with triple hinged top, 1.02m. wide. £6,150

HEXAGONAL

A George III mahogany brass
bound hexagonal cellaret,
15in. wide, 27½in. high.
(Graves Son & Pilcher)
£1,150

A George III brass bound
mahogany cellaret with
lead lined interior retaining
tap beneath, 19in. wide.
£3,800

A George III brass bound
mahogany hexagonal
cellaret, 28in. high, 17in.
wide. £3,850

George III mahogany hexagonal
cellaret, the lid opening to a
plain interior, the brass-banded
sides fitted with two brass loop
handles, 24½in. high.
(Butterfield & Butterfield)
£787

A late Victorian ormolu-
mounted mahogany wine-cooler,
the hexagonal lid with
pomegranate finial, the sides
with flower-filled entrelac-
moulding and laurel-wreath
handles, 29in. high.
(Christie's) £1,870

A George III mahogany brass-
bound hexagonal wine-cooler
with geometrically-inlaid and
banded hinged top enclosing an
interior fitted with lead-lined
divisions, 19in. wide.
(Christie's) £6,600

A George III brass-bound
mahogany cellaret-on-stand, the
hinged hexagonal top enclosing a
lead-lined interior with
compartments, 18½in. wide.
(Christie's) £5,500

An attractive George III
mahogany wine cooler, the
hinged cover with moulded
edge, bound with brass, 1ft. 7in.
wide.
(Spencer's) £2,900

A George III solid amboyna
cellaret, with brass carrying
handles to the sides, the hinged
top enclosing an interior fitted
with divisions, 20½in. wide.
(Bonhams) £1,800

OCTAGONAL

A late 18th century octagonal wine cooler, in exotic hardwoods, brass bound with side handles, 20in. wide. (Woolley & Wallis) **£1,050**

George III mahogany cellaret on stand, third quarter 18th century, the fluted stand with moulded square legs, on casters, 30¹/₂in. high. (Skinner Inc.) **£2,163**

A George III mahogany and brass bound octagonal cellaret with hinged top, 46cm. wide. (Phillips) **£2,400**

A George III brass-bound mahogany cellaret of canted rectangular shape, the hinged top inlaid with two satinwood octagonal panels each with a compass medallion, 26in. wide. (Christie's) **£13,200**

A Georgian crossbanded mahogany and line inlaid octagonal wine cooler, having tap to base on a stand with chased brass claw and ball feet, 18in. diameter. (Geering & Colyer) **£1,500**

A George III mahogany cellaret with octagonal hinged top enclosing a lead-lined interior, the frieze inlaid with a rounded rectangular panel, the tapering octagonal body inlaid with ovals, 19¹/₂in. wide. (Christie's) **£12,100**

A George III mahogany cellaret, of octagonal form, bound in brass, the hinged top enclosing a lead-lined interior, 25in. wide. (Bonhams) **£2,600**

A late George III mahogany cellaret of octagonal form, the ebony strung lid opening to reveal a converted interior, 20in. wide. (Hy Duke & Son) **£1,500**

A Chinese Export black-lacquer and gilt decorated octagonal cellaret on a later stand with an overall trellis design centred by oval floral medallions, first quarter 19th century, 25in. wide. (Christie's S. Ken) **£1,540**

A Regency mahogany oval wine cooler in the manner of Gillows with lead-lined interior, 27¼in. wide. £5,450

Georgian mahogany and brass bound wine cooler of oval form, measuring 2ft. x 1ft. 6in. (G. A. Key) £1,200

A George III mahogany oval wine cooler with line inlay, 24in. £2,600

A George II mahogany wine-cooler, the oval brass-bound body with lion-mask carrying-handles with later brass liner on partly imbricated cabriole legs, 26¼in. wide.
(Christie's) £6,380

A George II oval brass-bound mahogany wine-cooler of bombé shape, the sides with giltmetal carrying-handles, on short cabriole legs and hairy paw feet, 28in. wide.
(Christie's) £52,800

An early George III mahogany wine cooler, the oval brass banded body with carrying handles at the sides and zinc liner, the stand with square chamfered legs, 2ft. 1in. wide.
(Phillips) £2,200

A George III brass bound mahogany wine cooler with arched brass carrying handle and lead lined interior, 13in. wide. £8,600

A George II mahogany wine-cooler, the tapering body mounted with pierced carrying-handles, the waved shaped base edged with foliage centred by bunches of grapes, on hairy-paw feet, 27¾in. wide.
(Christie's) £165,000

A Regency mahogany wine cooler with a brass-bound rounded rectangular body enclosing a tin liner, 35in. wide.
(Hy Duke & Son) £1,500

OVAL LIDDED

A George III mahogany wine cooler, with hinged cover and two brass bands (third band missing), 24in. wide. (Lawrence Fine Arts) £2,970

A William IV brown oak wine cooler with hinged stepped oval top with lotus-leaf moulding, on stepped oval base, with anti-friction casters, 38¼in. wide. (Christie's) £4,400

A George III mahogany wine cooler, the oval lid enclosing a detachable tin liner, 26in. wide. (Christie's) £4,620

George III mahogany cellaret, 18th century, oval form, hinged lid, brass florette and ring handles, on square tapered legs. (Skinner Inc.) £1,401

A late George III mahogany and brass-bound wine cooler on later stand, the domed lid with later finial, 24in. wide. (Christie's) £990

A George III style mahogany brass bound wine cooler with oval fanned top centred by a turned handle, 28in. wide. (Christie's S. Ken) £825

George III brass-mounted mahogany wine cooler on stand, late 18th century, on a conforming stand above splayed square supports ending in casters, 19⅜in. wide. (Butterfield & Butterfield) £2,248

A Regency brass-bound mahogany wine-cooler, with hinged oval fluted top centred by an oval stepped finial carved with a patera, on stand with paw feet, 26½in. wide. (Christie's) £8,800

A George III brass-bound mahogany wine-cooler with oval hinged top enclosing a lead-lined fitted interior with slightly tapering sides with ring-handles, 26¾in. wide. (Christie's) £2,750

RECTANGULAR OPEN

A Regency mahogany wine cooler of rectangular shape with lead-lined interior and lead tray, on rosewood paw feet, 32½in. wide.
(Christie's) £2,420

A 19th century walnut cellaret or jardinière, stamped *Barbetti*, on tortoise feet.
(Dreweatt Neate) £2,400

A Regency mahogany wine cooler of sarcophagus shape with lead-lined interior, 31¾in. wide.
(Christie's) £6,380

A George III mahogany wine cooler on stand, of rectangular shape with tapering sides, on four fluted tapering supports.
(Lawrence Fine Arts) £6,160

A Regency mahogany and ebonised wine-cooler, on a part-reeded lotus-leaf carved turned shaft and concave-sided canted rectangular platform base and bronzed scroll feet, 30in. wide.
(Christie's) £5,500

A Regency mahogany wine cooler with lead-lined body, on ebonised claw feet, 28in. wide. £4,600

A Regency mahogany wine cooler with lead lined interior, formerly with a lid, 39in. wide. £4,700

A George III mahogany wine-cooler, on hairy-paw feet, the sides with brass carrying-handles, with later copper liner, 29¼in. wide.
(Christie's) £6,600

One of a pair of William IV wine coolers, each with moulded rectangular top around a lead-lined well, with gadrooned sides and feet, 35in. wide.
(Christie's) Two £8,250

RECTANGULAR LIDDED

Late 18th century George III mahogany cellaret, the sides with brass carrying handles, 17¾in. wide.
(Christie's) £2,901

A Federal inlaid cherrywood cellaret and stand, 1790-1810, 36in. high. £6,600

A George III carved mahogany cellaret with a hinged cavetto top and fluted canted angles, 43cm. wide.
(Phillips London) £2,500

A satinwood cellaret cross-banded with tulipwood and inlaid with burr-walnut ovals, 20in. wide.
(Christie's) £1,870

A George III plum-pudding mahogany cellaret, the sides with carrying-handles, the integral stand with square tapering legs and brass caps, 23½in. wide.
(Christie's) £2,200

A George III mahogany cellaret, with hinged serpentine-fronted square top enclosing a foil-lined interior with compartments, on square tapering legs, 16in. wide.
(Christie's) £2,200

A George III mahogany cellaret-on-stand, banded with rosewood, the hinged square top enclosing a later mahogany tray and compartments, 15¾in. wide.
(Christie's) £1,870

A Sheraton period mahogany rectangular wine cooler, with satinwood oval and line inlay, on square tapering legs, 21¾in. wide. (Geering & Colyer) £700

A late 18th century Continental cellaret, the domed top and front inlaid with oval panels in various woods, on primitive cabriole legs, 18in. wide.
(Tennants) £1,250

A Victorian mahogany sar-
cophagus-shaped wine cooler,
minus lining, in the Chippen-
dale-style, circa 1850, 29in.
long.   £725

A William IV ash wine cooler
with hinged coffered rectangular top, panelled tapering
body and plinth base, 43½in.
wide. (Christie's London) £715

A George IV mahogany wine
cooler of tapered form with
beaded coffered rectangular top,
with later interior, 26½in. wide.
(Christie's S. Ken)   £1,265

A Regency mahogany wine
cooler, the tapering front with
reeded pilasters, the sides with
carrying handles, on paw feet,
22½in. wide. (Christie's
London)   £1,485

A George IV mahogany wine
cooler of sarcophagus shape
with stepped hinged top
enclosing a lead-lined interior,
28in. wide. (Christie's) £935

A late Georgian small mahogany wine cellaret with
brass ring handles, 20 x 19in.
                             £900

A George IV mahogany wine
cellaret of sarcophagus shape,
the hinged cover with central
raised panel, on plinth base,
29¹/₂in. wide.
(Lawrence Fine Art)   £825

A Victorian mahogany
sarcophagus shaped wine cooler,
the hinged rectangular lid
carved with a panel of foliage,
the foliate carved frieze above
tapering sides, 25in. wide.
(Christie's)   £572

A Regency mahogany and brass
mounted wine cooler of
sarcophagus design, in the
manner of Thomas Hope, the
bevelled domed hinged top with
cavetto frieze, 2ft. 7in. wide.
(Phillips)   £5,800

SARCOPHAGUS

A George IV mahogany sarcophagus cellaret with hinged lid, lead-lined interior and Bramah lock, 33in. wide. (Christie's) £935

A late Regency cellaret of Gothic style, 64in. wide. £2,450

A George IV mahogany wine cooler, the frieze carved with scrolling acanthus, the tapering sides with carrying handles on paw feet, 29in. wide. (Christie's London) £1,980

A Regency small mahogany wine cooler with brass ring handles and paw feet, 16½in. high. £2,650

A Regency mahogany sarcophagus cellaret with revolving panelled doors enclosing a fitted interior for six bottles, 33in. wide. (Christie's) £3,080

A Regency mahogany wine cooler with bronze lion-mask ring handles, on paw feet, 17in. wide. £950

 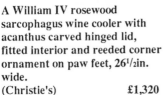

A William IV rosewood sarcophagus wine cooler with acanthus carved hinged lid, fitted interior and reeded corner ornament on paw feet, 26½in. wide. (Christie's) £1,320

An early Victorian mahogany sarcophagus wine cooler, the hinged top surmounted by bunches of grapes and enclosing a zinc-lined fitted interior, 33½in. wide. (Bearne's) £820

A Regency mahogany sarcophagus cellaret on stand, the architecturally moulded tapering body with gilt brass lion mask and ring handles and on lion paw feet, 20in. wide. (Bearne's) £3,100

SARCOPHAGUS

A William IV mahogany sarcophagus-shaped wine cooler with lead lined interior, 27½in. wide.
£1,100

A William IV feathered mahogany sarcophagus wine cooler, with fruit cast brass carrying handles to the sides, on paw feet, 42in. wide.
(Bonhams)   £1,600

A Regency mahogany sarcophagus shaped wine cooler with lead lined interior, on paw feet, 29½in. wide.
£3,300

An early Victorian mahogany sarcophagus wine cooler, the raised hinged lid with fruit and acanthus cresting, on paw feet, 27¹/₂in. wide.
(Christie's)   £1,760

William IV carved mahogany cellaret, second quarter 19th century, the coved rectangular top with canted corners opening to a metal-lined interior, 26in. wide.
(Butterfield & Butterfield)£1,261

An attractive early 19th century mahogany casket of sarcophagus cellaret form, the ovolo moulded hinged top with reeded edge, 78cm. long. (Henry Spencer)   £1,200

A Regency period mahogany sarcophagus-shaped cellaret with original inset brass roller casters, 26in. high. £850

A Federal inlaid mahogany wine cooler with lift top, 22in. wide.   £2,850

A large Regency mahogany and ebonised wine cooler in the manner of Gillows, with a lead-lined divided interior, 33in. wide.   £4,700

INDEX

OTHER LYLE PUBLICATIONS

A Fortune in Your Attic   £16.95
86248-146-5

Advertising Antiques   £16.95
86248-147-3

Lyle Price Guide Art Nouveau & Deco   £14.95
86248-139-2

Lyle Price Guide China   £14.95
86248-140-6

Lyle Price Guide Clocks & Watches   £14.95
86248-149-X

Lyle Price Guide Dolls & Toys   £14.95
86248-141-4

Lyle Price Guide Doulton   £14.95
86248-152-X

Lyle Price Guide Militaria, Arms & Armour £14.95
86248-148-1

Lyle Price Guide Printed Collectables   £14.95
86248-156-2

1001 Antiques Worth a Fortune   £14.95
86248-118-X

Erotic Antiques   £14.95
86248-130-9